First published in 1999
by The Scientific Medical Network
Gibliston Mill
Colinsburgh, Leven, Fife.
Scotland, KY9 1JS
Home Page: http://www.cis.plym.ac.uk/SciMedNet/home

© Scientific Medical Network and individual auth.

British Library Cataloguing in Publication Data
A catalogue record for this book is available from the
British Library

Library of Congress Cataloguing in Publication Data
A catalogue record for this book has been requested

Typeset in Adobe PageMaker by Brian Box, Fife, Scotland
Indexed by John Caton, Fife, Scotland
Printed and bound in Great Britain by
Beshara Press, Tewkesbury

Acknowledgement
We are most grateful to the Russell Trust for a grant towards
the production of this book

ISBN   0 9535333 0 1 (pbk)

CHAPTER 3: HEALTH, HEALING & WHOLENESS
Edited by Dr John Cosh

CHAPTER 4: TOWARDS AN INTEGRAL SCIENCE OF CONSCIOUSNESS
Edited by David Lorimer

Chapter 1
The Network, an Overview

David Lorimer

The Silver Jubilee of an organisation is a good time to take stock of progress, to look back over the previous 25 years and forward to the next 25. Before we look at the origins of the Scientific and Medical Network, we will briefly explore its current nature and aims. The Network was founded in 1973 and now has over 2,000 members in 54 countries. It questions the assumptions of contemporary scientific and medical thinking, so often limited by exclusively materialistic reasoning. It is an informal international group consisting mainly of qualified scientists and doctors, together with psychologists, engineers, philosophers, therapists and many other professionals. The aim of the Network is to deepen understanding in science, medicine and education by fostering both rational analysis and intuitive insights.

As an association of people deeply committed to the advancement of human knowledge and understanding in the fields of science and medicine, the Network encourages intellectual discernment and is wary of the consequences of ill-founded and sensational claims sometimes made in areas of pseudo-science. Its Members support the freedom to develop any worthwhile field of study, even if this means moving beyond theories currently considered plausible. They are prepared to explore frontier concepts and experiences. Many Members are of the opinion that these matters are best considered in terms of the view that human beings and the universe have a transcendent essence. This means taking seriously the possibility that paranormal phenomena and spiritual experiences may reveal other realms of reality, and that human consciousness has dimensions that extend beyond body and mind. This in turn implies a profound vision of the nature of the human being and that the challenges facing human society are intellectual, emotional and spiritual as well as material. Members are

Open to new observations and insights
Rigorous in evaluating evidence and ideas

Responsible in maintaining the highest scientific and ethical standards
Sensitive to the views of others

The Network links like-minded individuals, encouraging exchange of ideas and the cultivation of friendship. Because Members share a deep commitment to open enquiry and to truth in experience, they are prepared to ask searching questions about the nature of existence and the nature of the human being. The Network is committed to no dogma or creed. It seeks to pursue truth wherever it leads, to widen the intellectual horizons of science and of society as a whole, to stimulate research at the frontiers of human knowledge and experience, and to make the results of such research more widely known through education.

In the course of our discussions about the Network and its approach, it became progressively clearer that we could not formulate anything by way of a set of beliefs about the world that might be shared by even a majority of members. Instead we realised that there was a special way of asking questions and seeking for answers that characterised our best meetings and which is now expressed in what we call the 'Network Guidelines'. These are printed in every issue of *Network* as well as applied at meetings. They constitute the Network ethos as it is embodied by our members.

Open-mindedness:
- Bear in mind that good science is an open, self-correcting system; no theory or set of insights is complete or perfect. There is no Network consensus view.
- Be ready to consider constructive criticism and to submit your work to rigorous examination.
- Be prepared to revise your beliefs in the light of evidence and experience.
- Question your own assumptions and presuppositions.
- Maintain a broad frame of reference.
- Cultivate humility, honesty, humour.

Rigour
- Recognise that our views of reality are models.
- Be prepared to test your ideas.
- Try to define your terms clearly.
- Make it clear when you are voicing opinions and beliefs.
- Be able to state opposing viewpoints in argument.

Care for Others
- Have respect and empathy for others and be aware of their needs.
- Balance kindness and understanding with clarity and discernment.
- Be willing to listen and learn from others in the interests of trust and openness.
- Disagree sympathetically, sensitively and constructively.

The words in our current leaflet echo those expressed in the first newsletter circulated to Members, dated 18th January 1974, which states the immediate aim of building up a network of qualified scientists and doctors 'who have adopted or are inclined towards a non-materialist interpretation of the Universe and who have a sympathetic personal interest in studies of and research into paraphysical, parapsychological and spiritual matters and in action that might usefully flow from these'.

The next paragraph explains the rationale of choosing qualified scientists and doctors to spearhead the effort:

'The reasons for adopting this strict selective process lie at the heart of the whole plan. The view was accepted that, despite fairly widespread expressions of disillusionment with science and some dislike of the direction in which it appears to be leading the world, people in general do, in this materialistic age, look to scientists directly or indirectly as their intellectual and spiritual leaders. They no longer accept the opinions of others about the nature of the Universe or what constitutes reality except where those opinions seem to be substantiated by the findings of scientific or medical research. The method of compiling an ever growing body of facts, each related to and depending on those already established, leads to the development of a great scientific system of immense value and entirely valid and coherent within its own terms. But the limitations which this system imposes are seen to become ever more onerous. New discoveries, unrelated to what is already known in a scientific way, tend to be ignored for lack of adequate means of scientific expression. It has become essential for scientific research to be focussed to an increased extent on those areas where true advances in basic understanding of the human situation can be made. It seems to us that studies of what is often called (but may not be) the "paranormal", leading naturally into studies of the spiritual nature of a man and the Universe, have a vital contribution to make to this process, and that there is a need to bring the relevance of the results of good quality research in these fields to the notice of as many as possible of those scientists who have not hitherto had any particular occasion to take notice of it. What is needed therefore is an interpretation, good enough in quality to appeal to the trained minds of scientists, of the results being achieved. The part of our network dedicated to this work must consist almost exclusively of scientists because only they will stand a reasonable chance of being able to present material that will impress their colleagues sufficiently to make a timely and much needed impact on the direction of orthodox scientific thought. Scientists have the equipment and hold the key to the kind of research that will be done, and it is they whose interest must be aroused.'

The kind of evidence sought was spelled out as follows:

'It may be useful at this point to refine further our definition, still tentative, of the kind of material we are looking for to recommend to others. So far we have described it as follows:-

a) evidence (not proof) of planning by or purpose of some dynamic mind other than that that of any incarnate person connected with the research.

b) evidence of the existence of energies, laws and forms of life that cannot be directly apprehended by our normal physical senses.

c) evidence that the physical structure of living or inanimate things is dependent for its maintenance and growth on a more basic non-physical field.

d) well attested instances of higher sense perception (HSP). Professor E R Laithwaite's article "Inner Voice" in the New Scientist of December 20th appears to furnish an example of this.

e) well attested cases of mind functioning independently of the body (including out-of-the-body experiences).

f) evidence of the continuity of life after the death of the body.

g) the more than usually conclusive cases of healing through paranormal agencies (since there are so many cases of healing to choose from).

Newsletter 4 (August 1976) restates the aims of the Network as follows:

'To win greater acceptance by science and medicine of man's spiritual essence; to show that this is wholly consistent with current knowledge of the physics and chemistry of the physical body; to hasten the widening of intellectual horizons in research; to encourage recognition that the world's ills can only be cured by an improved attitude of mind – action will then flow from this; and to promote a climate of opinion that will make easier the pursuit of the nobler objectives and give only second place to material progress'.

Newsletter 5 refers to a 'Blueprint for Being' as a template for day conferences on contemporary approaches to teaching about Being, Knowing and Acting. The following themes would be addressed:

-   What to teach about the nature of human origins and ultimates
-   Is there an available body of knowledge that is indispensable to human self-realisation?
-   Can we offer a noble vision of human beings relationship to themselves, others and to the planet?

These questions remain to be posed and answered by every generation and bring us to George Blaker's piece. George played a pivotal role in the Network's inception and is now its President. His career in the civil service took him to India, where he was in direct contact with Gandhi, and saw him later on in a senior post in the Department of Education and Science.

Glancing Back and Forth

George Blaker

On thinking back, after 25 years, to the first few days and weeks of the creation of the Network I find myself remembering, with the utmost affection and respect, the sterling qualities of the founders. One inevitably compares the hopes and aspirations of that time with the achievements and further hopes and ambitions of the Network now. At that time, in 1973, we sought to engage the interest of scientists and medical people at the top of their professions. This was because we felt that somehow we needed to bring home to their younger and less experienced colleagues the absolute necessity for a majority of people in general to understand that without a transition from our evolving but materialistically based culture to a broader spiritually inspired understanding of the world and its inhabitants the new, just, fair, sustainable and peaceful world order that should succeed us could not become established.

We took the view that the Churches could not bring about this change because, despite the best intentions of many individuals within them, they were immovably shackled to a fixed past in a moving world that could only leave them behind. Perhaps if we had been contemplating the same situation 20 years later we might have thought that instead of the Churches perhaps the football or tennis or film stars or pop musicians, or all of them together, might have done it through the large popular following they enjoy. But in the conditions of 1973 we thought that scientists and doctors would be a better bet! It would be to them, as we saw it, that people would turn for credible explanations of why the human and world conditions were as they were.

So it seemed to us that a large measure of responsibility for moving public opinion forward would lie with the leaders of the scientific and medical communities, whether they realised it or not. Because of their achievements in their own academic and research fields it would be to the outspoken opinions of such thinkers that their more

***Photograph*: George Blaker**

junior colleagues would pay serious attention. It was therefore men and women of that calibre whom we sought to enrol.

That describes why we tried to find highly accomplished people to share our vision. But we also wanted to attract anyone, whether recognised in the world as accomplished or not, who felt inspired by the need for a spiritual understanding of life. We also thought that might help us to avoid becoming elitist so far as we could. Hence, too, membership at first by invitation only.

At another level there was a third group of people with whom we wanted to make contact. That group was the young who had not yet or had only recently passed through University or early job training, so as to offer them the opportunity of hearing about more comprehensive theories relating to the nature of the world that we knew they would not normally encounter in the course of their formal education. We believed they would readily recognise that the currently acceptable view that the world and all things in it were the random, purposeless result of gigantic physical forces was based on unspoken and usually unrecognised assumptions of a restricted character for which there was no proof that was not itself based on those same limiting assumptions. We wanted them to hear and think about the argument that a wider and less restricting view of life was both reasonable and possible. We wanted them to consider this before long years of training within the narrower system had closed their minds to anything freer and more comprehensive, as seemed to us to have happened to a rather large number of our contemporaries.

Our wish to engage with the young was put into effect by means of the "Wider Horizons" project. This was a week-long residential course for 18 to 25 year olds, limited for logistic reasons to 12 men and women each year. It was held first at Sidmouth, then often at Emerson College, with one exceptionally fruitful week on the island of Iona.

In its early days "Wider Horizons" was extremely successful. No particular philosophy or world view was taught, but participants were addressed by 6 or 7 Network members and other invited speakers, each giving, for one evening and one morning, their own views about the nature of life and the world and the place of humanity within it.

15

The "students" had full freedom to question the speakers as much as they liked, and to make their own contributions.

Many of the participants were thrilled with this. Some of the ideas they heard expressed for the first time harmonised with their own intuitive thinking and it seemed like a wonderful release. Some are still Network members. Many lasting friendships grew up among them and most of those friendships are still intact today. I know of at least three marriages that were contracted between people who attended the course and met there for the first time. All those marriages are still going strong today.

The founders who embarked on this included Sir Kelvin Spencer, Dr. Patrick Shackleton and, a month or so later, Dr. Peter Leggett. There were others too who were around and active in those early stages, some of whom are still with us, such as Geoffrey Leytham and Max Payne. Kelvin Spencer, some years earlier, had been Chief Scientist at the Ministry of Power, as it was then called. He had been deeply involved in all matters relating to nuclear science. Next was Patrick Shackleton, whose last job was as Dean of Postgraduate Medical Studies at the University of Southampton. He suffered badly from a bereavement and from cancer, from which he died less than four years later, but who nevertheless took a leading part in arranging the first "Wider Horizons" courses. Peter Leggett joined the group while he was still Vice-Chancellor of the University of Surrey, and, with Kelvin, we became very good friends, a result that seems to occur often within the Network. We all felt deeply the need to change the dominant intellectual attitude reigning in the world and were acutely conscious of the powerless inability of a handful of people on their own to bring about such a huge change. The fact that the motive was a spiritual one made it more difficult in the sense that few people, so far, would understand that or know what it meant – a goodness that is learned individually from experience and knowledge; but at the same time it was made easier by the knowledge of the help and support that Spirit would draw to itself from the universal source. Its timetable might be longer than we could appreciate. It might take a hundred years or more, though we hoped that something useful could be achieved in about 15 years. In the light of the continuing advance of evolution we could not foresee any time when the efforts of the Network would no longer be needed. We recognised that our project was a long term one, but also that it required an immediate start to be made.

We pondered sometimes on what it was that had brought us together, and we could not ascribe it to coincidence. We felt driven to the conclusion that there was a deliberate planned purpose behind it. In my vocabulary that meant inspiration by that strong benevolent power, working in all of us, that supports and encourages us when we are doing things that are truly beneficial to other people, or to the world or planet as a whole, but does not support or encourage us when we are doing something that is intended to or will have the effect of inflating the ego or doing damage in other ways.

Holding such views it became natural to me to see purpose rather than coincidence in many incidents that kept occurring in life, and I mean in all life, not only connected with the Network, though the Network had its full share of such events. I think of that voice on the telephone that said to me: "You do not know me. My name is Andrew Glazewski. I am a Polish Priest. I have heard what you are trying to do with science and if I have got it right I know of someone else who is trying to do exactly the same thing, but in medicine. He is Patrick Shackleton and his phone number is ….." Then he gave the same phone message to Patrick, with my phone number.

That was the first I had ever heard of either Andrew Glazewski or Patrick Shackleton. Patrick and I got together and after a whole day's discussion we were in agreement that we were both wanting to do the same thing. We decided that it would be ridiculous to go into competition with each other and that we had to work together. From the moment that decision was taken things that had held fire for both of us suddenly began to happen. A few weeks later the Network was born. A clear case, I thought, of constructive guidance; and there were to be other such synchronicities.

Without spending too much time on it we searched for more superficial factors that might have caused us to arrive at very similar or indeed identical conclusions about life. Our backgrounds and upbringing, education and life histories were all so utterly different that it seemed all the more remarkable and significant that journeys

17

along such diverse routes should land us all, toward the end, in a place from which we saw the same view of the world. We hoped that, with so many different ways of climbing the spiritual mountain, the similarly of views meant that we were arriving somewhat nearer the top – nearer, at least, than the place from which we began.

We had also learned that there are innumerable ways of scaling that mountain and that each of them merits respect from all the others. As opinions about the nature of life are not necessarily dependent on conclusions we are offered from within out contemporary culture, and as every life history is different, it follows that every final view adopted is almost certain to be unique. All the more remarkable, therefore, when these unique journeys finally arrive at the same place. This again seemed to point to a guiding hand or directing power, especially as the last and enduring landscape is a beautiful one.

So the founders wanted to discover and to bring together all people, but especially those from scientific and medical disciplines, who could accept that the systems in which they had been trained for many years were not as watertight and foolproof or as comprehensive and accurate as their instructors seemed to assume, but were underpinned by hidden assumptions that were wide open to challenge though this limitation was not recognised. We wanted to find those talented individuals who could accept that the section of reality that we measure and weigh is not the whole of reality, and most probably not even the major part of it. We sought trained minds bold enough to pursue the search for truth wherever the quest for it might lead.

I find it encouraging to look back at those 25 years and see the little group of our five original and at first rather hesitant members and to compare them with the 2,000 members in more than 50 countries and many hundreds of associates that we have now, and all the activity and exchange of thinking that has occurred in that time. Has that thinking meant any advance? How far are the founders' aspirations and ambitions still valid today? Has progress been made towards fulfilling them?

The three founders I have mentioned above have now all passed on into what all of them would have expected to find was an active and conscious life, probably more active and more widely conscious in another dimension, free of course from the physical body but still very much themselves, with a continuing sense of self. As time and experience built up they would expect that sense of self to become gradually more aware of the meaning and implications of the unity of all life. They would still be, at first, in a condition to which the whole of their past existence had brought them, and they would still find themselves with unimagined prospects slowly opening up before them.

If they were still in their earthly form now they would have been pleased to see, in the Network literature, such statements as the following, just to quote a few examples.

"The Network is still undergoing a period of organic growth and must remain flexible in its outlook."

"The Network has an important role to play in the next millennium as science gains an understanding of the true spiritual nature of mankind and becomes more integrated with many of the systems of ancient wisdom."

"The spiritual being of the Chair is an important factor in sounding the spiritual note of the Network."

References to *the radiant spiritual heart of the Network.*

"We have an ambitious vision …. We believe that this vision can transcend currently acceptable limits of scientific enquiry and lead to a fuller flowering of the human spirit."

The smiles of approval from our three imagined observers as they read those words will be moderated by just a hint of the reminder that we have a very long way to go yet. But it seems that on the whole we are keeping our faces turned towards the Sun and will be able to continue our journey forward in an atmosphere of goodwill and confidence.

***

Among those involved with the Network at an early stage and mentioned in George Blaker's piece above were Sir Kelvin Spencer (1898-

1992) and Dr. Peter Leggett (1912-1994). Kelvin had been chief scientist at the Ministry of Power in the 1950s and Peter Leggett was Vice-Chancellor of Surrey University. They had their own recollections about the founding of the Network:

Early Days of the Scientific and Medical Network – A Personal View

Sir Kelvin Spencer (1988)

Those of us who were in at the birth of the Scientific and Medical Network will share with me, I hope, a glow of satisfaction at the change of thought which is now occurring. I refer to a change in the way we interpret our total awareness and build a thought model to bring it into coherence. My recollections go back to two meetings at Exeter University Staff Club in the early 1970s. Three people who were at those meetings stand out in my memory: Patrick Shackleton, George Blaker, and a Pole who was both a priest and a scientist, Andrew Glazewski. We shared a feeling that modern science had become imprisoned in a framework much more confirmed than in those pioneering days some three centuries back. It was then that freedom of thought was won from a narrow Priesthood wedded to a theology that didn't fit the then contemporary world picture. It seemed to us at that Exeter gathering that science in the mid twentieth century had lost its way. Outstanding advance in materialistic science and the technology associated with it had deprived earthly life of meaning and purpose. Science strove to be 'value free'. Facts were confined to what could be verified by experiment and measurement, a process which excluded many aspects of human awareness. As Eddington expressed it in the 1920s –"Measurement became the measure of all that is". Mercy, Pity, Peace and Love were excluded from that scientific prison house.

The first of those Exeter meetings was chaotic, but the underlying thought was that science had restricted its field of endeavour too drastically. At that first meeting we didn't succeed in bringing our vague ideas to a focus. Yet a clear and coherent statement of aim was obviously needed if our small group was to expand and have a wider influence.

The focus needed was given at the second Exeter meeting. George Blaker was invited to summarise the outcome of the first meeting. He did it with a creative insight that put into a few words what we had been groping towards. In my recollection that second meeting was the birth of what became the Scientific and Medical Network.

Before the meeting ended we'd agreed that some of us present would write ambiguous letters to selected acquaintances. A few of us had recently retired from our professions after having won respectable positions in them. We each wrote to some of our professional friends. We could not guess how they might respond to a direct invitation to help forward the agreed aim, so ambiguity seemed expedient. The recipient could then interpret the letter in either of two ways: as a friendly correspondence between one still in harness and one who had shed the shackles of office, or he could read between the lines an invitation to take part in a great adventure. To our pleasant surprise many welcomed and accepted this disguised invitation.

That adventure has now been given the name – *Global Mind-Change*, by Willis Harman, whose book with that title has recently been published. Those who took part in these early days of the Network have, I think, reason to cheer their old age with the thought that they had helped, in however small a way, to trigger a change in thought. Of course our embryo group was but a pebble on the beach along with countless other pebbles. But the Network and its fellow workers here and overseas have since picked up many more on that beach which, in Isaac Newton's words, borders the vast ocean of Truth that lies all unexplored before us.

Too many scientists give the impression that they know nearly all that's needed to blaze the way to a better world. Yet compared with what we need to know – certainly how to achieve a world in which war plays no

Photograph: Sir Kelvin Spencer

part! – what we know now is little indeed. And alas too much of today's knowledge is but knowledge: a far cry from wisdom.

Recollections of Early Days with the Scientific and Medical Network

Dr Peter Leggett (1988)

Two factors were responsible for my association with the Scientific and Medical Network since shortly after it was founded – my life long interest in the spiritual implications of the paranormal, and meeting George Blaker.

Ever since the relatively early age of seven or eight I had been concerned with **purpose**, and in particular with "What is the purpose of human life?" In pursuing this quest I had drunk fairly deeply at several different wells, and in the early 1970s I was still searching, having found both orthodox religion and materialistic science unsatisfactory.

My first memory of George Blaker was in March 1971 when I was invited to say a few words at the annual meeting in Surrey University of the Surrey Naturalists' Trust (now the Surrey Wildlife Trust). This was followed a month later by dinner at the University during which we discovered our mutual interest in 'wider horizons'. This was the start of a very close friendship which has blossomed over the years, and has involved a keen interest in everything to do with the SMN.

During my time at Surrey University I had often wondered how such interests could find a place in the University. In 1973, greatly helped by financial assistance from one of the University's major benefactors, it proved possible to appoint a Professor of Philosophy, Shivesh C. Thakur, whose terms of reference included a major interest in the paranormal.

In January 1974, an informal seminar was held at Surrey on the subject of 'The Paranormal', to which 12 people came by invitation from

Photograph: Dr Peter Leggett

Taken at the University of Surrey

outside the University. Among these were George Blaker, Patrick Shackleton, and Kelvin Spencer. At their suggestion this meeting was followed in April 1975 by a weekend conference under the auspices of the SMN on 'Ideas on the extension of individual awareness beyond the two ends of earthly life'. About 50 people attended, and talks were given by Max Payne, Sir George Trevelyan, Paul Beard, Charles Davy and myself. Sessions were chaired by George Blaker, Patrick Shackleton, and Kelvin Spencer. The conference was judged a success by those who attended, and helped to bring the SMN into the open and to the notice of the scientific and medical professions.

Later that year the Youth Network came into being at Eileen Noakes' lovely house in Sidmouth, and in 1977 the SMN held its first 'May Lectures' at the Royal Society of Medicine in London. The overall theme was 'Science, Mind, and the Spirit of Man', and Fritz Schumacher was one of the speakers. Since then a 'Wider Horizons' week at Emerson College for a few 18-25 year olds, and a 'May Lectures' day in London, have become regular annual features of the SMN Calendar.

***

George Blaker writes about Peter Leggett:

Peter's deep interest in and invaluable contributions to the activities of the Scientific and Medical Network began as early as 1974, soon after its birth. I remember the early meetings in the Hog's Back Hotel, supposedly half way between Patrick Shackleton's house in Winchester and mine in Ockley, so close to Peter's University that he could sometimes join us. But his principal and most essential contributions to its development and work came with the activities he stimulated within and from the University itself, where his influence was paramount. He had always been interested in the apparent anomalies in the results of scientific research that did not fit into the expected or apparently emerging pattern. Instead of ignoring the data that seemed anomalous or erratic he wanted to focus on and identify the causes of the aberrations. He often questioned the assumptions underlying the materialistic view of the world generally taken for granted by most his colleagues. He had a deep interest in the spiritual implications of 'the paranormal'. He has published, in *Network Newsletter* No. 40, some recollections of those early years (see above) and yet one feels that that reference does not do full justice

25

to the beneficent effects of his life on those many people who met him or heard him give talks not only in the University but also in many other places round the country.

In the general area of his interest in the Network he experienced two disappointments. The first was that the Chair of Philosophy that he succeeded in getting established in the University did not operate, after his retirement, in the way he hoped it would. The second disappointment, shared I suppose with many other authors, was that he would have liked more people to read his three books that appeared in print between 1986 and 1990 and were reviewed in the *Newsletter*. His style of writing was not popular enough to make them best sellers; they were perhaps too concise, a price that had to be paid for being a top class mathematician.

He was a wonderful friend, yet I cannot feel any sense of loss, only of gratitude and joy for what he did in his life. We shared the view that life does not end suddenly with the death of the physical body but continues on its way, almost uninterrupted, through the incident of death.

***

Dr. Patrick Shackleton

Desna Greenhow

The role of Patrick Shackleton has been referred to by a number of people already. Here his daughter reflects on his part in establishing the Network.

My father, Patrick Shackleton, was, in 1973, at the end of a long and creative career in medicine. His philosophy had always been one of treating the whole person, to which his speciality as an anaesthetist was particularly suited. He used to say that his responsibility to patients stretched well beyond the task of keeping them stable and unconscious in the operating theatre. He was concerned with their well-being and frame of mind before and after the operation, and it was this empathy with the whole person which interested him most in his profession. He had little time for the mere treating of symptoms, or for the mechanistic approach of the technician. He was a great believer in, and practitioner of, the art of medicine, and was, as so many good doctors are, a natural healer himself.

Photograph: **Dr Patrick Shackleton**

His wartime was spent working with Sir Harold Gillies at his maxillo-facial unit near Basingstoke, where his warmth and enthusiasm, his pragmatic approach to patient care, and his open-mindedness to ideas for new techniques, won him many friends among war-wounded and colleagues. "Shack", as he was known, generated affection that was lasting. Many times when we were in circulation as a family he would be greeted as a long-lost friend by someone many years after he had given them treatment, encouragement and energy in their struggle to pull through some terrible wartime experience. (He would have denied that he had much to do with this beyond his normal work as a doctor.) At the height of his anaesthetic career he became senior anaesthetist at the Southampton Group of Hospitals. (He had turned down a very good offer to take over a private practice in London, and this was in keeping with his belief that medical care should be open to all, regardless of their ability to pay. He was one of the few consultants of his group to go into the National Health Service full time when it was initiated, and to refuse to take private work.) My father's obituary in *The Lancet* speaks of his time at Southampton, with the phrase, 'He saw that the key to a high standard of patient care is the stimulus provided to teacher and trainee by an interesting and effective system of specialist training. As a result of the priority he gave to postgraduate training, and of his own example of clinical excellence, he soon created one of the best departments of anaesthetics in England'.

From 1960 onwards he was lured into academic medicine as advisor in post-graduate medical education to the Wessex Regional Hospital Board, and then helped set up, with Donald Acheson and John Revons, the first new medical school this century, at Southampton. He became its first post-graduate dean, and received its first honorary doctorate. His ideas on post-graduate education allowed, once again, for a holistic approach. He was ever-anxious that doctors should have a constantly renewed approach to the profession and to patient care, and should refresh their views and their skills continually over the years, so as not to get hidebound in their dealings with the people in their care.

After his retirement, and at a time when he was in low spirits after the death of my mother, he was to prove that he still had a fresh approach and an enthusiasm which was to carry him, at the age of sixty-nine, into a new project which became the over-riding interest of his remaining years, and to which he had a great deal to contribute.

His marriage had been a very happy one, and, in the months after my mother died, his loneliness led him into a search for communication with her. In the process, he met a new group of people, and made some new, close friends, some of whom were interested in the paranormal. He began to think that there were great areas to be investigated that never were taken on by the mainstream researchers in science and medicine. He thought that one reason for this was the career structure, which meant that it was difficult to stick one's neck out to try to undertake research which was unprovable by conventional methods without losing all credibility in one's field.

In the summer of 1973 a good friend of my father's, Andrew Glaszewski, brought him together with George Blaker, who was having similar ideas with particular reference to scientific research, and to Kelvin Spencer, whose last job before retirement had been as Chief Scientist to the Ministry of Power. Kelvin described himself, in a letter to my father in August 1973, as "interested since 1917 in the less emotional aspects of the paranormal, and puzzled at the unscientific attitude of science to the subject." From then onwards, these three corresponded on an almost daily basis for the three and a half years which saw the setting up and development of the Network. My father and George Blaker formed the secretariat (of two), and Kelvin came in as frequent commentator and participator in all the stages of the gradual unfolding of the new initiative. I am lucky to have a folder of all of this correspondence, and would like to hand it over to the Network for the archive. It is delightfully readable as a tossing round of open-minded discussion by three articulate and warm-hearted friends. However, behind that was a strong sense of purpose about the Network's raison d'être, and some extremely hard work was involved. The first priority was to attract a membership of people with "scientific or medical degrees and doing (or in a few cases, retired from) a scientific or medical paid job, deeply interested in the field of psychical and spiritual studies, research, and consequent action."(Draft statement of Aims, 15th August,1973). By October, a combined effort had achieved a membership of twenty-five, which was to rise steadily from then on. Confidentiality was promised to members, leaving them free to express opinions that might not find favour with orthodox minded colleagues. This issue of confidentiality was a topic of discussion in these early days, and one on which Arthur Koestler, with whom my father had several fruitful meetings in the winter of 1973-4, felt strongly, that members should at least be known to each other, so that cross-fertilisation of ideas and research topics could flow. By April 1974, the idea of an open list, to include members who were happy to align themselves publicly with the Network had taken shape. (Confidentiality was still offered to those who preferred it.)

Koestler was at one with George Blaker, Kelvin and my father in feeling that regular newsletters were essential to keep the momentum of the Network going, and Newsletters 1 to 5 were produced by George and my father between Autumn 1973 and March 1977. The preparation and discussion of contents features in the correspondence, including reports of the various conferences and meetings staged by the Network in these years.

The work did become quite arduous, and my father had a fair amount of illness during this time. However, his enthusiasm carried him on very happily. In January 1975 Kelvin wrote to him, "A warm welcome to your 'late secretary.' I'm intrigued with the advance you've made in getting not only into contact with, but persuading to materialise those who've gone to the next world: and to materialise so completely that they - or rather she- can take down shorthand and manipulate a typewriter. For this is the construction that your words bear: your late secretary. The alternative - that she's unpunctual - I'll not entertain for a moment."

In 1976 the Network took on the organisation of the May Lectures, and it was decided that the first should be in May 1977 at the Royal Society of Medicine, with key speakers being E.F. Schumacher, James Robertson, Professor Derek Bryce-Smith and Dr. Peter Leggett, Vice Chancellor of Surrey University, who had been involved in many Network events over the previous years. Sadly, my father, who had been operated on for a tumour in January 1977, died three weeks before the fruits of his careful participation in the planning of this event took place.

Two quotations might serve to sum up his enthusiasm for the aims of the Network. The first is from a letter he wrote to another doctor in connection with the possibility that the Network might contribute to the Royal Commission on the future of the Health Service in 1976.

"Surely the aims of the Network include the emphasis upon a holistic approach to medicine and science; and our intention is to tackle in greater detail the problem of how we shall move from our present materialistic human situation into the new ethic and new system of values that we hold are essential for the future. What we should be doing, I hope, is to present a case for bringing back into the practice of medicine the concept of man as a spiritual being in a spiritual universe with a soul as well as a body and mind; and that disease is often (usually?) an imbalance somewhere in the relationship between the three components of man, and that the restoration of balance can be achieved by various routes other than the pharmaceutical suppression of a symptom. In other words, more humanity, compassion and understanding from the heart than purely intellectual and scientific thinking and action."

The second is from the address given at his funeral in May 1977 by his friend Tom Gaunt.

"His remarkable professional career has already been spoken of in *The Times*, and will be elsewhere, and I do not propose to say more now; except that the confidence he inspired has enabled men of differing outlook to come together under his leadership to discover new truths. Particularly, I am thinking of the Network, those meetings to discuss things scientific, medical, and spiritual, which have led to the May Lectures. I hope and believe they may be a permanent memorial to him."

***

Early Contact with the Network

Geoffrey Leytham

The next piece is by Geoffrey Leytham, formerly of the Department of Psychology in the University of Liverpool, who has been a Trustee of the Network for many years.

In 1973, I was at the University of Michigan, on sabbatical leave, when I received a forwarded letter from George Blaker and Patrick Shackleton, inviting me to join a group that they had just decided to form. The following quote is from their letter:

'We are trying to establish a network or private and informal list of qualified people in this country (and later abroad) who have had scientific or medical degrees conferred upon them by a university: who are or have been continuously employed on scientific work; and who have at the same time a sympathetic and personal interest in all or any aspects of paraphysical, parapsychological or spiritual studies, research and consequent action. It appears to us that these are the people who have the necessary training and background to be able to further the object we have in view'.

As an academic psychologist with spiritual inclinations, this invitation came as a breath of fresh air, and I immediately wrote back and said that I would be delighted to join. This decision has given me immense nourishment and many rewarding friendships over the last twenty-five years.

Sadly, Patrick Shackleton, a former Dean of the Postgraduate Medical School at Southampton University, became ill, and died on 29th April, 1977. In the Network Newsletter No.6 (May, 1977), George Blaker wrote a glowing tribute to his co-founder, and among other things said:

'The student seminars held at Sidmouth House with the object of widening the spiritual awareness of young people in training for their careers, at which many members of the Network assisted, gave him especial pleasure. The last was held within a month of his death, and he got up from his sick bed more than once, at no mean effort, to take part. Out of these emerged the vigorous "Student Network" which was particularly close to his heart'.

At that time, the total membership of the Network was around 150. Today it is over 2,000. Much of the credit for this expansion over the years is due to David Lorimer, who was appointed Director when the Network became a Charitable Trust in 1986. It was created with a view to attaining the following objective:

> 'The advancement of learning and religion in any part of the world by the study of the various aspects of truth presented through the arts, the sciences and all religions in which may be found spiritual truths necessary for man's fullest development through his understanding the laws of life and of living.'

The laws of life and of living. How can the diverse members of the Network contribute to the understanding of these laws? How can we achieve unity in diversity? The words 'man's fullest development' might provide us with a clue, as Maslow's study of self-actualizing people gives us some idea of what psychologically healthy people are like. He concluded that: 'In healthy people,... dichotomies disappeared, and many opposites thought to be intrinsic merged and coalesced with each other to form unities' (*Motivation and Personality*, 1954, 1970). It is a case of 'both/and', rather than 'either/or', and among many examples given, Maslow includes 'head/heart' , masculine/ feminine , and 'sensual/spiritual'. It seems reasonable to assume that mature organisations will exhibit similar characteristics to mature people, and it is hoped that the Network is developing in that direction.

Which dichotomies might prove relevant to our search for integration, synthesis and unity? The three mentioned above would appear to be apposite to our present position. When the British Psychological Society increased its membership from a small, informal group of academics, to around five hundred diverse members it found that there was a conflict between the more scientifically inclined academics and those in the more personal, applied fields. This was partially resolved by creating four sections for psychotherapy, education, occupational and social psychology. This experimental/experiential

33

split reflects the head/heart and masculine/feminine polarities referred to by Maslow, and is very much in line with the tough-minded/ tender-minded dimension of personality, found especially in research on divisions in political parties. The various groups in the Network cover approaches along this continuum, By 'fostering both rational analysis and intuitive insights', there is every possibility that rigour, evidence and experience will result in mutually acceptable views on the laws of life and of living, including a resolution of the sensual/spiritual dichotomy: going without, but also going within, seeking to replace the dogmatic religious/dogmatic scientific attitudes with a free spiritual outlook informed by a liberal science.

Allied to the above quest, is the mode of presenting the Network's views and findings. In these days of the communications revolution, there is a danger of information overload, and a consequent reduction in personal and social transformation in a healthy direction. Research into university teaching methods, using student learning as a measure of efficiency, indicates that talk and chalk lectures are the least efficient; that audio-visual aids improve their efficiency; and that the most efficient procedures involved student participation and immediate feedback. These findings support the old Chinese dictum: 'I hear and I forget. I see and I remember. I do and I understand.'

Thus, while conferences have their place, it is likely that Bohm's Dialogue format is better, and that even more efficient would be Heron's Co-operative Research, with people, rather than on or about them. Interactive computer programmes could be suitable to introduce the Network to schools and universities, but the residential student seminars, often lasting a week, and close to the hearts of both our founders, provide that human and personal interaction between young and old, which is so essential to learning and understanding. After all, it is the young that we must look to for the future of society and humanity, and if the Network can assist them in preparing for this responsibility, then it will have fulfilled some of its obligations as a charitable trust.

Personal Reflections on The Silver Jubilee of The Scientific and Medical Network

Professor Henryk Skolimowski

Henryk Skolimowski, who has divided his time between the USA, Greece, India and his native Poland, contributes the following personal note about the Network.

I joined the Network in its early days. There were all kinds of good alternative schemes in the air at the time, - the early 70s, yet the SMN struck me as a particularly worthwhile venture. It has proved to be so ever since, as it has continually grown in versatility and strength.

One of the things that struck me from the very beginning was the fact *that we started from the top of the pyramid;* (not from the grass root level, by inviting everybody; but by inviting the conscious, intellectual elite). Democracy is important, but excellence is also important. For me the Network has been the pursuit of diversity and excellence. The second thing that struck me favourably about the Network was the fact that the people within the Network did not try to compete with each other. The Network has never become an avenue for clashing egos. Instead it has been inspired and guided by the ideals of co-operation and unselfishness. This ethos, in my opinion, has been an important source of its success.

The third thing that has struck me is of a more subtle nature. Somehow we have followed the right path (the right as I wanted to say), right balance, right chemistry; and, dare I say, right alchemy. Obviously this right balance has to do with the calibre and character of the people within the Network. Yet, I have seen other people with character and quality, embarking on good schemes, which, nevertheless, have fizzled out. So we must have been doing some important things right. Perhaps we might wish to analyse what these were; or perhaps we might keep doing them without analysing too much.

Now, what about the next 25 years? This question should be considered very seriously. Very soon, we shall be in the new Millennium.

I dare say, much more will be needed of us as we enter the new Millennium. Are we prepared to give more? Are we aware what will be expected of us? One of the ideas which has been lingering at the back of my mind is: should we try to establish a new type of academia, a new type of university? We are all aware that present universities are not doing too well.

Another idea that has been visiting me is *that we should try to create a new, just, equitable, and sustainable world order.* This, I would propose, is one of the most important items for our work during the next 25 years. Of course, we should not abandon the exploration of the frontiers of knowledge, but the creation of a just, humane, world is a task of great importance. Personally, I have always felt good to be associated with the Network. There is a good ethos and good energy emanating from what we are doing. Although our Network is small, it is doing an important work. Let us realise it clearly.

The Network and Its Development

Dr. Peter Fenwick

Dr. Peter Fenwick is a neuropsychiatrist and neurophysiologist with a long standing interest in the nature of consciousness and brain function. He joined the Network in 1977 and agreed to become Chair of the Network Council for a trial year in 1986 – luckily for the Network, he still holds this position!

In the beginning.......the Network was almost a clandestine organisation. It was a forum for scientists and doctors who wanted to be able to discuss with their peers those things that (at that time) dare not speak their name at scientific gatherings. Consciousness for example, parapsychology, human spirituality, life after death and other such unmentionable topics. Joining was by invitation only.

I received such an invitation in the 1970s. I didn't know what the Network was, but it sounded interesting, so I said yes. I received a small Membership list and nothing else happened. But clearly I must have remained on the list because one evening in 1986 I was contacted by the former Vice Chancellor of Sussex University, Peter Leggett, who asked if I would like to become more closely involved with the Network, which was now becoming a charity, help write its constitution, and help guide it through its next phase of development. I said I had already too much on my plate, but provided the demands were minimal, I would be happy to do this for one year only. Fourteen years later, I am still here!

Setting up and organising the Council of the Network was great fun and working with David Lorimer was very exciting. The Wider Horizons programme for students, run by Paul and Cathy Filmore and Mariellen Romer, was already in existence, and was particularly valuable as it helped interested students to learn about the bigger picture of science and themselves. As we held our first meetings and members started connecting and networking it became rapidly apparent that the Network was something very special. Network meetings were stimulating affairs, as we could all discuss, with a degree of freedom that was not then possible in the academic workplace, ideas about the full nature of human beings and the structure and nature of the universe. It was impossible to go to a Network meeting without coming back changed. The fact that we felt able to use our intuitive as well as our intellectual sides gave these discussions added insights and a wider dimension.

This heady mixture produced by the meeting of network minds which were open to new ideas was network 'magic'. However, any forum for discussion of new territory and new ideas is valueless unless it is open to examination. We wanted people to be able to express new ideas in a safe environment, and yet be prepared to re-examine their beliefs if these were questioned. We recognised that in these circumstances members were open and vulnerable and that the special network magic would arise more easily if guidelines were formulated to protect them at such times.

The Network grew and we had our first AGM - at Dartington, on an idyllic summer's weekend. The sun shone, we lounged on the grass, discussed the growing Network and expanded to fill the Universe. Perhaps one should never try to recreate a perfect experience, so we haven't yet returned to Dartington, but each AGM has had its own special quality. The second AGM, at King Alfred's, Winchester, was

Photgraph**: Dr Peter Fenwick (L)**
David Lorimer (R)

'Gaunts House' **1991**
By Mike Brown

notable as the venue for the first Saturday entertainment - a tradition that has gone from strength to strength ever since, with each year a mixture of heady new talent and old favourites. 1993 was notable as the year of the first Continental AGM, held at the lovely old Abbey of La Bussiere, near Dijon. Throughout these growing years the newsletter also grew, under David's editorship, becoming thicker and meatier, metamorphosing in the 1990s into *Network* and finally into an imposing A4 journal with a cover in full colour.

We have now been in existence for 25 years and have grown at the rate of about 8% a year from a small invited group to a world wide organisation of two and a half thousand members, which includes many leading members of the scientific community, amongst whom are two Nobel prize winners. Although most of the main meetings take place in London or the South of England, there are now several autonomous local groups throughout the country, each of which tends to develop its own particular style and focus of interest.

Throughout the last 25 years the Network has continually re-invented itself so as to meet the changing needs of its members. It no longer has any need, for example, to hide its light under a bushel - it is possible now, for example, for serious scientists to express an interest in consciousness, and even to start to discuss spiritual topics. The aim of the Network now is to stimulate, educate, and allow its members to grow. We keep abreast of the cutting edge of science, particularly as it relates to consciousness, for the new scientists of the 21st century will be true Galileans, understanding the complexities of the modern outside world. But much more important, they will also have looked inwards and learned to understand the inner thrust of their own spiritual nature.

This is an ambitious vision, a new way of thinking about the world and our relationship to it. It is a way, grounded in the achievements of modern science, and in the creative exchange of pioneering ideas, that also facilitates the full development of inner creativity in its members. The mission of the Network is to promote the development of this new way of thinking, by encouraging critical judgement and an ethos of genuinely open enquiry. We believe that this vision can transcend currently acceptable limits of scientific enquiry and lead to a fuller flowering of the human spirit.

Reflections and Directions

David Lorimer

Soon after I was invited to join the Network in 1983, when I was teaching at Winchester College, I drove over to Ockley to meet George Blaker. He took me out to a local pub and mentioned in the course of lunch that I was just the kind of person he was looking for to take over the running of the Network! I was somewhat taken aback, but the idea grew on me and three years later I was collecting files and papers from his house and driving back to Gloucestershire to start work with my new electronic typewriter. At first, I received little mail and did not even need a secretary. We had no computer until 1988 and all records were kept on a card index file. There were just over 400 members and a number of associate members or friends who received the newsletter in return for a token subscription. Then, gradually, activity began to pick up. The 1987 May Lectures were attended by 150 people and we arranged a series of autumn lectures in an inaccessible part of St. Thomas's Hospital.

By the summer of 1989 we decided to hold a residential Annual Meeting and spent a couple of glorious days at Dartington Hall with some sixty members out of the total of 600. Since that time the membership has more than trebled and now stands at 2,000 in over fifty countries, with a further 800 associate members. We have experienced a considerable growth in international membership, which makes up nearly 40 per cent of the total. Since the election of Kevin Ashbridge in 1992, the Council has always had at least one representative from Continental Europe and bi-annual Continental Members' Meetings have been instituted as well as country groups in The Netherlands, Switzerland and Germany. In 1993 we took our Annual Meeting abroad for the first time, and again in 1996. The growth of membership has made local groups a viable proposition so we now have a twenty such groups operating all over the country with more in the process of formation. We also have a small number of interest groups meeting on a regular basis and whose activities are reported in the Network News and Notices section of the Review.

In 1992 we had the chance to take over the organisation of the annual Mystics and Scientists conference which celebrated its 20th Anniversary in 1997 and which resulted in the publication of a book compiled from the lectures *The Spirit of Science* (Floris Books). This led to a raising of our conference profile and the staging in 1995 not only of the Mystics and Scientists conference, but also to a major meeting withProfessor Ilya Prigogine, a conference in St. Petersburg and the first Beyond the Brain conference in Cambridge with the Institute of Noetic Sciences. This has helped establish our track record as conference organisers and has in turn led to the production of video and audio recordings now sold through our trading arm Wider Horizons, set up in 1995. Although our Wider Horizons course for young people is currently dormant (see George Blaker's description above), an increasing number of UK members are now giving lectures in schools through our Schools Scheme. We now have over ninety members participating and send our material to more than sixty schools.

Another major recent development has been the establishment of our Web Page with the help of a grant and a great deal of hard work by Claudia Nielsen, Paul Filmore and Levente Toth. More recently, Kevin Ashbridge has served as our web master and will hand over to John Caton during early 1999. His major innovation is the monthly updated Members' Directory that now appears in the private area of the web. The office moved from the South of England to Fife in Scotland at the end of 1996. We now have four main computers, one for each full- or part-time member of staff, plus a laptop and a portable miniature Psion, useful for writing book reviews on long-distance flights!

Over the period, the newsletter has metamorphosed from 32 small pages to the 72 double column pages A4 format Review. We are indebted to John Miller for all the editorial work he has put in since 1993 to make the presentation and layout so professional. Unfortunately John died rather suddenly in May 1998, but his good work is being maintained in the new arrangements we have with our local printers.

One of the biggest differences in format is in the book review section, which has been steadily built up over the past few years; ten

years ago there were perhaps half a dozen short reviews per issue whereas we now have up to forty main reviews plus nearly a hundred other shorter ones per issue!

At the beginning of 1999 we are now poised to expand our activities with the inception of a new educational initiative and the inauguration of the George Blaker Foundation as its vehicle. We know that many people share our approach, views and concerns and are working for a deeper and more humane world-view that recognises the essentially spiritual nature of human life, a science that incorporates a profound understanding of human consciousness, a medicine that treats the whole multi-dimensional person and an education system that is more than just a training of the mind and memory.

What Does the Network Stand For?

Max Payne

Max Payne concludes this introduction by asking what the Network stands for. It is a question as relevant now as 25 years ago when the founders began their deliberations. Max was invited to join the Network by Peter Leggett, and has been a very active Member ever since. Formerly a lecturer in philosophy at Sheffield Hallam University, he is currently Chair of the Trustees of the Network.

What does the Scientific and Medical Network actually stand for? This is the question potential members ask when they are wondering whether to join. It is also asked by long standing members who know that they belong to something valuable, but who do not quite know what it is. A cynical answer is that, like all organisations, the Network stands for itself. It has risen from nothing in the last 25 years. It has organised a large number of successful events, conferences and seminars, and it has a devoted membership; the main aim of the Network is to continue going on as it is. This answer plainly will not do. A deeper answer, and perhaps the final answer, is to be found in the Network guidelines. We seek to express open-mindedness, rigour and concern for others. But the question remains, open-mindedness and rigour for what?

The Network has no corporate views. It proclaims no dogmatic manifestos.

Members publish their research, write their books and make their public pronouncements totally on their own authority. They may reveal that they are members of the Scientific and Medical Network if they wish, but they may not claim to have its backing for what they say. Yet most members of the Network are committed to the existence of a spiritual dimension. They believe that there is more to reality than space, time and matter, and the mind of man can touch that fuller reality. Why then does not the Network make the reality of the spiritual its major platform, instead of burying its recognition of the spiritual in the small type of its literature? Why do we pretend to be neutral when we are not?

Before this question can be answered another question comes first. Why have a "Scientific and Medical" Network at all? What is special about science? There are three key answers.

(a) The 20th century has been moulded by science and its attendant technology. It is by far and away the most triumphant form of knowledge mankind has ever possessed. We are the children of our times and can start from no place else.

(b) The official world view of science is materialistic and anti-spiritual. Any reaffirmation of the higher experiences of human consciousness has to confront scientific knowledge as it is at present structured. If the scientific world-view is to be transformed, it is has to be met on its own terms. . The people best qualified to do that are scientists and medical professionals themselves.

(c) Paradoxically the way to widen the horizons of science is through the self-awareness of science. The process of scientific inquiry is far more fundamental than the structure of scientific knowledge. The most powerful way to reaffirm the spiritual in our times is to claim that if only science is consistent with its own principles, science will recognise the reality of the dimension of spirituality.

Scientific knowledge is perpetually advancing in detail, but during the history of science the whole structure of scientific has undergone dramatic paradigm shifts. Modern science began when Ptolemaic astronomy and Aristotelian mechanics were supplanted by the mechanics of Galileo and Newton. 20th century science in its return replaced Netwon with Einstein and the hard massy atom with quantum theory. The paradigms of science, and the total world-view of science have changed, but the process of scientific discovery has remained the same. Science is an open self-critical inquiry based on a cyclical system of theory, deduction, experimental confirmation or refutation. The ideal of science is expressed in the basic regulative principle of the Lorenz transformation in relativity theory. Science seeks that description which is true for all possible observers whatever their particular perspective.

Science is the most successful form of knowledge the world has ever known. It has revealed the inner most energies of the atom, the complex secrets of the genetic code at the heart of the living cell, and has discovered that we live in a universe so vast that it exceeds the limits of our imagination. The reality revealed by modern science is so far outside the limits of human experience that it can only be talked about in enormous negative and positive powers of ten. The human mind does not know what 10^{32} seconds or 1011 years means. They are simply numbers that if used in calculations yield the right answers. Yet vast as the fabric of scientific knowledge is, it systematically excludes the central core of human experience including the very self-aware creativity of the scientist that makes science possible. Man's inner knowledge of himself is outside science, and the attempt to reduce a human being to the categories of external scientific knowledge is as inadequate as it is degrading. Any attempt to come to grips with the dimension of spirituality must go beyond the limits of science as we know it today.

Yet at the same time as we must seek to transcend science we have no better model for a valid truth seeking inquiry than science. The greatest challenge to the Scientific and Medical Network today is to show that the inquiry into the paranormal and the spiritual can be subject to the same discipline of impartial truth seeking as physics and astronomy. In science there is a point of neutrality beyond the most zealous advocacy of the most well attested theory. The point of neutrality is the point of the final and ultimate question - in the light of all the evidence, is this true? This is the position of totally impartial judgement in the pursuit of truth. It is an almost impossibly exacting position, and the amazing thing is how often science manages to reach this point.

It is possible to regard the whole history of human civilisation as a vast and as yet uncompleted spiral. With the rise of science in the modern age mankind moved from societies ruled by custom, emotion and belief into a more coldly rational age. A more participatory view of reality gave way to more clinical and objective perspective. Science displaced religion. We are now on a higher curve of the spiral. We are coming to recognise that reality is wider and higher than the objective material world of space and linear time. The task before us is to return to a better and wiser perception of spirituality carrying with us all the disciplines of the open self-critical truth seeking process of science. The paradigm examples of the scientific process is the way Newtonian physics was replaced by Relativity, or the Einstein / Bohr correspondence on quantum physics. In both cases the process of inquiry was seen to be more important

What this means in the exploration of the wider dimensions of human consciousness can be seen in two examples. There is impressive evidence that about 5% of those having a cardiac arrest, but who recover, have a "Near Death Experience" of moving through a tunnel into an ocean of light and love Those who have had the experience consider it evidence that human personality can survive the death of the body. Sceptics have asserted that this is what can happen to consciousness when the brain is short of oxygen. Alternatively it is suggested that an NDE the right temporal lobe of the brain connects with a universal state of non-locality in a 10 dimensional universe.

Again the evidence for telepathy and the far vision of distant objects is well documented. This appears to be straightforward evidence for consciousness operating outside the brain, and therefore for consciousness being something separate from matter. It could be, however, that someone might come up with impressive evidence for telepathy being a function of modulated neutrinos operating in a non-local fashion. Such a theory would put the whole question of the relation of mind to matter into a new perspective.

The role of the S.M.N. is to raise these questions and to catalyse a dialogue at the highest level in order to seek for the answers. It should not proclaim as final some theory of the way the universe fits together, because it is almost certainly bound to be wrong. The spiritual dimension of human experience exists and is supremely important. The search for goodness, love, truth and beauty is intrinsic to our nature, how it fits with matter, time and death is an open question as far as the human stage of existence goes.

This quest for truth and neutrality as to the answer becomes even more important if we explore further what the Network really has to be about. The Aristotelian schoolmen talked about mechanics and motion, but only Galileo dropped two balls from the leaning tower of Pisa to see what actually happened beyond ideological or intellectual commitment. Science has not always lived up to this high standard, of course, as the history of the theory of continental drift, or the inability of orthodox science to come to terms with the evidence for paranormal phenomena shows. However it is only necessary to look at the history of religion to see how admirable the example of science is. Religion is split up into a large number of major and minor groups, all totally in conflict with each other, although all claim to be in touch with ultimate spiritual reality. Not only are the great traditions utterly distinct , but each one is fragmented into smaller and smaller sects quarrelling ever more bitterly over ever tinier details of their faith. Does the Holy Spirit proceed only from the Father, or from the Father and the Son?. Just exactly how many times must the name of Amida Buddha be repeated to ensure re-birth in the Paradise of the Pure Land? Does the authority of the Bishop of Rome really extend to the power to release a soul from the travails of Purgatory?

If the great spiral is leading us back into spirituality, it is necessary to ensure that intuition leads us to transcend the intellect. We do not want emotion to drag us backwards to level below the rational. We must reverence and preserve the methods of scientific critical rationality. In the 20th century there has been a great gulf between science and spirituality. The Network stands with one foot each side of the divide. Its role is to build a bridge over the abyss. It should not lead over and walk away from the problem.

I have little doubt that the challenge of our rapidly moving times may force the Network to be adopt a higher profile on the spiritual dimensions of reality, and the necessary disciplines to be followed in order to be more open that reality. We may well, and indeed should, examine the moral responsibilities we have as individuals towards our fellow men and women, society and the ecosystem of the whole planet. But in all these things we must not lose sight of our central guiding compass direction: the impartial, self-critical and open search for truth.

Chapter 2
Science in Transformation

Edited by Chris Clarke

Introduction

S cience denotes the activities of a group of people, scattered across
the globe, teaching these practices to their successors; and it
denotes the material—ideas, perhaps knowledge, maybe even
occasionally wisdom—that flows from these activities. It is hard to
speak in generalities about such a multi-faceted thing, but we can
unhesitatingly say that we are now seeing major changes in science,
from whichever facet we view it. In this chapter I will be presenting
aspects of these changes that seem to me to be the most exciting. First,
however, I want to relate these movements to the wider institutional
picture.

Over the period 1973-1998 covered by this book, science has
changed in ways which both mainstream scientists and more radical
thinkers might describe as "transformation", though their emphases
would be different. Those in the mainstream, comparing science as
practised now with science at the start of this period, would see how
science has begun to free itself from its internal boundaries. While
universities may still package their work into departments labelled
"Physics", "Chemistry", "Geology", the real action is taking place across
traditional boundaries. Discussions of research strategy are marked not
by these old categories but a variety of new hybrids, such as Bio-
electronics, Earth Sciences, Environmental Engineering and so on.
Science is thus coming to be seen more as a single unified area of
enquiry. This unification is important; but the more radical scientist
would go further and in addition point to sciences in the making which
span even wider gaps, a key example being the study of consciousness,
which bridges quantum theory, psychology and biophysics. More than
this, they may argue (as Mae Wan Ho does below, for example) that
what is happening is not just a different way of cutting the same cake,

but a fundamentally different way of doing science, a way that emphasises the synthesis of elements into wholes as well as the analysis of systems into parts. From this point of view, science seems to be moving to the point where questions about our own place in the universe can at least be asked in a scientific context, if not answered!

How you view this depends on your conception of science. I remarked that it was the activity of a certain group of people, but what exactly is it that they are doing? It used to be thought that science was the process of progressively uncovering the nature of an absolutely existing external reality, gradually moving closer to a final revelation of all its laws and of all the objects that have come to exist as a result of those laws. On this conception the scientists' task is to exercise their ingenuity to discover what is already there, waiting to be found. It is as if the Grand Picture has already been painted in nature, but is only given to us in pieces like a jigsaw, and it remains for science only to fit together the pieces in order to reveal the picture. As with all jigsaws, there may be different strategies to be adopted in working on the task, but in the end it is the same picture that will emerge.

Some of the newer scientists regard this view as bunk, and I would certainly agree with them. I take from the old view of science that its defining property, what distinguishes it from pure art, is its quest for universality and for a particular sort of understanding, which ensures that its deliverances go beyond the merely personal. Its accounts are true not just for me and for those who are prepared to bend their imagination to mine, but for all inquirers who approach the matter with the tools appropriate to the phenomena in question. I also take from the traditional view the conviction that the accounts of science do not merely *reflect* experience, but they encapsulate experience so as to give an understanding of what could happen in nature and what could not happen. The understanding yielded by science is not merely a comfortable "ah" after the event, but the ordering of events according to their degree of possibility or impossibility, in a way that is always in some sense predictive. In the classic traditions of science, I accept that the pusuit of this quest involves many surprises and false turns before these qualities are achieved, so that science is very far from being a

49

construction of the human mind, but must be in constant dialogue with the intractability of nature.

To conclude from all this, however, that the picture delivered by science is independent of the way we approach the matter is a complete non-sequitur. There is abundant evidence (such as the description quoted below by David Peat of "Blackfoot Physics", and the analysis of Goethean science by Bortoft) that the picture depends crucially on the order and on the manner in which the pieces are found and placed. This means that our conception of science, indeed the very nature of what scientists do, is not merely starting to change from fragmentation to holism; it is starting to change from observation to participation. The activity of the scientist plays a part in determining what emerges. More than this: the quality of being of the scientist plays a part in what emerges.

These changes in science have occurred in part because of social and economic forces: the decline of authoritarian structures, the increase in the proportion of those participating in education in the West, the supremacy of technologically driven capitalism, the growing awareness of the consequent ecological crisis. And in part they have arisen because of the development of entirely new techniques within science itself. To understand this we need first to look at the new concepts and new mathematical tools that have made change possible, beginning with the concepts that arise from the quantum realm. In particular, this area has produced, by analogy or perhaps more than analogy, the idea of a participatory universe, with the scientist as a determining factor in the nature of reality.

Quantum Theory

Let us begin this section with a glance at terminology. Science is full of "theories" - of magnetism, continental drift, evolution and so on - accounts that explain some particular class of phenomena in terms of laws or mechanisms appropriate to that particular class. At first glance, "quantum theory" seems to be a theory in this sense, covering the class of atomic (or smaller) phenomena. But closer examination shows something very different. While it would be meaningless to apply ideas about convection in the earth's mantle to anything other than continental drift, the concepts of quantum theory are so general that they can be applied to *anything*. An indication of this is the fact many specific theories, such as magnetism or acoustics, come in two versions, classical and quantum, with the quantum version formed by applying quantum concepts to the classical theory. In other words, quantum theory is not in fact *about* anything in particular. Rather, it is a collection of ideas within which one can develop particular theories about particular phenomena.

A further confusing issue is the fact that there is no agreement as to what quantum theory actually is. Right from its start there were two versions (then called matrix mechanics and wave mechanics) which seemed at first to have little to do with each other, and several different varieties of interpretation, and this variegation has continued ever since. Surprisingly, this does not make the subject vague. Its procedures can be taught, and in almost all areas of application, apart from when it is pushed to extreme limits, its practitioners are never in any doubt as to what is or is not allowed in the subject. Those who do quantum theory have no problem; the difficulty lies with those others, philosophers or popularisers, who try to classify and unify this body of practice. Coming from the outside, it is painfully difficult to get to grips with what seems to be a confusing plurality of approaches. One can think one has learnt quantum theory by reading a single book, but one only knows quantum theory after one has taken one's place within a community of people using a variety of techniques, and after one has learnt how these different techniques translate one into the other. Those who proclaim that "quantum theory tells us that the world consist of waves", or "the world consists of many parallel universes" are confusing a particular dialect of a language with a model of reality. The phenomena that the language describes, however, are real and universally valid, and so it is to these phenomena that we need to turn, adding pinches of salt to the alternative linguistic descriptions that we are forced to employ when discussing them.

From its beginning, quantum theory has pointed to the active, participatory role of the "observer" in determining how phenomena can emerge, although there has been disagreement as to who or what an "observer" is. For Wigner it was the immaterial consciousness of the living scientist, for Daneri it could be a photographic camera. For Penrose, interestingly, it is any sufficiently massive object that records the phenomenon; though when that object also happens to be a brain, its action gives rise to consciousness. Experiments over the last 25 years have addressed the related questions: how extensive in space is the effect of the observer? and are the effects of different observers interrelated? The fundamental experiment that explores this, which has developed into many variations, will be described shortly—the 'Aspect Experiment" named after Alain Aspect who performed it in its most decisive form, or sometimes also after Friedman and Clauser who first developed the experiment. It shows clearly that the states of many entities, when handled quantum mechanically (in shorthand, their "quantum states") can be *entangled*, in a way to be described. Erwin Schrödinger, one of the principal founders of Quantum Mechanics, once remarked that its most significant feature was the possibility of the entanglement of states. The ethical implications of entanglement will be developed by Mae-Wan Ho later in this chapter.

The enormous implications of the experimental detection of effects due to entanglement are twofold, corresponding to the two questions above. First, there is in principle no limit in space to the extent over which an observation sheds its influence. Second, while each observation is entirely unconstrained by other observations, the joint action of two or more observations can manifest additional phenomena which involve aspects of the combination which are more than the sum of the separate parts. It is as if each cell in our body were exercising complete freedom within its own terms of reference, and yet the totality of the cells had areas of freedom that emerged solely through the relationships of the cells, in which the body as a whole could find expression without thereby constraining the freedom of the individual cells.

The Aspect (FCA) Experiment[1]

The experiment is based the vital fact that light, like all physical entities, has both a particle aspect: if one uses a light-intensifier (of the sort used in military surveillance, for example) to amplify the image of a very weak source of light, then one can see the random speckles of individual photons—particles of light—arriving at the intensifier. In addition, it has a wave aspect: each photon is associated with vibrations of electric and magnetic fields, and these vibrations determine what happens when the photon passes through, for instance, a lens of a pair of *polaroid* sunglasses, or a prism whose faces are specially coated so as to be sensitive to the direction of these vibrations. Such prisms (figure 1) split a beam of light into two beams in which the electrical vibrations that make up the light take place in two different directions. We could, for instance, arrange things so that in one beam the electrical vibrations were taking place horizontally, while in the other they were taking place vertically. Physicists say that the two beams have 'different polarisations'. If we were to rotate the prism, then these two directions would also rotate, while keeping the same relation to each other and to the prism. If, now, the intensity of the beam of light is reduced to the point where it consists of individual photons passing through the prism one at a time, then each photon will emerge either in the horizontally-vibrating beam or in the vertically-vibrating beam. Since photons are indivisible, there is no alternative. But if we had set up the prism at a different angle, then the division would not have been into horizontal and vertical, but into two different angles.

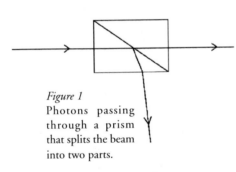

Figure 1
Photons passing through a prism that splits the beam into two parts.

Having got these details out of the way, I can now describe the Friedman-Clauser-Aspect experiment. Many night clubs (and also a local Italian restaurant, a favourite in our family, when it celebrates birthdays among its clientele) sometimes switch off the main lights and

53

turn on ultraviolet ones, at which all white garments glow blue because of the fluorescent dyes used by detergent manufacturers. The molecules of these dyes absorb light of one colour (in this case, ultraviolet) and then re-emit it a moment later at a different colour (in this case, blue). Some dyes can be set up so that, when a molecule absorbs a single photon of light at one colour, it later emits two photons in quick succession at another colour. The experiment makes observations on these pairs of twin photons coming from a single molecule, analysing their polarisations using two of the prisms just described, one for each photon, placed on opposite sides of the tube containing the dye, at some distance from it.

What happens depends on how the prisms are oriented. When both are aligned in the same way, then the same result is obtained from both: either both photons pass through or both are reflected (it cannot be predicted which of these happens on any particular occasion). In other words, the photons are not acting independently. In itself this is not surprising, since they have a common origin and so might be expected to have similar behaviours.

But as one thinks more about this, the behaviour starts to seem puzzling. Suppose, for example, that one of the photons, the left, say, passes through its prism. Then it is determined that the right must also pass through its prism; there is no choice about what the right one will do, once we know what has happened to the left one. So now there are two possibilities.

1. The first is that the right photon never had any choice in the first place, in that it was somehow fixed from the start that it would go through. But in that case it must have been fixed from the start that the left would go through, as well, since either both go through or neither goes through. So on this possibility the whole system has a fixed reality which we passively observe. This, however, is contradicted by the basic observations of quantum theory, that whether or not a photon goes through a polarisation-sensitive prism is randomly determined with probabilities that depend on the angle at which the prism is set. (This part of the argument is linked to the crucial element in the version of the experiment performed by Aspect, who demonstrated this randomness by altering the effective angle of the prism while the photon was already in flight.)

2. The second possibility is that it remains open what is going to happen to the right photon until we observe the left one. This possibility seems really strange, for it means that our knowing about the left photon somehow affects the right photon.

Careful observations of what happens when the prisms are at different angles now shows that the first possibility is wrong: quantum mechanics, with its uncertain reality not fixed in advance, is in fact operating. (The details, while not too complicated, involve a little elementary mathematics: see Penrose [1989].) So we are left with the second option: not only is the reality of the situation constructed by a dialogue with the observer, but the pair of photons respond to this dialogue in a co-ordinated fashion, even though they are separated by a large distance, so large that it is possible to choose the angles of the prisms after the photons have left the dye. The two particles form a single whole, dynamically determining its reality, even though the component particles appear to be separated in space. There is an underlying unity of being between the particles which overrides the separateness of space.

Though this experiment is concerned with the more exotic reaches of physics, its implications are enormous; what seems a tiny result about an obscure area of science spreads like a virus through the whole of scientific thought. The importance of separation in space is the bedrock of the scientist's view of reality; it is tied up with a view of space and time as absolute structures on which all else depends. Yet here is an influence, a kind of harmony, which seems to ignore spatial distance. Physics is rooted in atomism, the doctrine that ultimate reality consists of separate particles in the void, that interact only through external forces and collisions, yet these particles share an inner unity of being.

Metaphysical Foundations

Before moving on to mathematics, the second of the mental tools which have played such a part in transforming science, I insert a reflection on the metaphysical implications of the changes, and particularly of the changes stemming from quantum theory. With this confirmation by the FCA experiment of the key principles of quantum mechanics, 3 features emerged.

- It was possible that the universe was radically interconnected— interconnected at the level of being, not just at the level of causal interactions (at least this was true in the very restricted form manifested in the Clauser-Friedmann-Aspect experiment).

- The picture of the universe given by classical physics, in which there was a definite state-of-affairs at each moment of time, changing according to completely prescriptive laws, became very hard to maintain. Of the various versions of the classical picture, only Bohm's very sophisticated variation was tenable, but this had the drawback of its far greater complexity in com parison to quantum theory; if Bohm's theory were not used, the indeterminism of quantum theory had to be accepted as an integral part of nature.

- The indeterminism (or "freedom", to use a positive term) of nature emerges progressively and independently at greater and greater levels of complexity.

Rejection of the classical picture leads to an "ontological vacuum": quantum theory has no agreed answer to the question, of what does the universe consist? (Entities carrying names like "protons" and "neutrons" become logical principles, not building blocks.) This ontological vacuum engenders not despair but opportunity, for rethinking our metaphysics in a way that takes account from the start of the participation of the observer, the interconnectivity of the parts, and the indeterminacy of phenomena. In such a rethinking, the nature of mind can play a central role—as discussed by Willis Harman in his essay elsewhere in this volume.

New Applications of Mathematics

Mathematics has been traditionally associated with the old mechanistic, non-participatory picture of the universe. Galileo, for example, wrote

> This grand book the universe ... is written in the language of mathematics, and its characters are triangles, circles, and other geometric figures without which it is humanly impossible to understand a single word of it; without these, one wanders about in a dark labyrinth.[2]

In Galileo's world, only these mathematical properties of nature were "real"; all the other qualities of our experience are added by the psychology of processing our sense-data. This association of mathematics with the Galilean world-view is endorsed below by Bortoft, writing on alternative Goethean science. But what sort of mathematics are we talking of here? The mathematics of classical physics was a discipline that dealt with precise numbers and their unambiguous prediction. What seems to be emerging as characteristic of new areas of science is not the abandonment of mathematics, but the application of branches of mathematics that deal with more qualitative aspects of nature. Alan Maine describes these intriguing developments below.

Mathematics for the New Science

Alan Mayne

Introduction

During recent millennia, mathematicians have created their own world, with many different but interlocking sub-worlds. This world seems real to them and it cannot be described by words alone; it also requires symbols and pictures to convey its meaning (Stewart 1995, p ix). Indeed it has both subjective and objective aspects. It springs from the imagination and artistic creation of mathematicians and scientists, but it brings many deep insights into the laws governing the physical universe. Parts of its wonder arise from the sheer beauty of many of its laws and phenomena; other parts reflect the wonder of the universe itself. For example, this wonder is evident in many of the recent developments of nonlinear mathematics, which has advanced explosively in recent decades. It also appears in the structures of great generality that modern mathematics has formulated. It shines like a lighthouse in the remarkable Fermat's Last Theorem, whose statement was so simple and elegant, but whose proof was formulated only recently after centuries of struggle (Aczel, 1996).

In general, mathematics is extremely valuable in philosophy, science and even in human affairs, because of the tremendous precision and versatility of its 'language'. It has linguistic tools of great power that complement those of written and spoken language. Thus the applicability and relevance of mathematical language may be much wider than most people suppose, because of the infinite variability and generality of approach that mathematics can in principle provide. Mathematics can be qualitative as well as quantitative, and mathematical processes are not bound to be *algorithmic*, thus they are not bound to follow explicit sets of rules. This opens up the possibility that mathematical language could have useful applications to describing spiritual experiences and discussing ethical problems, *without* devaluing their human meaning and quality.

Nonlinear Mathematics

Many of the more recent developments in nonlinear mathematics have become well-known to the public, partly because of their very broad practical significance, and partly because some of them produce highly artistic coloured images. They include catastrophe theory and the more general theory of singularities, the theory of fractals, chaos theory, and complexity theory. The realisation, that nonlinearity occurs very extensively in the universe, is totally transforming our scientific and thus our philosophical world views.

It is not very easy to define 'nonlinearity' in a way that can be understood by non-mathematicians. A 'linear system' can be defined very roughly as one whose whole is the sum of its parts. More generally, in a 'nonlinear system', the whole is no longer equal to the sum of its parts, and may be greater or less than this sum, or sometimes greater and sometimes less, according to its nature. Linear systems are generally very much easier to handle mathematically than nonlinear systems, which are so intractable that important advances in their understanding began, only about 100 years ago, with the work of Henri Poincaré. Practical solutions of most nonlinear equations and nonlinear systems became feasible only with the advent of modern computers. For similar reasons, most of the mathematics of physics was linear during its first two centuries or so, and only after that did nonlinear dynamics begin to be developed as an important practical theory.

From about the 1960s on, nonlinear mathematics began to branch out from nonlinear dynamics into new sub-branches such as catastrophe theory and the more general theory of 'mathematical singularities', the mathematics of fractals, chaos theory, and complexity theory. The following subsections briefly describe each of them in turn, but with special emphasis on chaos theory and even more on complexity theory.

Catastrophe Theory

Catastrophe theory was created by René Thom, who was a pure mathematician but also a 'natural philosopher', who thought deeply about the natural order and how it is reflected in scientific theories. Being founded on a branch of mathematics called 'differential topology', catastrophe theory is qualitative, not quantitative, but it is well adapted to describe and even predict the 'shape' of certain processes. As such, it can provide insights complementary to those obtained from quantitative mathematical analyses and calculations. The book *Catastrophe Theory* by Woodcock and Davies (1978) provides a good preliminary explanation of catastrophe theory and some of its applications for non-mathematicians. It outlines the seven 'elementary catastrophes', each indicating how a particular type of sudden qualitative change of system behaviour can occur. It then gives examples of how catastrophe theory can throw light on problems in physics, chemistry, biology, animal psychology, human psychology, sociology, politics, and economics.

Fractals

In 1975, Benoit Mandelbrot coined the term 'fractal' to describe broken up shapes that are irregular and have the same degree of irregularity at all scales. A fractal object is 'self-similar' in that it looks similar when examined from nearby or at a distance. Many fractal shapes occur in nature, for example, coastlines, mountains, clouds, and the forms of many plants; the distribution of galaxies in the universe is fractal. Mandelbrot's (1983) book *The Fractal Geometry of Nature* presents the basic mathematical theory, and gives many illustrations of fractal shapes and patterns, some in colour and of great beauty. For briefer descriptions, see Chapters 10 and 11 in Hall (1992). Peitgen & Richter's (1986) book *The Beauty of Fractals* includes many additional coloured and black and white illustrations of fractals.

Chaos Theory

The book by Lorenz (1995) is a fascinating general introduction to chaos theory by one of the mathematicians who pioneered its development. Especially as it has many illustrations of beautiful mathematical curves and patterns, it is generally accessible to non-mathematicians, although elementary mathematical concepts are sometimes used. It explains the basic phenomena of chaos, and describes various natural phenomena where it arises. It concentrates most attention on chaotic phenomena which occur in weather; accurate weather forecasting is *not* possible after a fairly short time span, at most a few days long, which depends on the specific situation in which the forecast is made!

Lorenz includes a most interesting account of how, during his meteorological researches, he himself was led to discover the particular chaotic phenomenon, which later became known as the 'butterfly effect'. Some types of weather, like other chaotic phenomena in general, are *extremely sensitive* to their initial conditions. That is why the flapping of a butterfly's wing can affect the unfolding of other events many miles away! Though this effect is totally unpredictable!

Near the end of the book, readers are given some indication of how they can use programs on their personal computers to generate their own home-made chaotic visual displays! The last chapter outlines some of the relationships between chaos theory and other parts of nonlinear mathematics, including complexity theory, cellular automata, and fractals.

James Gleick's (1998) book *Chaos* is the best-known popular exposition of chaos theory, and an excellent survey of for those without mathematical knowledge. It gives a fascinating account of its evolution as a new branch of nonlinear mathematics during the 1960s and 1970s, and outlines examples of its many applications to science and technology and to practical applications like weather forecasting and stock market prediction. The book edited by Nina Hall (1992) gives further examples of scientific and other applications of chaos theory.

Complexity Theory

The books by Waldrop (1993), Lewin (1993), Casti (1994), and Cohen & Stuart (1994) show how scientists in many different disciplines are abandoning the linear, reductionist thinking, that has dominated so much of modern science, and are exploring new concepts about interconnectedness, coevolution, nonlinearity, structure, order and chaos. These pioneering new thinkers are combining their new ideas, explorations and experiments into an entirely new way of thinking, a new paradigm, about nature, life, human social and economic behaviour, and the universe itself. This is a most promising breakthrough in unified scientific thinking, reaching farther than general systems theory, because it penetrates so much more effectively into areas of practical application.

Although the first two books deal with advanced scientific concepts, they are written in very readable styles like that of Gleick (1998) on the mathematics of chaos. They discuss, from complementary viewpoints, the work of the remarkable Santa Fe Institute for the study of the sciences of complexity, in New Mexico, USA, with which many if not most of these scientists have been associated at one time or another. By introducing the personal stories of the lives and thinking of those most directly involved, and vividly conveying the excitement of the areas in which they are working, these three books are as 'hard to put down' as any thriller! They bring out the essence of the new ideas that they discuss, even though the detailed implementation and application of those ideas can only be understood by the appropriate 'experts'. They have useful lists of further reading for those who wish to explore the relevant mathematical and scientific ideas further.

Both Waldrop and Levin emphasise certain striking features of the emerging 'science of complexity', that is still so new and wide-ranging, that it is hard to define it and determine its boundaries. Complexity research addresses many questions arise in many scientific disciplines, indeed often cut right across them. These questions concern the origin of life, the nature and development of living organisms and their ecosystems, biological evolution, the human brain, human economies, and so on, even the nature of the physical universe itself. Nobody yet knows what these questions have in common, but each of them refers to a complex system, where very many independent agents interact with each other in very many ways. The agents' interactions are so rich that they always allow the system as a whole to undergo spontaneous self-organisation. The system is adaptive, in the sense that it actively tries to turn surrounding events to its advantage. It has a kind of dynamism that makes it qualitatively different from static objects that are only complicated. All these complex systems can also bring order and chaos into a special type of balance, often called 'the edge of chaos'.

Complexity scientists find these common themes so striking, that they see an underlying unity common framework and a common theoretical framework for complexity, that would illuminate both its natural and its human phenomena. At the Santa Fe Institute and elsewhere, they believe that they have the mathematical tools to develop it, including nonlinear mathematics, the mathematics of chaos, computer simulation, automata theory, artificial intelligence, artificial neural networks, cybernetics, general systems theory, evolution theory, and ecology.

In his book *Complexification*, Casti (1994) draws on his experience of working at the Santa Fe Institute to show how complexity theory can become the basis for a science of surprise. It shows how the theory challenges and gives counter-examples to each of the following 'conventional intuitions'. Small gradual changes in causes lead to small gradual changes in effects. Deterministic laws give rise to completely predictable effects. All real-world truths are the logical consequence of following a set of rules. Complex systems can always be understood by analysing them into simpler parts. Surprising behaviour results only from complicated interactions between a system's parts that are hard to understand.

Cohen and Stewart adopt a complementary approach to Waldrop and Lewin, by enquiring how simplicity in nature is generated from chaos and complexity. They ask why simplicities exist and can persist in a complex universe, and derive simplicity from the interaction between chaos and complexity. They find that many different complex systems contain the same simple large-scale patterns, because such patterns do not depend on detailed substructure. The first part of the book is about what science knows, states the conventional reductionist view, and presents science as a developing set of ideas, not as a fixed body of established knowledge. The second part considers what to think about what science knows and does not know. This area is a more mysterious world, to be presented through images and metaphors, rather than by formal definitions and descriptions.

The final chapter shows the nature of the relationships between simplicity and complexity, and introduces the concepts of 'simplexity' and 'complicity'. Simple rules tend to emerge from underlying order and complexity, in systems whose large-scale structure does not depend on fine details of substructure. The closely related concept of 'simplexity' concerns the emergence of large-scale simplicities as a direct result of rules, and is guaranteed by these rules. At the same time, interacting systems tend to coevolve and mutually change each other, and their simple beginnings lead to a growth of complexity, that cannot be explained in detail, but whose general course can be understood and predicted. 'Complicity' is much more subtle, intricate and convoluted than 'simplexity'; it enlarges the range of possibilities, but can be recognised by 'meta-rules', which are large-scale universals.

In his book *Thinking in Complexity*, Klaus Mainzer (1997) critically analyses the successes and limitations of scientific approaches based on complexity theory, its systematic foundations, and its historical and philosophical background. Its chapters consider the relationships between complex systems and the evolution of matter, life, mind-brain, artificial intelligence, and human society. Its epilogue on ethics discusses ethics in relation to responsibility and freedom.

In his book *How Nature Works*, Bak (1996) introduces a concept of 'self-organised criticality' to explain various complex patterns that repeatedly occur in nature and in human affairs. He gives examples from various branches of the natural sciences. Then, in Chapter 11, he points out that economies show various forms of instability, despite the almost exclusive emphasis of the mathematical theory of economics, until recently, on 'economic equilibria'. Like many other systems, economies are liable to fluctuations of activity that can occasionally be very large. From this point of view, very severe depressions *could* occur in the future, and it is still not clear how far financial and economic policies by governments can prevent a major, worldwide depression during the next few years.

Anderla et al. (1997), the authors of the book *CHAOTICS*, use the perspective provided by what they call 'chaotics', a combined mathematical theory of chaos and complexity, to develop what they view as a truer understanding of the processes of the real world. They suggest various ways in which it could be applied it to contribute to the improvement of the human situation.

General Mathematical Structures

Mathematical modelling, general systems theory, and cybernetics provide a general framework for discussing similar basic structures arising in different branches of knowledge. One of the final sessions at the International Cybernetics Conference in August 1998 discussed the scope for applying knowledge about general mathematical structures to cybernetics and other branches of science, and formulated preliminary plans for setting up an international study group for this purpose. Category theory was considered to be especially significant in this respect.

Probability theory, mathematical statistics, and fuzzy set theory lead to broader, more general views of causal categories (including 'acausal synchronicity') and scientific methodology in general. Peterson (1998) describes a fascinating journey into the ambiguities and uncertainties of randomness, which is a part of everyday experience that we associate with chance, uncertainty, and chaos. Randomness occurs in many systems in daily life, and plays a fundamental part in quantum physics.

At a deeper level, Gödel's Theorem shows that systems of mathematics have certain limits, so that it is *not* possible to prove or disprove every possible proposition about a mathematical system *within* that system. This could have important consequences for the limits of scientific and philosophical understanding and for the nature of artificial intelligence. These topics are discussed in Chapter 8 of John Barrow's (1998) book *Impossibility.*

Category Theory

Category theory is a generalisation and extension of *set theory,* which has played such a fundamental part in mathematics in the past. It helps overcome some of the problems and paradoxes that have arisen in set theory, and its methods have been remarkably successful in some other branches of mathematics. It also has applications to computer science, where it is related to the concepts of *object-oriented programming* that are becoming increasingly important. It also has applications to cybernetics and could be relevant to theories of the classification of knowledge. I do not know of any popular or semi-popular exposition of category theory, but the book edited by Gray (1984) gives a good idea of the range of its mathematical applications.

Probability Theory and Statistics

Probability theory and statistics have many applications to all branches of science and technology, ranging from quantum physics to practical affairs. During recent years, the analysis and perception of risk have been discussed increasingly, as more publicity has been given to both man-made and natural disasters. Thus they have become important challenges to the science, engineering, and technology (SET) community. Probability theory can be applied to making quantitative estimates of various types of risk, but it is often difficult to calculate these estimates due to inadequate information about the situations in which they occur and the unquantifiable nature of many types of uncertainty. In some cases, public concern about risk even leads to increasing skepticism about the advantages of scientific research, so that an appropriate system is needed for measuring risk. John Adams

(1995) discusses risk mainly from the psychological viewpoint of how people perceive risks and behave in various types of risky situation.

Conclusions

Although their roots go back for many years and sometimes for over a century, the different sub-branches of the mathematics of nonlinearity have radically transformed not only mathematics itself but also the scope of its applications to science, technology, and human affairs. Many people who are non-mathematicians have thereby gained some knowledge of what it can do, and much appreciation of its beauty and its wonder. At the same time, advances in category theory, probability theory, and statistics exemplify the many ways in which more general concepts of mathematical structure are increasing the applicability, scope, and power of mathematics.

Alan Mayne is editor of 'New Paradigms Newsletter' and author of a number of resource books for the new millennium.

The Nature of Life and Evolution

In the classical picture as I have characterised it, the world is a deterministic machine with separated parts, a view which reinforces the Darwinian concept of evolution in which the only interaction between individuals and between species is that of competition. Indeed, competition is a denial of interaction: the species affect each other only through the intermediary of a common resource—food or space—which is becoming depleted. This in turn fitted well with social Darwinism, the carrying over of the notion of unrestricted, non-interacting competition into the functioning of society, and with this came the pernicious amorality of the market place. It is perhaps profitless to search for which of these factors came first in a causal chain; it is sufficient to note their interdependence.

With changes in our view of the universe, and changes in society, the Darwinian concept of evolution could no longer be accepted uncritically. A landmark in this was Lyn Margulis's 1970 book *The origin of eucaryotic cells* which demonstrated what has now become an orthodoxy, that the cells which make up all the dominant species on earth today arose not from competition but from collaboration, in which different organisms came together to work for their mutual good, and eventually fused into a single entity. Since then, the role of collaboration has become increasingly clear. But how are we to think of evolution (it its general sense of "unfolding") in the light of this new conception? Surely we have to start to reenvision what we mean when we talk of an "organism", how an organism is related to its environment, and what are the factors that bring organisms together and lead to their inner transformations. We also have to rethink the nature of any possible ethics that flows not from Darwinian competition but from organic wholeness and collaboration. Below I reprint three essays indicating possible paths in this rethinking. First, Rupert Sheldrake describes the change that is needed from a mechanistic to an organismic paradigm, and outlines its implications. These ideas are then further developed in more detail by Mae Wan Ho, who describes the nature of the organism and its ethical implications. Then Theodore Roszak describes the new concept of evolution, which starts to implicate the role of mind in the process. Mae-Wan Ho significantly picks up the quantum idea of entanglement that I discussed above, and draws out from it its own particular ethical implications.

Widening the Framework of Biology[2]

Rupert Sheldrake

I believe that the study of living organisms could be far more exciting, fruitful and attractive if the framework of biology were widened.   I give examples of inexpensive research that could help open up its frontiers.

In the life sciences, teaching and research are severely limited by an outmoded ideology.   Since the collapse of communism, academic biology is one of the few domains in which a narrow orthodoxy retains a near-monopoly of power. In most other areas of modern life we are used to pluralism and debate. In politics, for example, it is taken for granted that different parties will have different views. The same is true in the arts, and indeed within the churches. Even in the hardest of hard sciences, physics, there is a diversity of opinions on fundamental questions. The fantastic theory that the universe splits into a multiplicity of parallel universes every time a measurement is made is seriously debated. Extra dimensions, once the hallmark of metaphysical speculation, now come cheap; for example, the currently influential superstring theory has ten, nine of space and one of time.

Institutional biology stands in stark contrast to all this liberal pluralism, a living fossil of an earlier age. Its still-dominant paradigm, the machine theory of life, is over three and a half centuries old. In the scientific revolution of the seventeenth century, Descartes and his fellow mechanists explicitly rejected the old doctrine, taught all over medieval Europe, according to which not only people but also plants and animals were shaped and organized by invisible souls. This was, in turn, one version of the animistic thinking found in traditional cultures all over the world. The English word 'animal' reveals these assumptions through its derivation from 'anima', the Latin word for soul.

The mechanistic theory proclaimed that the universe and everything within it were soulless. Plants and animals, and the human body too, were inanimate machines, devoid of any mysterious life-principle. The only exception was a small region of the human brain, the pineal gland, in which the rational mind interacted in an unexplained way with the machinery of the nervous system. The modern theory is essentially the same, except that the supposed seat of the mind has shifted a couple of inches into the cerebral cortex. Many modern mechanists seek to dissolve the mystery of the mind by asserting that consciousness is nothing but an aspect of the physico-chemical functioning of the brain.

From the seventeenth century right up to the 1920s, the mechanistic school of biology was opposed by vitalists, according to whom living organisms are truly alive, animated by a life principle not reducible to the physics and chemistry of inanimate matter. Mechanists denounced vitalism as heresy, or dismissed it as a superstition that would be swept away by the progress of rational understanding. Vitalism is the ultimate in scientific incorrectness.

This historical background helps explain why institutional biology is so attached to the mechanistic paradigm, in spite of the many problems it causes. Here are some of them :

- Factory farming is a logical outcome of the mechanistic theory of life. But like vivisection, it arouses increasing opposition from those who see animals as fellow creatures, rather than inanimate machines.

- The reductionistic spirit of modern biology has been intensified by huge financial investments in genetic engineering and biotechnology. The gulf between laboratory research and our direct experience of animals and plants grows ever wider.

- Despite the strenuous efforts of neo-Darwinian evangelists, the theory of evolution by blind chance and purposeless selection cannot be proved, and is continually challenged and questioned.

- Consciousness remains inexplicable in mechanistic terms.

- Psychic phenomena have refused to go away, despite being denied for decades by institutional biology and academic psychology.

- Despite the successes of orthodox medicine, there has been an astonishing growth of alternative forms of therapy. These are usually ignored by official medical research institutes and medical schools. An open-minded and pragmatic approach to healing is impeded by mechanistic prejudices.

- Many central problems of biology remain unsolved in mechanistic terms: for example the development of embryos, the inheritance of instincts and the navigational abilities of animals like homing pigeons. Mechanists always promise that a mechanistic understanding will be achieved some time in the future, but this is no more than an act of faith.

- Although mechanistic biology is founded on the denial of animating principles within living organisms, in practice these vital factors are reinvented in a mechanistic guise. The "genetic program", for example, is a purposive, mind-like entity that goes far beyond the mere molecules of DNA. And the "selfish genes" of Richard Dawkins are endowed with the power to "mould matter", "create form", "build survival machines to live in" and even "aspire to im mortality". The real paradigm of modern biology is in fact a form of crypto-vitalism.

The main alternative to the mechanistic paradigm today is not a return to old-style vitalism, but the holistic or organismic approach. Instead of taking the machine as its central metaphor, it treats living organisms as organisms. The machine metaphor has no privileged claim on our thinking. It is not supremely objective, as its proponents often assume, but intensely anthropocentric. Only human beings make and use machines, and only recent human beings at that. The mechanistic theory projects technological habits of thinking onto all of nature.

The philosopher Alfred North Whitehead proposed in the 1920s that the metaphor of the organism could unify the sciences, and transcend the old vitalist-mechanist controversy. From this point of view, not only microbes, plants and animals are treated as organisms, but also atoms, molecules, crystals, societies, planets, solar systems and galaxies. The Gaia hypothesis, the idea of the Earth as a living organism, is one example of this approach. The new cosmology provides another. Rather than seeing the universe as a machine slowly running out of steam, since the 1960s the cosmos has looked more like a developing organism, starting very small, and developing ever more complex patterns of organisation within itself as it grows. Embryos behave like this; machines do not.

The holistic approach emphasises that at each level of organisation, organisms have an integrity that cannot be understood simply from a study of their parts. Within biology, one way of thinking about this wholeness is in terms of biological fields, such as the morphogenetic fields that shape the developing forms of plants and animals.

I have proposed that such fields are responsible not only for morphogenesis, but also for the organisation of instincts and behaviour, for mental activity and for the co-ordination of individual organisms within societies. The generic name for these organising fields is morphic fields. I postulate that these fields have an inherent memory, given by a process called morphic resonance, involving the influence of like upon like through space and time. The result of this process is that each member of a species both draws upon and contributes to a collective memory. In the human realm, a similar conception is already familiar in the form of C.G. Jung's notion of the collective unconscious. These ideas are developed in detail in my book *The Presence of the Past* (Collins).

In my book *Seven Experiments that Could Change the World: A Do-It-Yourself Guide to Revolutionary Science* I describe seven different ways in which inexpensive research could open up science in general and biology and psychology in particular. One example concerns the uncanny powers of domestic animals. Most households in Britain contain pets, and these are the animals we know best and observe most intimately. This vast body of experience has been ignored by institutional science, and even by parapsychologists. But if we pay attention to the plentiful evidence, rather than dismissing it, several common patterns emerge, some of which suggest the existence of modes of communication at present unknown to science.

The behaviour on which I have concentrated concerns the ability of dogs and cats to know when their owners are coming home. The animals go to a window, door or gate to wait for their owners, often half an hour or more before their return. In many cases, this reaction cannot be explained in terms of routine or the expectation of people at home, because the absent person returns at irregular and unexpected times. For example, over twenty people have told me that their partners work irregular hours and do not usually telephone to say when they are coming, but they know from the pets' behaviour when their partner is on the way home, and prepare a meal accordingly.

Several people have, at my request, carried out simple experiments by coming home at random times and by unusual means, for example being driven by a friend in an unfamiliar car. Their dogs still reacted, usually responding at the very time they set out to come home. In some cases when people took taxis, the dog reacted not at at moment they got into the taxi, but when they telephoned for it. Several such experiments have been recorded on video, and further research of this kind could well be carried out in student research projects. The results so far suggest that pets can pick up their owners' intentions from miles away in a manner that cannot be explained in terms of conventional senses or physical forces. This could be called a psychic or telepathic effect, but I prefer to think in terms of a morphic field linking pet to owner.

Another line of research concerns the well-known feeling of being stared at from behind. This effect implies that the mind of the starer can reach out to touch the person stared at, and has many implications for our understanding of consciousness. Again, this phenomenon has so far been neglected by science, and yet it can be investigated by simple experiments that cost almost nothing. Some have been carried out as student projects in schools. The results so far suggest that the effect is real, and cannot be explained in conventional scientific terms. For details of experimental procedures, see my world wide web site (www.sheldrake.org).

Research on subjects such as these has been inhibited for decades by taboos against the "paranormal". But the phenomena themselves are normal enough. Millions of people have experienced them, and their existence is usually regarded as a matter of common sense. Such phenomena imply the existence of invisible interconnections so far ignored by science. But they only seem paranormal if "normal" is taken to mean "mechanistic".

I believe the development of science is better served by opening up such fields of enquiry rather than by putting them out of bounds. We need a broader theory of life, and I look forward to liberation of biology from the dogmas of mechanism.

Dr. Rupert Sheldrake is author of a number of controversial books, including 'A New Science of Life', 'The Presence of the Past' and 'Seven Experiments that Could Change the World'.

© **Times Supplements Limited, 1996**

The Physics of Organisms and the Naturalistic Ethic of Organic Wholeness

Mae-Wan Ho

The Fall from Grace

The biblical account of our common ancestors' fall from grace has always held a special fascination for me, because it can be read in so many ways. One reading is a parable of our estrangement from nature, as the result of which, we are forever condemned to know her from the outside. Cartesian mind-matter dualism, at the basis of western science, did begin by separating mind from body and isolating observer, as disembodied mind, from 'objective' nature observed. It has resulted in a knowledge of alienation, which is reductionist, fragmented, devoid of value and meaning, and divorced from life.

Another more interesting reading is that, in the beginning, our ancestors were happy and content in the garden of Eden, i.e., nature, in a mindless, innocent sort of way, until Eve tasted the fruit of the tree of knowledge and discovered reason. Presumably, she began to think for herself, telling Adam he should do likewise, thus bringing upon them the wrath of God, a benevolent despot who likes to keep humanity innocent and happy. So he castigated them both, told them they were shameful, guilty and sinful, and shut them out of nature forever. He admonished them not to think for themselves, but instead, to have faith, to bear children, to atone for their sins and wait for redemption. The irony is that once Eve has tasted the forbidden fruit - knowledge - which enables her to know nature more intimately, she and her children are seduced into doing it ever since. I believe it is possible for her children to find their way back to the garden of Eden through knowledge. Perhaps, God, being really a decent sort of fellow, knows that anything forbidden is bound to be seductive, and has actually meant for us to know, to redeem ourselves through reason and imagination.

Redemption through Knowledge

So it is that the same tradition of western science, now pushed to its limits, is leading us back to a participatory knowledge that is probably universal to all traditional indigenous cultures world wide. My book (Ho, 1993) is an attempt to outline a participatory 'indigenous western science' which is fully contemporary. It is 'participatory' because the knower places her undivided being - body and mind, intellect and feeling - squarely within the known, which is all of nature. And it is 'indigenous' because, like all knowledge gained through immersing oneself within nature, it is an unfragmented whole - encompassing science, humanities and art, ethics and religion-that we live by, that gives meaning and value to life. In these respects, I part company with perhaps the majority of scientists for whom science holds no meaning for life, and must be divorced from personal experience in any event, to maintain its 'objectivity'.

The Theory of Organisms and Organic Wholeness

I take, as my starting point, Whitehead's view that we cannot understand physical reality unless we have a theory of the organism. I draw on many areas of contemporary physics - from non-equilibrium thermodynamics, condensed matter physics to quantum optics - as well physiology and biochemistry in order to illuminate the nature of the organism. I then show how there is no separation between the so-called 'hard' sciences such as physics and chemistry and the 'soft' sciences such as psychology and philosophy, and furthermore, that understanding the organism holds the key to understanding our selves and our relationship with nature.

The theory of the organism is about perceiving organic wholes, perceiving ourselves as such and at the same time, an integral, inseparable part of a greater whole that is ultimately all of nature. The organic whole is something very special, as Whitehead and Bergson both tried to tell us. It is a plurality that is singular, a unity that is multiplex and diverse, an actuality that contains within it all potentials.

74

It differs radically from the conventional notion of the 'whole' that belongs in the mechanical era - a collective or co-operative with a division of labour - a whole that can be taken apart, like a car-engine, and put back together again. Even the notion of nested hierarchies, or Arthur Koestler's holons, fails to capture the essence of an organic whole, for nested hierarchies, like Chinese boxes, can also be neatly decomposed. More-over, hierarchies imply that the 'higher' controls the 'lower', like the line-management that the present Government has foisted on our universities, many of which are in grave danger of congealing into a solid mass of bureaucratic, apathetic immobility.

An organic whole, in contrast to a mechanical whole, has no controller nor parts which are controlled. It is dynamic and fluid, its myriad activities are self-motivated, self-organising and spontaneous, engaging all levels simultaneously from the microscopic, molecular, to the macroscopic. Instead of 'control', a more accurate description is 'communication'. An organic whole is a system maximally communicative so that adjustments, responses and changes can propagate 'upwards', 'downwards', 'sideways' in all directions at once in the maintenance of the whole. An organism is always thick with activities at all levels - all co-ordinated and constitutive of the whole. The organism has therefore no preferred level. We may choose to define hierarchies and to restrict our description to the 'social', 'behavioural', 'biological', biochemical' or 'genetic' level, but only with the realisation that the whole will always elude us. The organic whole has no decomposable parts or levels, it is a coherent whole. This does not mean we cannot break it up to study the pieces, as we have been doing for several centuries in the west. But the isolated part is a mere shadow of its life in the whole. An enzyme molecule, for example, has a rich and diverse 'cytosocial' microenvironment within the cell - consisting of other enzymes, proteins, ions, and metabolites - in which it expresses its full potentials. It is only within the past decade that enzymologists are realising how we have been misled by their work on single, purified enzymes in dilute solution.

The Coherent Wholeness of Being

The coherence of organisms that I am talking about has all the properties of the ordinary meaning of the word: correlation, connectedness, a consistency in the system, and so on, and something much more.

Think of the 'I' that each and everyone of us experience of our own being - a consciousness that is resolutely and concretely singular. Although we know we are made up of innumerable cells and astronomical numbers of molecules of all kinds, we never experience ourselves in the plural, nor as a mixture of separate states. This experience of a singular 'I' is none other than the intuition of our own organic wholeness, our inner process with its dynamic heterogeneous multiplicity of succession without separateness, a succession of qualitative changes which melt into and permeate one another with no definite localisation or boundaries, each occupying the whole of our being within a span of feeling that Bergson refers to as 'pure duration'. The intuition of organic wholeness as pure duration is quite precisely captured by the notion of coherence within quantum theory.

The quantum coherent state is a 'pure state' - an indivisible, indecomposable unity that contains within it the potential of all states, each permeating the whole. It is a seemingly paradoxical state that maximises both global cohesion and local freedom. For coherence does not mean uniformity, or that everybody is doing the same thing all the time, quite the opposite is the case. The coherence of the organism is radically and quintessentially pluralistic and diverse, and at every level, from the structured, multi-enzyme complexes inside cells, the organisation of diverse cells into tissues and organs, the polymorphism of natural populations to the variety of species that make up natural ecological communities, and the kaleidoscopic, multicultural earth which makes life enchanting and exciting for us all.

Think of a particularly good performance of a grand ballet, or better yet, a large jazz band in which everybody, by doing his or her own thing, is perfectly in tune, in step with the whole, with the audience also participating in the occasion, becoming one with the performers in the music and the art. When we multiply such a performance as many times over as we can, increasing the number and range of performers and stretching tempo much, much further, and in both directions, we come close to imagining what happens in an organism such as ourselves. Within our body, the grandest ensemble of song and dance goes on, ranging over seventy octaves, from localised chemical bonds vibrating, molecular wheels turning, micro-cilia beating, waves propagating on all scales, to fluxes of electrons and protons, flows of metabolites and ionic currents within and between cells and tissues - activities spanning ten orders of magnitude of space, yet all constituting a coherent whole. The individual and the collective are one, with all the potentials of the pure state open to it. It is very likely that sustainable social and ecological communities function in the same way, over larger space-time domains.

The coherent state is also a state of 'non-locality' of space and time. For, within the volume in which coherence holds, there is no time-separation, so changes can 'propagate' in no time at all, and similarly, within the coherence time, there is no space-separation, so distant sites become neighbouring. This is very far removed from the ordinary commonsensical and mechanical notion - to which most of us have been thoroughly schooled - that objects are separate from one another, each of them having definite boundaries and outlines, and a simple location in linear, homogeneous space and time. Instead, the organic space and time of real processes are heterogeneous, non-linear, multidimensional and non-local, and hence thoroughly entangled with one another. As Whitehead says, 'each volume of space, or each lapse of time includes in its essence aspects of all volumes of space, or of all lapses of time'. It will take us a long while to recover the full intuition of non-local organic space time, which I believe, our common ancestors used to have, and a number of traditional indigenous cultures have retained it to the present day.

The Naturalistic Ethic of Universal Mutual Entanglement

An organism is a domain of coherent activities, perceiving, generating and structuring space and time. Its boundary is dynamic and fluid, extending and contracting with the extent of coherence. An organism could be an individual, a society, or indeed, the whole earth and beyond. Each organism, in the act of becoming itself; enfolds the environment consisting of other organisms into a unity residing in a 'self', while aspects of the self are communicated to others. The realisation of 'self' and 'other' are thus completely intertwined. The individual is a distinctive enfoldment of its environment, so each individual is unique. But it is also constituted of others in its environment and simultaneously de-localised over all individuals. The society is thus a community of organisms mutually de-localised and mutually implicated, or entangled. Individuality is relative, for an organism can be part of the life history of some larger, more complete entity. Ultimately, the entire universe is one organic whole constituted of a convocation of organisms that are mutually entangled in a multi-dimensional, non-local space-time of organic processes. That, and that alone can provide the rational basis of a naturalistic ethic: for any act against others is inevitably an act against the self The awareness of mutual entanglement - the organic oneness of all being - is the guide to coherent, or moral action. It also defines for each and every one a unique role in a participatory universe from whom we draw comfort and strength, and to whom we direct our creative action and love, which is at the same time, the fulfilment and love of self. We are, so to speak, at home in the universe.

The naturalistic ethic is thus integral to participatory knowledge, which is a way of life. Ethics is not something separate, to be grafted on to a knowledge system divorced from life, which therefore vehemently denies there can be such a thing as a naturalistic ethic. The currently dominant ideology is neo-Darwinian sociobiology. It tells us in no uncertain terms that we are really selfish bastards even when we are apparently good. Freudian psychology dovetails neatly with that view, and both are completely in line with the usual interpretation of the biblical account of the fall from grace: we are all branded with Original Sin. So, how can we be good? We can only frighten our children into submission, into behaving *as if* they are good by threatening them with punishment from father, and ultimately, God the Father. Fortunately, people *are* really good, and even though they have been misled into evil by alienation and ignorance – and organised religions of all kinds have a lot to answer for that – they can recover their indigenous 'goodness' through knowledge that they can feel and think out for themselves, and not just depend on the pronouncements of prophets or gurus.

The most significant development of contemporary western science is thus a re-affirmation of indigenous participatory knowledge at the 'fundamental' level of physical reality. It is the knowledge of universal, organic wholeness which is consonant with individual as well as collective experience, and that is how meaning is possible. Meaning depends on something deeply felt, that is communicable to other beings entangled with our own being. Words are not for naming or defining things. They are potent signs for invoking a shared reality which we never cease to participate in creating. And as reality is created and enriched, so too is meaning. A significant sign shapes and reshapes its content, which in turn conjures new signs. Reality is meaning, and meaning, reality. There is no 'objective' reality apart from us, just as we have no meaning apart from nature.

The participatory knower, therefore, acknowledges her power to shape and transform reality, and hence also her responsibility for the knowledge, always guided by an ethic of universal oneness that needs no external schooling. There is no piety involved in participatory knowledge, for it is above all, joyful, playful and spontaneous. It is always innocent, because it has no motive other than that it stems from our desire to know the breadths and depths of nature ever more intimately, and in countless ways to express the deep delight of mutual entanglement which is the well-spring of all creative action and understanding. Participatory knowledge knows no bounds nor boundaries. There is no fragmentation into disciplines, no demarcation into secular versus sacred domains: it is at once sublime and practical. It is one, and integral to life. By living our life as parent, builder, gardener, labourer, artist, scientist, all, we participate in celebrating and creating reality.

Acknowledgement

I thank Peter Saunders for commenting on earlier drafts and for suggestions to improve the manuscript.

Dr. Mae-Wan Ho is Reader in Biology at the Open University

Evolution and the Transcendence of Mind

Theodore Roszak

Where is evolution going? For most biologists, the answer is: everywhere and no where. Standard Darwinian theory understands evolution to be a free-for-all, governed by random combinations of DNA and lucky environmental selection. Living things evolve in all directions, occupying any niche for which their genetic roulette prepares them. 'Survival of the fittest' means the survival of those that 'fit' the shifting ecological contours of their habitat. The process is ceaseless, shapeless, mindless.

Evolution and the Enlightenment

Darwin, we must recall, created his theory of natural selection during the high noon of dog eat dog capitalism. Malthus and the Manchester School were never far from his thoughts. The prestige of classical economics has long since faded; but evolutionary biology remains linked to the image of ordered randomness once seen in the competitive free market. Natural selection is the biological version of Adam Smith's 'invisible hand'. In both cases we have dynamism without design, vitality that describes no vector. Both ideas claim to be value-free, but they are far from being philosophically neutral. Classical economics was invented to chase government from the marketplace; similarly, Darwinism was quickly seized upon to drive God from the state of nature. The universe ran by itself; no central planning agency was needed. But such biological laissez faire has always been troubling to those who see the history of life on Earth as an adventure rather than a succession of accidents, The uncertainty set in early. Alfred Russel Wallace, co-founder of natural selection, was among the first dissenters. He agreed that natural selection explains adaptation; but in his eyes adaptation was essentially conservative and unenterprising. It moves in a purely horizontal direction, moulding plants and animals to their environment in ever more specialised and so inflexible way. Overarching natural selection, Wallace saw a more daring, vertical movement which boosts evolution toward higher levels of complexity and consciousness.

The Evolution of the Brain

If evolution were merely a matter of survival by adaptation, we might still be a planet of hearty bacteria. Clearly, something more dramatic and risky has been going on. Life has been building itself up into more delicate, sentient forms. And in the vanguard of this vertical thrust, we find the most remarkable development of all: the human brain, an organ that vastly transcends the competitive advantage we may once have needed to outsmart our primate rivals.

What is the status of art and music in evolution, Wallace asked. Do they perhaps point toward a destined goal beyond physical survival? Fascinated by the transcendent impulse of the mind, Wallace, in his later years, was drawn to spiritualism and parapsychology as possible keys to human nature.

Standard biology has a conveniently minimising category for the brain's strange excursion into cultural creativity: hypertrophy. Excess - perhaps the sort of excess that often proves fatal, as it may have with the dinosaurs who went to extremes in body-weight. But a name is not an explanation. And there is surely something odd about so dismissive a treatment of the very mind that brought forth evolutionary theory. If we value the quest for truth, as every scientist must, are we to regard the brain that searches for truth as no more than a luxurious surplus of electrochemical circuitry?

Mind in the Cosmos

Following Wallace, countless evolutionary philosophies have pondered the place of mind in nature. All have agreed that it is the frontier of evolution. Admittedly, this is a self-serving view. The whales and the oak trees are in no position to dispute the role we assign ourselves as the vanguard of life on Earth. We announce that status, but only the silence of our fellow species surrounds us. Yet the claim need not be made arrogantly; nor need it ignore the hazards and responsibilities that befall pioneers. It can, indeed, be a humbling and civilising lesson to see ourselves at the forefront of a grand, cosmic vista that dwarfs the selfish passions and petty distractions of the moment.

But it is one thing to decide that mind is the leading edge of evolution; another to decide what 'mind' most essentially means. Whose mind do we choose as our model? Here is where controversy sets in. Scientists understandably cast human nature in their own intellectual image, preferring the analytical and empirical habits that characterize their professional life (but which may actually have little to do with great paradigmatic breakthroughs like Darwin's own discovery of natural selection). Such an approach to the evolution of intelligence is well illustrated in Carl Sagan's book *The Dragons Of Eden*. For Sagan, intelligence is wholly a matter of problem-solving and tool-making, practical talents to which natural selection easily applies.

This Robinson Crusoe/Tom Swift* image of mind is good, solid eighteenth century science. John Locke, David Hume, and Benjamin Franklin would have heartily approved. Here is the mind as a rational instrument without shadowed corners or hiding places. It is the mind of Homo faber; closed to dreams and unsettling visions, never in need of psychiatry or spiritual counselling. We are left to wonder how such a mind could ever make itself sick with unbridled fantasy or thwarted desire. In the evolution of efficient intelligence, why would not the burden of neurosis have long since been selected out? We are reminded that Freud, searching for the secret of madness, turned to the Romantic poets for insight, just as C.G. Jung, seeking the archetypal roots of consciousness, turned to myth, religion, and alchemy.

Artificial Intelligence

Not surprisingly, Sagan's study of mind finishes with an enthusiastic chapter on artificial intelligence, obviously the way ahead for the brain as data-processor. Conceive of the mind as a computer, and the computer is bound to look like a rather promising mechanical mind - possibly a better one than the human original. It calculates faster, files more datafollows logical rules more accurately, even plays chess better

*Hero of a series of early 20th C. American boys' adventure stories by Victor Appleton

than most. It uses words and numbers with unambiguous precision; it does not sleep, dream, lie, forget, goof off or go crazy. Is it not everything a mind should be?

There are many computer scientists who would agree. If evolution points toward better mental data processing, then the best data processors of the future may not be flesh and blood. It is not only science fiction that now flirts with the possibilities of human obsolescence. Imagine, at the present rate of progress, two or three more centuries of research in artificial intelligence and genetic self-replication. Imagine the two fields of study coalescing into one science. What wonders of transhuman evolution might then be within reach of our technology!

'The amount of intelligence we humans have is arbitrary,' observes computer expert Marvin Minsky of MIT, 'it's just the amount we have at this point in evolution.' There are people who think that evolution has stopped, and that there can never be anything smarter than us. Minsky has called the brain a 'meat machine' which, like all machines, can be analysed, adjusted, and improved upon.

In the same vein, Robert Jastrow of NASA believes that 'Human evolution is nearly a finished chapter in the history of life. That does not mean the evolution of intelligence has ended on the Earth. We can expect that a new species will arise out of man, surpassing his achievements as he has surpassed those of his predecessor Homo erectus. The new kind of intelligent life is more likely to be made of silicon.' Jastrow thinks this evolutionary leap to sentient computers may still be a million years off In the meantime, one can foresee problems along the way. Artificial intelligence is, after all, a technology. Like all technologies, it is somebody's property. That is a significant difference between computers and human brains. Brains - some brains - can be hired or bribed, but they cannot all be owned; data banks and computer software can and are. They are more and more owned and programmed by governments, corporations, and the military, interlocking super-institutions that use computers in their own interests. In a world of increasing military/industrial concentration, to imply that artificial intelligence is superior to human intelligence - to advertise it as the inevitable next step in evolution - is to deliver the persuasive power of facts and figures into ever fewer hands. As speculative as they may seem, such evolutionary vistas are not politically inconsequential.

There is another danger to which the computer model of mind opens us. It ignores a basic lesson of evolution: over specialisation kills. In an industrial economy, crisp logic and rapid data management are supreme necessities of life. But an urban-industrial society is only one possible human habitat, and perhaps not a long-lived one. The computers themselves may accelerate the pace of life beyond human tolerance to the point at which confusion, misjudgement, or the slightest lapse of attention are unaffordable. If the arms race were ever to resume, the thermonuclear war machine - the most highly computerised system yet developed - would soon reach that degree of inhuman exactitude.

To narrow our criterion of mind to fit the needs of the industrial style of life, to make our selves wholly dependent on the computer technology that that style demands, may be a prescription for extinction. Even in strict Darwinian terms, variety is the secret of adaptability; it is also what makes life interesting.

Boundless Mind

Fortunately, outside the small, busy world of the Artificial Intelligentsia, philosophers of evolution have celebrated many other dimensions of mind. Nietzsche and George Bernard Shaw envisaged the evolutionary Superman as artist and philosopher. Teilhard de Chardin believed it is the saints who will usher us to the culmination of human development. The systems theorist Erich Jantsch (in his book Design for Evolution) regards love and the 'feminine element' as the rejuvenating force of human evolution. Henri Bergson placed mystic intuition at the forward edge of the elan vital. He argued that the task of the mystic (whom he saw as an emergent new species) is to humanise technology so that it might liberate us from material necessity for a higher, religious calling. 'Man will rise above earthly things only if powerful equipment supplies him with the requisite fulcrum. He must use matter as a support if he wants to get away from matter. In other words, the mystical summons up the mechanical.'

To emphasise, as these philosophers do, the evolutionary role of the compassionate, the creative, the mystical is a useful corrective to the current fascination with computerised intelligence. It reminds us that, where the means of mass destruction have reached so awesome a level, our survival depends more on the saints who set humane goals than on the technicians who provide ingenious means. Norbert Wiener, the founding father of cybernetics, knew as much; he warned us that 'know what' comes before 'know how'.

The mind is bigger than logic and mathematics; bigger than any machine it invents. But it is just as important to realise that the mind is bigger than art and religion as well. It is bigger than anything we can stand away from and view critically as an option - which is, quite simply, every element of human culture. Indeed, the mind is so big that we cannot see its boundaries any more than we can see the edge of the universe. Whatever we say about it (including what I say here) becomes one more idea within it capable of being debated and negated.

Nothing so characterises the mind as its inherent elusiveness. It cannot encompass itself That paradox is an evolutionary one. It is grounded in the fact that, at a certain point, evolution reaches a reflexive state which generates the idea of evolution. Whatever 'direction' means in evolution, it has something to do with evolution's capacity for self-envelopment through consciousness.

Over the past two generations, evolution has become the most comprehensive scientific concept since Newton's laws of motion. Beyond living things, it is now invoked to explain the creation of matter out of the Big Bang, the spontaneous organisation of pre-biotic molecules, the development of stars and galaxies. The human mind, which alone reaches out to grasp the cosmic process from which it has emerged, clearly holds a special, frontier position in evolution. But it is not any one focus or fascination of the mind that points the way forward; it is the whole mind (or as much of it as any of us can experience) exercised in a condition of graceful integration.

There are certain forms of mysticism, like Zen Buddhism, with its open, non-discriminating style of meditation, that bring us close to appreciating the expansiveness of the mind. The impish humour of Zen stems from the ability of the mind to stymie itself with paradox and become larger by the act. But it may not be beyond computer science to find the same wise delight in the mind's often comic effort to capture itself. In mathematics, Gödel's theorem of incompleteness states that the axioms of any formal system cannot be wholly proved from within the system itself Thus, no logical system can ever come full circle and bite its own tail. There will always be a gap that has to be filled from outside.

Computer scientists differ in their evaluation of Godel's theorem. One interpretation by Professor Hao Wang holds that '...the human mind is incapable of formulating (or mechanising) all its mathematical intuitions. If it has succeeded in formulating some of them, this very fact yields new intuitive knowledge'. This seems to me as a non-mathematician to be a stiffly logical way of describing the mind as the Zen masters did: 'a sword that cuts but cannot cut itself, an eye that sees but cannot see itself'

Perhaps, then, with a bit of humility and a sense of humour, computer science can help us learn something about the mind's radically transcendent nature. After all, it is the human mind that invents artificial ones (as much for the fun as for the utility of it) and then has room left over to defy the logic or grow bored with their predictable correctness. That 'room' is the evolutionary margin of life still waiting to be explored. What computers can do represents so many routinised mental functions we can now delegate and slough off as we move forward to new ground. The machines are behind us, not ahead.

Prof. Theodore Roszak is professor of history and general studies at California State University, Hayward and author of many books , including 'The Voice of the Earth'.

Alternative Science

The previous essays have been drawing out the implications of modern science, implications often not appreciated by its practitioners themselves, pointing the way to an inner transformation of Western science that emerges from its own internal logic. But what if science has started off so completely on the wrong footing that it is incapable of changing sufficiently? Are there entirely different ways of doing science, which we might now be able to incorporate wholesale into our world view? Goethe thought that this was the case, as he attempted to develop such an alternative; his approach, which has growing numbers of adherents today, is described in the next essay. Following this, I review the ideas of David Peat, that we can find in the indigenous non-Western cultures of the world an approach that fully embodies the ideals of a participatory approach to the world, stressed by Mae-Wan Ho in her earlier essay. The two views have in common the concept of an organic connection between the "observer" and the larger world, but in the case of Peat's indigenous science, this connection becomes so profound that the word "observer" is no longer appropriate, and we become actors in the drama of nature.

Goethe's Organic Vision

Henri Bortoft

Most educated people know that Goethe was a great poet, writer and dramatist, but many are unaware that he spent a great deal of his time on science. He developed an alternative kind of science, which he himself thought very important. Near the end of his life he considered that he was not unequalled as a poet, but his scientific work was his greatest achievement, especially in his work on colour.

This judgement has been marked down as a mere eccentricity of the great man, and for a long time people simply took it that Goethe had misunderstood the nature of science and wasn't really a scientist at all. But fortunately today we are in a much better position to understand him, largely because of the tremendous changes in our understanding of science that have taken place since the 1960s, after the seminal work of Thomas Kuhn and many others. This is usually referred to as the new philosophy of science, the new history of science, and so on. As a result, we are now in a much better position today to see how Goethe's alternative science really is a science, not an alternative to science, and above all not simply a rather romantic activity you can go off and do if you don't like science. It is indeed a kind of science that has its own discipline, its own modes of discovery, its own modes of conception.

It is not so easy to grasp the idea of an alternative kind of science because we all start off with a presupposition of what science is about. We are barely aware of this, owing to the unconscious nature of presuppositions but the task of philosophy is to bring presuppositions to the surface. In this case, our education and long-standing cultural viewpoint tell us that science began when people 'came to their senses'. Instead of speculating, they saw how they could gain knowledge of the world directly from sense experience. So the picture grew up that science was based on observation augmented by experiments, and that knowledge is built up in this empirical fashion.

The Development of Modern Science

If that were the case, it would be difficult to see how there could be an alternative kind of science. Surely there can't be two different sciences? However, we have discovered in recent decades (although it was actually well known before - we can go back to Kant, and even long before that to Plato's *Thaetetus)* that we do not actually gain knowledge directly from sense experience when it comes to doing scientific work. Modern science did not begin when people simply used their senses to find out about the world. From its very inception (let us take Copernicus as a convenient starting point for the modern scientific movement), science has been based on the idea that the experience of the senses is illusory, and that reality is discovered by going behind the sensory to find out what lies beyond that in the form of mathematical relationships. These *mathematical* relationships are what in modern physics we call the Laws of Nature.

Copernicus maintained that what we see is entirely an illusion of the senses. We see ourselves as standing on a stationary Earth with the Sun going round, and so on. Copernicus says, No, that is an illusion; in fact the Sun is in the centre and is not moving; the Earth is moving around the Sun, as well as moving round on its axis, and this produces the illusion we experience with the senses. So the first step in modern science was to say that the world as we experience it is an illusion. Do not trust the senses, they are not trustworthy, we must find out how to go behind them by various means of thinking, especially mathematical thinking.

Copernicus was looking for harmony and symmetry in the cosmos. In so doing he was reflecting the Renaissance aesthetic ideal, which was very familiar to people at that time in painting, architecture and sculpture. They recognized in his work an expression of the same ideal of symmetry and harmony applied to the structure of the cosmos. His was one of the reasons why it received so much positive attention from the small number of people who were able to take it on. Behind this idea of symmetry and harmony was the fundamental philosophy of Neoplatonism, which in one of its forms was responsible for the main transformation of thinking in the Renaissance. That philosophy expressed the idea that the Sun is the representative of God, and must therefore be in the centre. Neoplatonism also contributed the idea that reality is not given in the appearances. The appearances are illusory, and we must look behind them for reality in mathematical, numerical and geometrical relationships. This is just what Copernicus was doing.

I mention this because it is an example of the formative effect of cultural-historical context on the very form which scientific knowledge takes. For a long time this has been missed out in accounts of science, which therefore make it look as if Copernicus must have made some kind of empirical discovery, perhaps by making some new observations. If you look in his work there are no new observations whatsoever in it. We have now discovered that science possesses *an intrinsic historicity,* which means that scientific knowledge contains a historical dimension within it. We all know that science is extrinsically historical, we can say, for example, that Orsted discovered electro-magnetism in 1819, or whatever. But in this case we are saying something much more profound: that there are cultural-historical factors entering into the very formation of scientific knowledge, giving it the shape that it has at a particular time, and therefore that science is *intrinsically* historical. Quite astonishingly, Goethe understood this and, as a result of his disappointment at the reception of his work on colour, he made a very thorough investigation into the history of science. This investigation has never been published properly in English because it tends to be missed out of various editions of the *Colour Theory*. Goethe came to the conclusion that 'the history of science is science itself'. He came to understand that scientific knowledge was not empirical in the way that he and others had believed, but depended on factors from the cultural and historical context to give it its form. This is astonishingly modern: we have to leap ahead a century and a half to Kuhn and others before we begin to get a similar appreciation of this factor.

The Mathematical Movement

The mathematical movement in science developed out of this Neoplatonic context. The key thing to remember about modern science, (the science from the early part of the 17th century and the Renaissance), is that it is mathematical. Its empiricism is the empiricism of experiments, which are mathematical projects because they are concerned with measurement. Mathematical physics, the great success story of the last few centuries, starts off from the illusions of the senses. Galileo said that our sensory experience of motion is an illusion; a force isn't needed to keep something moving, which of course is completely contrary to common sense. The great missionary figure of mathematical physics, Descartes, went the whole hog. By incorporating the philosophy of atomism from ancient Greek philosophy lock stock and barrel (as also did Galileo) he maintained that more or less everything that we experience in our world is an illusion. It's all an illusion produced by the senses - colour, smell, taste, sound: these things are simply not there in the world. The real is what can be handled by mathematical methods. This is the basis from which modern science developed.

Now we can see what Goethe did. He said that you didn't have to follow this pathway once you saw that science does not in fact have its own intrinsic foundations. There is no scientific method that has an absolute foundation which guarantees its own validity. Science itself is a cultural-historical movement. Once that is realised, we see that we can approach nature in this mathematical way - and it is a great achievement to do so, we allow it to be in its mathematical mode.

However, we can also see that there must also be other modes of approach to nature with appropriate means. Many of the conclusions of physics are actually methodological, reached because we can't deal with qualities mathematically. We disguise this fact by saying they're not real but merely subjective.

However, Goethe saw that this was unnecessary; we need not falsely ontologise what is really a methodological distinction. He saw that we could do what all of us, through our normal education, believe that science does anyway, but which science in fact doesn't do: *to start with experience.* He said that everything we need to discover about the world is to be found by going into experience directly, not by looking behind it or beyond it. There is more to the world than meets us at first sight; there is a depth within the world as it appears, but that depth is to be found within the world and not behind it. Goethe took an entirely different approach and found *wholeness* in the depth of his experience of natural phenomena – hence the title of the book which I have just written. [3]

Cultural Influences on 18th Century Thought

Setting aside Goethe's work on colour, I want to focus on the way that his work on plants illustrates a new, organic way of thinking. To understand this we have some work to do, because it is only too easy to misunderstand Goethe as a result of seeing him through our familiar ways of thinking. We are somewhat in the position of the son who saw double (in the traditional story told by Idries Shah), whose father said to him, 'Son, you see two instead of one'. 'How can that be?' said the boy, 'for if it were I would see four moons up there instead of two'. That is our position at this moment! We are seeing a lot of things that we actually believe are part of the fabric of the world but which in fact we are bringing to it by our way of seeing. This happens when people approach Goethe, and consequently they often interpret Goethe in ways which eclipse his organic thinking. We must recognise our own way of seeing. We must first be clear about the mathematical style of thinking that is so important in the development of the modern Western mind. The English in particular are shy of mathematics, but I shall not talk about anything mathematical. I shall talk about a *style* of thinking, the style that developed as a result of the great success of mathematics in the modern period, especially through its greatest achievement - mathematical physics.

Stephen Toulmin's excellent book, *Cosmopolis - The Hidden Agenda of Modernity,* has developed this with some thoroughness. He points out that, at the time of the development of mathematical physics, cultural contextual factors made it so propitious for mathematical methods to fill the vacuum left by a period of extreme scepticism during the Thirty Years War; the fight between Protestantism and Catholicism. People no longer knew what to believe and had come to the conclusion that knowledge and certainty were impossible. Descartes and others thought that this vacuum could be filled by mathematics. They had the idea that a mathematical approach would enable them to reach certainty. That was the cultural mission of mathematical physics, which became so influential.

The mathematical style of thinking tends to decontextualise everything. We talk about numbers, we talk about five, six, seven and add them up in various ways, but we don't really particularly care if they represent five apples or five motorcars; they are decontextualised. Any concrete situation becomes abstract, which means that it is independent of space and time. Then there is the idea that there are foundations from which we can proceed by means of a method that gives us certainty. For example, in geometry Euclid's *Elements* had just become more accessible at this time. It was thought to be a wonderful thing, and would have an exciting effect on men's way of thinking. They could, for example, prove theorems about triangles. This was an astonishing idea developed by the Greeks: actually to work things out in the abstract. So here we have an idea of certainty which is divorced from experience.

But in considering Goethe's science, the crucial idea is *unity,* which is carried with the mathematical way of thinking. The mathematical idea of unity is the idea of 'unity in multiplicity', or of a 'unity *underlying* multiplicity'. If we were to draw, for example, various triangles and attempt to look at them in a purely sensory way, we would see that they actually looked quite different. But if we take these triangles (they are, in fact, merely images of triangles, because the lines of a mathematical triangle have zero thickness), we can make discoveries about what all triangles have in common, e.g. the sum of the interior angles is equal to two right angles - a unity underlying the multiplicity of all triangles. This is the kind of idea of unity that we have. We take a multiplicity of different things, and subtract from them all the respects in which they are different to leave what they have in common; then we say that is the unity underlying multiplicity. We are looking for what is self-identical in all the different particular cases. This is how the mathematical laws of nature are conceived. Any particular case now has no interest in itself, i.e., its *particularity* has no interest. It is only of interest in as much as it is seen as an instance of the universal. So the particular in the mathematical style of thinking is always subsumed under the universal. The universal is the authority and the particular simply does as it is told.

We are reminded here of the language of Platonism, and Western philosophy is full of this kind of thinking. We remember the importance of mathematics for Plato, and how Plato talks about 'the one over the many'. The idea that there is a unity underlying multiplicity is a principle that applies to many different instances, but these are no more than instances of that principle. Here is a quotation from one of Plato's early dialogues, *Laches,* which is concerned with the virtue of courage: 'what is the common quality, which is the same in all these cases, and which is called courage?' And here is another, this time from the dialogue *Euthyphro* dealing with piety: 'Isn't it true that in every action piety is self-identical?' In both these cases we can see that unity is conceived in the form of unity in multiplicity'. Again, in the dialogue *Meno,* where Plato (Socrates in the dialogue) is concerned with virtue itself, and not with particular virtues, we find him asking the question: 'What is the character in respect of which they don't differ at all, but are all the same?' Clearly this takes the form of looking for unity in multiplicity by getting rid of all differences to find what is the same, self-identical, in all of them. This is the language of Plato's dialogues, which expresses the same *style* of thinking that we find in mathematics. In Plato this subsequently (in the *Republic,* for example) crystallised into a separation into two worlds (at least it did in the way that Plato was understood in the West) - the absolute world of the universal and the transient world of the particular. So there is the Platonic Idea of absolute Good, absolute Beauty, and so on, with a two-world dualism which came to dominate the Western metaphysical tradition. Furthermore, this ontologically dualistic style of thinking is found at the heart of mathematical physics in the 17th century, where the Platonic Ideas become identical with the mathematical laws of nature, and are conceived as being ontologically distinct from the matter they act upon. As one contemporary philosopher, Gary Madison, succinctly puts it: 'Metaphysics is alive and well and lives on in modern physics'.

In Toulmin's book there are many illustrations of the impact of this style of thinking from the 17th century onwards. He shows how the abstract, decontextualised style of thinking, for which the universal takes the form of a unity underlying multiplicity, leads to the idea of a universal method of science: a universal science of medicine, universal principles of law, universal moral principles, and so on. In the latter case this reaches a peak in Kant's *Critique of Practical Reason.* When we look at it (also knowing Kant's own predilections and his keenness to put mathematical physics on a firm epistemological foundation in his earlier *Critique of Pure Reason),* then we can see that Kant's second *Critique* is effectively the mathematical physics version of moral philosophy - but very well disguised, because we have to look at the style of the thinking, not the content. We say that he is dealing with moral judgements, and he is, but he is dealing with them in a style of thinking which is mathematical. The ultimate expression of this is the very idea of universal human reason, the key idea of the Enlightenment. If we look at what was said about this, we can easily recognise that it is the apotheosis of the mathematical style of thinking. It was believed that this would provide a sure foundation on the basis of which different people would come to the same conclusions about moral principles, aesthetic values, principles of government, etc. - in the same kind of way that they would come to the same conclusions about the geometrical properties of triangles. In other words, they would find a unity in the multiplicity that would be free from all relativity and hence true for everyone under all circumstances.

Multiplicity in Unity

Having laid this foundation, we can now begin to explore Goethe's way of seeing the organic world. I want to focus on his fundamental idea that, in some sense, all the different organs up the stem of the growing plant (leaf; sepal, petal, stamen, etc.) are one organ. We must understand in just what sense they are 'one organ'. The term which Goethe uses for this in German is *Urorgan,* which is usually translated into English as either 'primitive organ or archetypal organ'. Both of these are unsatisfactory: the former because it too easily evokes a Darwinian image, and the latter because it is inevitably associated with Platonism. It is this idea that I want to focus on, because it clearly conceives the *Urorgan* in the form of unity underlying multiplicity. Goethe went further and considered the entire plant kingdom as being in some sense one plant, which he called the *Urpflanze.* Here again, we find this usually translated as 'primitive plant' or 'archetypal plant', and the same problems apply. It is particularly difficult to avoid thinking of 'archetypal plant' in any other than a Platonic way, as a unity underlying the multiplicity of plants.

Goethe has usually been interpreted through this mathematical style of thinking. In any one of a number of widely available books we read that Goethe was seeking the underlying unity beneath the diversity of living forms, that he was seeking the general plan common to all plants and the simplest form from which all specialised organs had been removed. I remember in one case reading that Goethe, under the influence of Plato's theory of universals, was transfixed by uniformities and commonalities in nature. As we shall see, you can't get further from Goethe than that!

It is quite understandable that Goethe should be interpreted in this way, for we have seen how modern science developed in a cultural-historical context of Neoplatonism, and that the mathematical style of thinking expresses and reinforces this, leading us to conceive unity in the form of unity underlying multiplicity. However, around the time when Goethe was developing his ideas on morphology (he coined the term), there was a growing interest in what came to be called 'unity of plan' in anatomy in Germany it was called 'transcendental anatomy', and 'philosophical anatomy' in France. As Adrian Desmond has shown in his extraordinary book, *The Politics of Evolution,* this kind of thinking had a quite considerable effect in England in the decades before Darwin. The 'unity of plan' morphology of Geoffroy Saint-Hilaire, for example, was popular in some circles because it was thought that it would lead to the discovery of laws of the organic; this would be the biological equivalent of the laws of physics and would confer proper scientific status on the doctors coming out of the new medical schools. But 'unity of plan', as we have seen, is reached by removing all differences to arrive at what is common; if this is thought to be the archetype, then that is Platonic, mathematical thinking.

Although it seems inevitable that Goethe would have been understood in the light of this context, he was in fact doing something radically different. This is why it is so important that we begin by recognising that, as a consequence of our own cultural-historical context, we see unity in the form of unity in multiplicity, and that, in a manner akin to the son with double vision, we project this into what is there. To understand Goethe's organic vision we have to turn the idea of unity and multiplicity, the one and the many, inside out to our accustomed mode of thinking. Here are some of the things Goethe said about the plant - and again, it's important to experience the *form* of what he says by listening to the language. At the beginning of *The Metamorphosis of Plants,* he says that by careful observation we shall learn to understand the laws of transformation by which nature 'creates the most varied forms by the modification of one single organ'. He refers to 'The process by which one and the same organ presents itself to us in manifold forms', which amounts to what has been called meta-morphosis. Elsewhere, he wrote that 'It had occurred to me that in the organ of the plant which we ordinarily designate as leaf, the true Proteus is hidden, who can conceal and reveal himself in all forms. Forward and backward the plant is only leaf'; 'It is a growing-aware of the form with which again and again nature plays, and in playing, brings forth manifold life', and finally 'The thought becomes more and more living that it may be possible out of one form to develop all plant forms'. It is clear just from these fragments that Goethe is thinking in a thoroughly dynamical way, and that the dynamical mode of unity is such that, far from excluding difference by looking for what is common, it includes diversity within it.

In his book *Goethe's World View* (1897), Rudolf Steiner said that Goethe sought to see in a way which 'brings the diversity back into the unity from which it originally went forth'. Now if we follow the form of this we can see that it is quite different from saying that he looked for the unity underlying diversity, for what the diversity had in common. In fact, here we are coming at it from the other side. Goethe doesn't start from the finished product as if he were an onlooker. It is a key part of his thinking to try to follow its coming into being: he doesn't start with different organs or different plants, and ask what they have in common; he tries to get into the process to participate in the coming into being, so that he can see these different organs (or plants) emerging from an original unity. He comes to the view that there is, in the case of the organ, only one organ and that it manifests differently in different places on the plant. So for him the vegetative leaf, the petal, the stamen are one organ manifesting differently. He comes at it from the other side: instead of looking for unity underlying multiplicity he turns it round and looks for 'multiplicity in unity'. He tries to come out of the unity intuitively into multiplicity, instead of trying to derive the unity intellectually from the multiplicity. This has the effect of turning the one and the many inside out, from 'unity in multiplicity' to 'multiplicity in unity'.

Organic Thinking

However, this does not mean that Goethe thinks that this unity is broken up. We have to learn to think in a new way. We can gain some assistance here from the process of hologram division. Everyone knows that if a hologram is divided into two, say, then instead of having two halves of a hologram we have two whole holograms - even though each is physically half the size of the original. The result is quite uncanny: whatever the original hologram was of, the subject, we would now have two. It has been divided materially, but optically it is indivisible because it remains whole. How different it would be if we divided a photograph! But how many holograms are there after the division?

To begin with we would want to say that there are two, and there are materially, but *optically* there is only one, not two, because each is the very same one. Because we can't do this process of division in the same way with a photograph, we would have to make a copy instead - and then there would be two photographs, one and another one. But this is not so with the hologram, where it's more like 'one and very same one' instead of 'one and another one'. This is multiplicity in unity in which there are not two, there is one, but is not one numerically. There is another kind of one, which is one in the *form* of two.

This is what happens organically in the process of vegetative reproduction. We can take a fuchsia plant, for example, break it into pieces and grow each bit into a new plant. Each of these new plants is *organically* the original one. The plant is divided and yet remains whole (so really it is indivisible!), so that here again we have one in the form of' multiplicity in unity', where each one is in fact the very same one because there is only one plant. In England there is a species of potato called the King Edward. This is not allowed to pollinate but is propagated vegetatively by planting seed potatoes. This means there is only one King Edward potato plant, and it is the original one that by division has now turned into billions of potatoes - each of which is still the original plant. In his book *The Countryside Explained,* John Seymour says that 'It would be interesting to know how many billions of tons that first King Edward plant has developed into during its life!'

What we begin to catch here is a sense of multiplicity within unity as an *intensive* dimension - a dimension that is within One itself. It is helpful to distinguish this from the numerical 'one' by writing it with an initial capital letter, so that we can distinguish the intensive dimension of One from the extensive dimension of many ones. This is the way that Goethe is seeing when he talks about the *Urorgan* and the *Urpflanze,* not in the way that looks externally for unity underlying multiplicity. When he says that 'one and the same organ presents itself to us in manifold forms', and calls this organ Proteus, then he is thinking in the mode of this intensive dimension of One of an organ which is always the very same One but differently. There is now difference *within* unity, which is therefore self-difference - in contrast to the unity that excludes difference in favour of self-sameness.

This notion of self-difference can be further illustrated by means of the hologram. It is possible to make a multiple hologram in which several different images can be formed on one and the same hologram without being confused - as would happen with multiple exposures in a photograph. Each different image is the whole hologram, not part of it, and by changing the angle at which it is viewed, a series of images unfolds, one after the other, as if it were one image metamorphosing into different forms of itself. This provides us with an almost uncanny way of catching the idea of the self-difference of multiplicity in unity. Goethe himself described a dynamical experience of this kind. He tells us that he closed his eyes and visualised a flower 'right at the centre of the organ of sight'. When he did this 'new flowers sprang out of this heart, with coloured petals and green leaves', and that 'there was no way of stopping the effusion, that went on as long as my contemplation lasted, neither slowing nor accelerating'. We should read this intensively, not extensively as if it were many plants, one after the other. This is One Plant, manifesting itself differently. What Goethe means by metamorphosis - whether in the organs of the plant, the members of a single plant family, or the plant kingdom as a whole - is just this dynamical self-difference in which the One produces different manifestation of itself (Proteus). He does not mean that one manifested organ turns into another one in an extensive sense as if a petal turned into a stamen, for example.

Anyone can practise this way of seeing for themselves. It is, for example, possible to see a particular family of plants in its organic mode. It is an enlivening experience to observe the different members of a family such as the *Rosaceae* (rose, blackberry, strawberry, apple, etc.) and begin to see them as One plant in the form of multiplicity in unity. How different the *experience* of this is from that of looking for what these different plants have in common. But sometimes even quite a simple situation can provide us with what David Bohm used to call a 'template for thinking' in a new way. An ambiguous figure such as the duck'rabbit is a case *(see picture)*. The whole figure can appear as a duck or as a rabbit - the

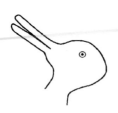

duck is not part of the figure and the rabbit another part. Playing with this can quickly give us a sense of the intensive quality of self-difference and multiplicity in unity - there are always some who object that this is 'only subjective', but it is only being used as a 'template'. However, when we work with the organic then in addition we find that it is *intrinsically* dynamical - as in Goethe's experience of the unfolding plant forms 'becoming other in order to remain itself' in Ron Brady's succinct phrase.

Darwin also seems to have come up to this point, especially in his work on barnacles, but then to have missed its significance: instead of seeing the phenomenon he wanted to explain it.

This is Goethe's organic style of thinking, in contrast to the mathematical style. The key to it is in the way that he turns unity and multiplicity inside out, so that something can be different from itself without becoming other than itself. His organic vision thereby escapes from the limitation of the one-sided kind of Platonism, with its emphasis on what is always self-identical, a mode of thinking that has had such an impact on the development of the modern mind. In particular, it liberates us from that impoverished unity which is reached by excluding difference in favour of what things have in common, which is an ontological cul-de-sac from which nothing can come for the simple reason that everything has been excluded from it. Just as mainstream science has affected our whole way of thinking in all aspects of our culture, then so too could Goethean science, with its organic style of thinking, have an effect on other areas of our culture beyond the confines of science. Now that we are moving towards one world in the form of cultural homogeneity, becoming everywhere the same as a consequence of global technology, Goethe's organic vision of a different kind of unity may well be timely. When Goethe died, it was said that he would not be understood for a hundred and fifty years. I suggest that this time has now come.

Henri Bortoft is author of 'The Wholeness of Nature: Goethe's Way of Science'.

Review of David Peat's Blackfoot Physics (1996)

Chris Clarke

(Page numbers are indicated [thus])

Goethe's science, radical in its approach, starts to stretch the boundaries of what is and what is not science, and alter the values and attitudes that we bring to science. A yet more radical questioning comes from the work of David Peat, who in his book *Blackfoot Physics* brings his study over many years of the cultures of Indigenous American people to bear on the whole question of how we understand and relate to the world around us. He argues that these peoples have systematic and sophisticated ways of doing this, which have as much claim as our own methods to be called "science," if by that we mean a "connected body of demonstrated truths" (Oxford English Dictionary).

Peat's book constitutes a far-reaching demolition of the notion that science is a discovery of pre-existent "facts," independent of the cultural patterns of the surrounding society. His discussion makes it clear that the Western concept of science - investigating only things that are independent of particular human subjectivity, independent of human values and meaning - is itself a highly culturally-specific enterprise. This kind of detachment from human concerns is specifically characteristic of Western thought from 1600 almost to the present day, and it is even now coming to an end. In *Blackfoot Physics* we have a picture of an alternative, in which human concerns, emotions and senses are not seen as irrelevant distractions, to be screened out, but as essential parts of a dynamic universe, aspects of our humanness that are to be trained and perfected in the growth of wisdom in order to perceive the full truth.

Before we can approach this alternative way of doing science, we need a radical change in our worldview. It is not a matter simply of modifying in a peripheral way our conventional picture. To illustrate this, David Peat describes how, in a discussion between indigenous and western people at the Fetzer institute, "the discussion came round to the Mic Maq worldview and the question was asked 'Why does ice heal?' When a hole has been made in the ice for fishing, sometime later the ice will be found to have healed over ...... [W]hen faced with the question of the ice that heals we had to begin to let go of everything we had read and had been taught about Western physics ... I had to allow my mind to move into another world, a world with totally different approaches and insights ... only then could I respect how complete and meaningful it was." [43] So his book encourages us to "move into another world."

Once we have started to move into this world, we realise that each element of what we think of as science could change, starting with the concept of *knowledge*, which is central to our conception of science. Science, for us, is about heaping up this stuff called knowledge, adding increasingly many bricks to the edifice of knowledge until the building is complete. The view of Indigenous societies is, however, totally different. "Knowledge, to a native person, cannot be accumulated like money stored in a bank; rather, it is an ongoing process better represented by the activity of coming-to-knowing than by a static noun." [55] In some respects "Polanyi's *tacit knowledge* comes close to the Native American's vision of coming-to-knowing" [66], but it is more consciously articulated that this. Knowledge is something that is explicitly valued and developed; it is a process that very tangibly present in the stories and songs of the society.

The knowledge of Indigenous science must be passed from one generation to the next, but it is not *given* from one to the next. "You cannot 'give' a person knowledge in the way that a doctor gives a person a shot for measles." [59] Instead, "In a traditional society children learn by watching and hanging around rather than through structured teaching, questioning, or experiment." [71] Moreover, this sort of coming-to-knowing is not abstracted, but rooted in the society itself and (a crucial but difficult concept) rooted in the landscape surrounding that society. "Knowledge in the traditional world is not a dead collection of facts. It is alive, has spirit, and dwells in specific places." [65] For example,

The skills necessary to build an Algonquin canoe are tied to a particular landscape, to the trees that grow there, to the game that can be trapped, [62] This concrete rootedness is bound up with the way in which *story* is used as the main way of articulating and preserving this form of knowledge. Peat stresses that "The stories told by traditional people come out of their direct experience and are ways of teaching that are very different from the simple imparting of facts." In a meeting of a local school board, for example, the way the local school was working was brought out when one man present simply told a story from his own childhood. "The old man had no need to analyse the philosophy of the local school board or discuss the relative value of different worldviews. He simply told a story, and, in the context of that school board meeting, the story brought into focus some of the things that people were sensing and feeling about the school's affect on their community." [57] As David Abram (1997) has noted, it is no mere accident that such stories are specific to the place where they occurred. Drawing on material from Basso, he describes how the Apache stories used for advising on socially cohesive behaviour are always finished with the tag-line "It happened at ...", concluding with a place-name which, in their language, was always evocatively descriptive of the landscape at that point. In this way, Abram claims, "a topographic place becomes the guarantor of corrected behaviour, the visible presence that reminds one of past foibles and that ensures one's subsequent attentiveness." [159]

There is thus a fundamental difference between Western knowledge systems, where the knowledge is a static body of theories that are abstracted from their specific concrete occurrence, projected into a Platonic realm of pure ideas, and the Indigenous knowledge systems where knowledge is not only dynamic, but is inseparable from the concrete. As Brown (1982) puts it when talking about the symbolism of the purification lodge, "It is important to note that to the Plains Indian the material form of the symbol is not thought of as representing some *other* and higher reality, but *is* that reality in an image." [43]

A consequence of this embodiedness of coming-to-knowing is the way in which the knowing has effect on the person. In the West, knowledge is imagined to stand apart from the knower, with no personal implications. "Within a traditional society, however, knowledge is a process that transforms and brings with it obligations and responsibilities... [K]nowledge for them is profoundly different. It is a living thing that has existence independent of human beings. A person comes to knowing by entering into a relationship with the living spirit of that knowledge." (66-7)

There is also a profound difference in the way this knowledge is articulated, which bound up with the structures of Indigenous languages. The rootedness of the knowledge is reflected in the rootedness of language in the sounds of the natural world, so that "[w]hen my Haida friend Woody Morrison speaks in his native tongue he tells me to listen to the sounds of the ocean, to the waves breaking on the shore, and for the cries of birds and the calls of animals."(85) As a result, language is structured so as to reflect the experiences of the world of the Indigenous societies, a different experiential world from ours. As we have already noted in the case of "knowledge" versus "knowing", "... European languages are noun-oriented ... Many Native American languages do not work this way. They are verb-based." (128) Thus our science is full of abstract (noun) entities: electrons, fields, states and so on, where as Indigenous science deals with processes. Peat illustrates this in discussing the translation of a phrase describing a healing by means of song. Conventional translations would say that the healer (noun, subject) is singing. But "[w]hat is really happening is 'singing' - the action, the process. The healer cannot really say that it is 'he' who is singing; rather the process of singing is going on....The image that began to emerge from that phrase was of a sick person and a healer and a process of singing taking place. The singing is the primary reality, for it did not originate with either person, nor was the healing something that passed in a transitive way from one to the other. The singing sings itself. The healing heals." (144-5)
We thus start to have a quite different metaphysics of action in the world. Instead of entities that impinge mechanically on each other, we have emerging processes. This in turn is reflected in a different emphasis in the handling of time, which Peat illustrates by reference to the Indigenous Australian concept of The Dreaming.

To the Australian Aborigine the Dream Time or the Dreaming, when the ancestors walked the land and created the landscape, is not a historical "time past" but a living time that has not passed away, one in which a person can still participate through dreams, visions and ceremonies....

> To the Native mind time is alive, and, if it must be pictured as a flowing river, then it is a river in which the mind is free to swim and move. Time does not exist apart from, and independent of, the spirits of nature and the lives of the people; its processes must be constantly acknowledged and renewed. [199] [I was led] to speculate that the very nature of time, within Indigenous science, is different from what we in the West normally experience. Or, to put it more precisely, that Indigenous people have access to dimensions within the spirit of time that we have forgotten.[203]

Peat [235] discusses how the expression of this in language was identified some time ago by Whorf, who pointed out that in the Hopi language the tenses that we use to express time are replaced by a distinction between what Whorf called the *manifesting* and the *manifested.* Importantly, the manifesting "comprises all that we call future, *but not merely this:* it includes equally and indistinguishably all that we call mental—everything that appears or exists in the mind, or, as the Hopi would prefer to say, in the *heart,* not only in the heart of man, but in the heart of animals, plants and things, and behind and within all the forms and appearances of nature, in the heart of nature [itself] ..." (quoted by Abram, (1997)[192]. If Whorf was correct (and this is a disputed area), it means that in this different metaphysic of emergent processes, the mental is inextricably bound up with the physical, to the extent that there is little meaning in differentiating the two.

The centrality of language to this aspect of Indigenous Science poses the same sort of difficulty as the centrality of mathematics to Western Physics. We are not dealing, as Chomsky maintained, with universal human ideas that can be expressed indifferently in various languages. Rather "Within Indigenous science, thoughts are inseparable from language. The language that is spoken is not simply a medium, or a vehicle for communication, rather it is a living thing, an actual physical power within the universe." [224] Not merely is the structure of language crucial, but its very sounds (rooted, as we have already seen, in the sounds of nature) are essential. Peat recounts how, when getting into a deep question with a Native friend, "he will remark, 'Well, in Blackfoot we say ...' and produce a pattern of sound for me. Or he may pause and sing to himself very softly as he tries to discover a way of putting the vibrations, and all that they convey, into the particular linguistic structure demanded by English." (222)

Despite this, there are suggestive parallels between this Indigenous metaphysic and ideas in quantum physics, particularly in its quantum logic form, though in view of the integrity of the Indigenous worldview Peat is more cautious here than in his earlier books. I was particularly struck be the way in which the "manifesting" is so like the quantum state, which in quantum logic is defined as the pure potentiality that is bound up in the current state of affairs, the range of incompatible and cohabiting possibilities that first are given order by establishing a particular context, and then are selected from in actual manifestation. On this view, the distinctive feature of quantum mechanics is the way in which context (technically, the "observable") enters in determining the frame of reference within which manifesting takes place[4] Peat's account reflects this exactly, while adding crucial differences concerning the involvement of the human person, when he writes:

> Within Indigenous science, context is always important. Nothing is abstract since all things happen within a landscape and by virtue of a web of interrelationships. The tendency to collect things into categories does not exist within the thought and language of, for example, Algonquin speakers.
>
> This leads to a profoundly different way of approaching and thinking about the world. For, in the absence of categories, each thing is mentally experienced on its own merits, and for what it actually is. Rather than indulging in comparison or judgement, Indigenous speakers attempt to enter into relationship with them. (233)

The question that arises from all this for me is, how far has David Peat demonstrated that the Indigenous societies have a science, as opposed to a body of culture-specific practical wisdom? Yet this question unasks itself as soon as it is examined closely. As I remarked at the start of this review, Western science is arguably just as culture-specific in its structure and focus as Indigenous science. And the distinction between "pure knowledge" and "practical wisdom" is a Western dichotomy which Indigenous peoples would not recognise. I want to enlarge on this second point in the light of Peat's discussion of healing, before returning to his general analysis of the sense in which there can be said to be an Indigenous science.

To take the example of healing and medicine, the ideal for us is represented as the acquisition of pure knowledge, which is then applied to the construction of specific remedies for specific diseases. We see here the separation of knowledge and practice, thinking in terms of nouns (remedies) rather than processes and contexts, and categorisation in terms of diseases separated from social context. All these are alien to Indigenous thought. Peat argues that the coming-to-knowing of Indigenous science, as an active process of relationship between society and the world, *in itself* has a healing effect. Reflecting on the way in which "[w]ithin a relatively short period of time after the arrival of the first Europeans, between 90 and 95 percent of the population of the New World was wiped out," [121] he writes "The vision of a garden of Eden has, to some extent, been confirmed by the work of scientists who have examined the skeletons of early peoples. Evidence points to the fact that, before contact with Europeans, The People were remarkably free from diseases. Indeed epidemics seem to have arrived when Western civilization began to encroach upon the Americas. ... Why were they so free from disease? Could it perhaps have been something to do with their beliefs, science, society and way of life? ...In a very real sense, human beings create the conditions for their own illness, out of their dreams, beliefs, values, social structures, and thought." [110, 115]

Our categorisation of a remedy in terms of a context-independent 'thing' is again alien to their thought. "A Native medicine may contain the same biologically active molecule [as a Western medicine] and yet, as far as I understand it, Native healers would not consider these two medicines to be identical..." [131] This is because "Spirit is part of the ontological existence of medicine. When medicine is passed around the circle there is an exchange of the spirit , with some people giving

spirit to it and others taking spirit." And he goes on to show how striking is this context-dependence when it comes to the preparation of a remedy: "Suppose a non-Native person spends several hours searching for a particular rare plant and finally spots one. His or her natural inclination would be to pick it at once, but the Native person will pass it by. It is only when they discover the third such plant that they will feel able to take it...This third plant is a gift from Mother Earth and, as with all gifts, if a person is to take it, it can only be as part of an exchange, The spirit of the plant must be acknowledged, for the medicine person seeks to come into a relationship with its power. ..."
The Medicine chapter of this book illustrates the way in which echoes of these ideas have always have an implicit place in conventional medicine, despite its idea of a base of pure knowledge, a place that is now becoming more explicit.

The penultimate chapter of the book gives a point by point analysis of the sense in which Indigenous science is similar to, and different from, Western science, in the context of a classification of their different aspects. His scheme is worth reproducing in detail as a summary of the argument:

Western Science

Experimentation	Instrumentation	Observation
Prediction	Mathematics	Representation
Control	Objectivity	Distancing
Freedom of external social values		Uniformity
Models	Causality	Technology
Progress	Fragmentation	Explanation
Authority	Truth	Transformation

Indigenous Science

Spirituality	Location	Observation
Initiation	Cosmology	Causality
Role of Humanity	Harmony	Ceremony
Elders	Artefact	Practice
Spirit	Dreams	Visions
History	Maps	Symbols

Subjectivity	Relatedness	Understanding
Sanction	Transformation	Path
Sacred mathematics	Sacred space	Representation
Technology		

David Peat's commentary on these points raises a series of fascinating issues regarding the way in which our own science could change in order to serve us in the ecological and social crises that now face us. For example, on the question of experimentation, he notes that although indigenous science does not set constraints on nature in the way that is essential to much of Western science, "there may be a sort of experimentation that is of an inward nature—an experimentation of the mind, so to speak. In a holistic world in which each part enfolds the whole, it becomes possible to enter into the inscape of the smallest insect, plant, or leaf and zoom outward into the whole universe. Sa'ke'j Henderson has suggested that the People's relationship with plants, animals, rocks, and trees serves them as a sort of electron microscope." [251] We have here a totally new way of knowing, only occasionally touched on in Western science (as in Barbara McClintock's work referred to in the feminist scientific critique of E Fox Keller, 1985), a way of knowing that carries with it a moral involvement with what is known.

There has rightly been a great wave of interest in Indigenous American wisdom as a guide to the human predicament. Peat's book is vital in showing us the way in which this wisdom impinges on our own scientific practice, and in showing us how to approach it with the openness and willingness to be transformed, which is the essential precondition to its understanding. It is a landmark book in our quest to enlarge the scope of science for the new millennium.

Prof. Chris Clarke is professor of applied mathematics in the University of Southampton.

References

Abram, David (1997) *The Spell of the Sensuous,* Vintage

Aczel, Amir D. (1996) *Fermat's Last Theorem: Unlocking the Secret of an Ancient Mathematical Problem.* Four Walls Eight Windows, New York & London.

Adams, John (1995) *Risk.* UCL Press, London.

Anderla, Georges et al. (1997) *CHAOTICS: An Agenda for Business and Society in the 21st Century.* Adamantine Press, London.

Bak, Per (1996) *How Nature Works: The Science of Self-Organized Criticality.* Springer, New York, & Oxford University Press, Oxford.

Barrow, John D. (1998) *Impossibility: The Limits of Science and the Science of Limits.* Oxford University Press, Oxford & New York.

Bortoft, Henri (1996) *The Wholeness of Nature* Floris, Edinburgh

Brown, William Epes (1982) *The Spiritual Legacy of the American Indian,* Crossroad

Casti, John L. (1994) *Complexification: Explaining a Paradoxical World Through the Science of Surprise.* Abacus, London.

Clarke, Chris J S (1996) *Reality through the Looking Glass: science and awareness in the postmodern world.* Floris, Edinburgh

Cohen, Jack and Stewart, Ian (1994) *The Collapse of Chaos: Discovering Simplicity in a Complex World.* Viking, London & New York.

Gleick, James (New ed. 1998) *Chaos: Making a New Science.* Minerva, London.

Gray, J. W. (ed.) (1984) *Mathematical Applications of Category Theory.* American Mathematical Society, Providence, RI, USA.

Hall, Nina (ed.) (1992) *The New Scientist Guide to Chaos.* Penguin Books, London & Penguin Books USA, New York.

Ho, Mae-Wan (1993). *The Rainbow and the Worm - The Physics of Organisms,* World Scientific, Singapore.

Jones, Edwin (1989) *Reading the Book of Nature* Ohio University Press, Athens

Keller, E Fox (1985) *Reflections on gender and science* Yale uUniversity Press, New Haven

Lewin, Roger (1993) *Complexity: Life at the Edge of Chaos.* Dent, London.

Lorenz, Edward (2nd. ed. 1995) *The Essence of Chaos.* UCL Press, London.

Mainzer, Klaus (3rd. ed. 1997) *Thinking in Complexity: The Complex Dynamics of Matter, Mind, and Mankind.* Springer, New York & London.

Mandelbrot, Benoit B. (3rd. ed. 1983) *The Fractal Geometry of Nature.* H. H. Freeman, New York.

Peat, F David (1996) *Blackfoot Physics* Fourth Estate, London

Peitgen, H.-O. & Richter, P. H. (1986) *The Beauty of Fractals.* Springer, New York and London.

Penrose, Roger (1989) *The Emperor's New Mind.* Oxford University Press, Oxford.

Peterson, Ivars (1998) *The Jungle of Randomness: Mathematics at the Edge of Certainty.* Penguin Books, London & Penguin Putnam, New York.

Stewart, Ian (1995) *Nature's Numbers: Discovering Order and Pattern in the Universe.* Weidenfeld & Nicolson, London.

Stewart, Ian (1998) *Life's Other Secret: The New Mathematics of the Living World.* Penguin Books, London & Penguin Putnam, New York.

Waldrop, M. Mitchell (2nd. ed. 1993) *Complexity: the Emerging Science at the Edge of Chaos.* Viking, London & (1st. ed. 1992) Simon & Schuster, New York.

Woodcock, Alexander, and Davis, Monte (1978) *Catastrophe Theory.* E. P. Dutton, New York.

[1] Abridged from Clarke (1996)

[2] This article first appeared in the *Times Higher Educational Supplement* on 2 July 1996 and is reproduced by permission

[3] Bortoft (1996)

[4] See my account in (Clarke, 1996)

Chapter 3

Health, Healing and Wholeness

Edited by Dr John Cosh

Introduction

"I dress his wounds: God heals him"

This was the modest response of Ambrose Paré, leading surgeon in 16th century France when praised for his surgical successes. To be precise, his words were: "Je le pansay: Dieu le guarist". Experienced in dealing with the terrible wounds of battle, and the almost equally terrible treatments then in vogue, such as cauterisation with boiling oil, he developed simpler methods and used bland herbal applications. He saw that such treatments did no harm to his patients' tissues, and allowed healing to take place. The healing process he saw as a divine gift to man.

A modern surgeon would be very unlikely to use Paré's words, but would have to agree with him in principle. The most sophisticated medical and surgical technology can only succeed by working with the body's own power of healing and regeneration. The more our methods permit or enhance those powers, the more successful are the results.

There is a growing awareness today that healing and health are intimately related to our inner state, emotional and spiritual. As multilevel beings, we are only truly in a state of health when we achieve a harmonious inner balance between all levels of our being. There is nothing really new about this awareness, for since antiquity some physicians at least have acknowledged the influence of the mind on the body, although Plato evidently thought otherwise, as quoted, below, by Prince Charles.

The spectacular advances of medical science over the last century have distracted us from this broader vision. The division of medical practice into specialties has done something to bring about a facile acceptance of separation between mind and body. Clinics and their specialists deal in psychiatry, or medicine or surgery or their subdivisions, and can claim with some justification not to have the right to trespass on each other's territory. Sir William Osler, a physician of wide experience, warned, a century ago, that overspecialisation in medicine would have its costs as well as its benefits. It was he who taught his students that "It is as important to know what sort of patient has the illness as it is to know what illness the patient has".

The flourishing worldwide interest in complementary medicine is a salutary reminder that the public feels somehow that science in medicine is not enough. More personal attention and understanding, more time, and simpler traditional remedies are wanted. The role of healer in the functions of doctor, nurse or therapist must not be lost in the ever increasing pressures of medical practice. How to unite the benefits of complementary medicine with those of conventional medicine is exercising many minds today. The urge for integration is widely felt.

The contributors to this chapter have much to say on these topics: how to build a sense of wholeness into the concept of health: to integrate complementary therapies and healing with scientific medicine: to appreciate current evidence for the unified working of mind and body: and to see that in training our medical students and junior doctors the concept of healing is not lost under a welter of scientific knowhow.

The Prince of Wales has for some years expressed an appreciation of the values of complementary medicine. Feeling a need for it to be recognised alongside orthodox medicine, it was he who initiated the Foundation for Integration in Medicine. His words on this subject, already published in the press and quoted in the Network Newsletter (April 1998, No.66, 14-15) are repeated here.

Integrated Healthcare: A Way Forward?

H R H the Prince of Wales
(Reprinted from the Daily Telegraph)

In recent years there has been an enormous growth in the use of complementary medicine - not only in Britain, but also in other European countries, the United States and other parts of the world. More and more people are turning to homoeopathy, herbal medicine, acupuncture, osteopathy and a wide range of other treatments - mainly paid for out of their own pockets. In Australia, for example, a recent study estimated that people spend twice as much on complementary medicine as they do on orthodox pharmaceuticals. I believe that this trend reflects a growing concern with the use of more and more powerful drugs and a potentially rather impersonal approach to healthcare. There is a feeling - not only among patients, but among GPs, nurses and other mainstream health practitioners too, that there needs to be greater integration and interprofessional collaboration in patient care and that we can each, as individuals, play a greater role in contributing towards our own health and wellbeing. Health should be much more than the mere absence of disease or infirmity; and we should strive to ensure that everybody can fulfil the full potential and expression of their lives.

This is not to deny the value of the dramatic scientific discoveries, for example in molecular biology, that have enabled Western medicine to make leaps in our understanding of the disease process and how to treat it. Serious illnesses and injuries that were once regarded as untreatable, can now be   cured and new forms of treatment are being developed all the time. I am confident that this trend will continue, supported by the dedication of researchers and medical practitioners and the generosity of private individuals, in addition to initial spending by governments around the world. It is vital to human progress that it should. Yet we know that new medical treatments and procedures can be costly to develop, and sometimes costly in application. As medicine becomes more sophisticated and more ambitious, so the costs have tended to rise.

Against this background, it hardly needs saying that we should try to make best use of all our available resources. That is where complementary medicine could have an important - indeed, vital role to play, in supporting and complementing current orthodox medical practice. Often it seems that complementary medicine can bring a different perspective and fulfil a real human need for a more personal touch which, in turn can help unlock the individual's inner resources to aid the healing process. The goal we must work towards is an integrated healthcare system in which all the knowledge, experience and wisdom accumulated in different ways, at different times and in different cultures is effectively deployed to prevent or alleviate human suffering. There is much that all the different traditions of medicine can learn from one another.

Over the past two decades I have supported efforts to focus healthcare on the particular needs of the individual patient, applying the best and most appropriate forms of treatment from both orthodox and complementary medicine in a more integrated way. I have been greatly encouraged to see the progress which has been made in increasing the range of choice available to the individual and to the medical practitioner.

These changes in attitude were reflected in the BMA's report *Complementary Medicine: New Approaches to Good Practice,* published in 1993 and a report by the General Medical Council *Tomorrow's Doctors* in the same year. Some complementary treatments are now available within the National Health Service and an independent Survey for the Department of Health in 1995 showed that almost forty percent of GP partnerships in England provide access to complementary medicine for NHS patients, either by undertaking these treatments themselves or by delegating them to complementary practitioners. Acupuncture, homoeopathy and osteopathy were most frequently used.

There has been progress in education and in standard-setting too. There has been an increase in the number of accredited university courses for students wishing to study for a career in a number of different complementary medical professions. Two of these - osteopathy and chiropractic - have recently become regulated by Act of Parliament and some of the other professions are working hard to establish credible and effective systems of professional self-regulation.

But there is still a great deal to do. Last year I asked a group of leading individuals from different scientific, educational and healthcare backgrounds for their advice on how we could make further progress. We quickly identified four priority areas:

> *scientific research into the safety and effectiveness of complementary medical therapies, how they work, how they could be improved and where they are most likely to be helpful;.

> *the development of formal standards and systems of professional regulation, to provide effective safeguards for the public;.

> *improved education and communication, to promote a sharing of ideas and the basic skills and principles of professional conduct essential for all healthcare practitioners, to improve the quality of care;

> *effective delivery mechanisms to provide integrated healthcare to the public.

Accordingly we established four Working Groups to consider each of these priorities, and produced a draft report which was circulated for comment to a large number of individuals and organisations with an interest in orthodox and complementary healthcare. These included royal colleges, leading researchers, medical schools, consumers of healthcare and bodies representing practitioners of complementary medicine.

The Prince of Wales's Initiative on Integrated Healthcare

In October 1997, on the occasion of the publication of a report on Integrated Healthcare the Prince of Wales said:

The results of 18 months discussion and consultation were published in 1997 in a new report entitled *Integrated Healthcare: A Way forward for the next Five Years?*. I pay tribute, in particular, to the dedication and commitment of those who chaired and participated in the Working Groups. I believe they have advanced the cause of integrated healthcare and shown the way forward for further cooperation and partnership.

For me the most heartening finding of the work so far has been the very wide measure of agreement between orthodox and complementary practitioners on the need for this initiative to succeed. It seems to me that we have reached a defining moment in our attitude towards healthcare in this country. I believe that we have a unique opportunity to take stock and consider how we can make the very best use of all our precious healthcare resources. We cannot afford to overlook or waste any knowledge, experience or wisdom from different traditions that could be brought to bear in the cause of helping those who suffer. We must respond to what the public are clearly showing they want by placing more emphasis on prevention, healthy lifestyles and patient-centred care. Integrated healthcare is an achievable goal. It is one we cannot afford to miss.

Conference on Integrated Healthcare, May 1998

In introducing this conference and welcoming contributors, Prince Charles took as his text a quotation from Plato:

> "The cure of the part should not be attempted without treatment of the whole, and also no attempt should be made to cure the body without the soul, and therefore if the head and body are to be well you must begin by curing the mind: that is the first thing. For this is the error of our day in the treatment of the human body, that physicians separate the soul from the body"

He ended his speech with the wellknown Medical Litany of Sir Robert Hutchinson:

> "From inability to leave well alone;
> From too much zeal for what is new and contempt for what is old;

118

From putting knowledge before wisdom, science before art,
  cleverness before common sense;
From treating patients as cases;
From making the cure of a disease more grievous than its' endurance;
Good Lord deliver us."

And on another occasion, addressing an audience of psychiatrists Prince Charles commented as follows:

"I believe that the most urgent need for Western man is to rediscover that divine element in his being, without which there never can be any possible hope of meaning to our existence in this earthly realm"

HRH The Prince of Wales is Patron of the Foundation for Integrated Medicine.

Holistic Medicine

Hertha Larive

Modern medicine and surgery can be brilliant in treating with disorders affecting a single bodily system, and in dealing with acute crises and trauma. But deep seated and chronic illness involves more than one system, often with social, emotional and psychological overtones. Here the holistic approach is needed, appreciating a patient's multilevel requirements; time, patience and understanding are called for. Hertha Larive is herself a holistic practitioner, counsellor and healer.

Holistic medicine is based on four precepts:

1.   The multilevels of existence:

SPIRITUAL.
MENTAL   - Psycho/Spiritual
EMOTIONAL
PHYSICAL - Bio-energy

2. The body is a homeostatic system, self healing and self regulating.

3. Each patient is a unique and special individual.

4. The cooperation of the patient and his/her ability to take responsibility is essential.

One of the principles of the holistic philosophy assumes that an important relationship, interaction and interdependence exists between spirit, mind, emotions and the physical body, together forming the whole constitution of man. Any disturbance, imbalance or inhibition affecting any part of the dynamic whole will result in some kind of pathology.

Health is seen as the harmonious relationship and homeostatic balance between the many systems of the body. Health depends on the operation of a number of subtle levels in our nature, both subjective and energetic, influencing our wellbeing.

The holistic view accepts that we are more complex than outward appearances suggest, and that the "Whole" is much greater than just the sum of the parts. Only those therapeutic models that take account of this will truly heal. Some models would also include the influence of past lives and karma, as well as frustration of soul purpose and intention in a person's life as important factors in disease processes and patterns of behaviour. The cultural background of race, education and religion, of work and experience, of family and wider relationships all play a part in the development of disease and as potential sources of stress. Personal expectations and assumptions, self image and particularly FEARS of life, death and failure are sure promoters of disease and may keep a person in a constant state of stress.

This is not all: what of a person's character? The quality of character concerns the strengths, achievements, aspirations, intentions and the spiritual resources that are called upon. It concerns the inherent goodness and truth in a person and all that reflects the element of the Divine in their nature. This is the psycho-spiritual intelligence that is called upon for healing and transformation and for understanding the challenge of illness. A person's character also concerns their ability to express and receive love, their need to transcend the lower ego and to relate to others in a right way.

Here also is the importance of the patient's self understanding of what has led to his condition, for a patient knows himself as no other person can. In my experience a patient's insights are tremendously valuable. for they lead on to their understanding of the need for personal cooperation and responsibility for recovery.

The practice of holistic medicine is hugely demanding. It is not possible to find adequate training, as it requires a deep understanding of its philosophy and principles This cannot be acquired through theoretical study only but, in addition, by practice as a way of life: the map is not the same as the territory. The more the practitioner understands from practice, the more he can teach by example to the patient, who can recognise the practitioner as one who has learned the truth by experience.

The usual authoritarian stance of the medical specialist, with disempowerment of the patient, needs to be replaced by a relationship of respect as equals in a collaboration of mutual learning, insight and understanding, with loving empathic support and encouragement from the practitioner. As the patient learns to understand himself, meeting his own needs and taking responsibility for his own wellbeing, so he becomes empowered and autonomous.

Finally I should like to make it clear that the Holistic method may require many specialists to participate in the recovery of a single patient. Specialists in any or some of the following may be needed: allopathic medicine, nutrition, herbalism,, homoeopathy, acupuncture, manipulation, various forms of physical therapy, relaxation, psychotherapy, healing and prayer. As the wellbeing of a patient depends on healing at several levels, no one practitioner usually has all the competence and skills to meet all the patient's needs.

In Holland recognition of the value of a holistic model of practice was emphasised when a commission was set up in 1978 to examine and report on complementary and alternative medicine. As a Principal of a College for part time study over six years of esoteric philosophy, psychology, healing and the holistic model, I was invited to participate in the Commission's study. In view of the lack of hard evidence for the efficacy of these methods, the Ministry of Health laid down the following criteria for their evaluation:

How much did the therapy serve the psychosocial needs of the patient?

How much did it educate the patient in healthier lifestyles, thereby having a preventative role?

Valuation of the fact that more time was needed for a patient to have a holistic consultation than a conventional medical consultation.

Could the therapy, when successful, be financially less costly?

It was recognised that these criteria were different from those applied in conventional medicine, and it was acknowledged that complementary therapies often offered more psychosocial support to patients.

In response to the WHO initiative encouraging nations to evaluate traditional systems of medicine, with possible reduction in costs, Holland's commission examined practices in that country over two years. The result was a six hundred page document making recommendations to the Ministry of Health in favour of changes and initiatives of a very supportive nature to complementary therapies.

Any study of the dynamic human "Whole" which does not acknowledge the interactions and interdependence of systems and organs with the rest of the whole will not discover the true nature of the cause and development of disease. The true nature of disease often appears quite unrelated to any pathology that is not related to the "Whole"

Treating symptoms and dealing with the body only as separate systems unrelated to the whole can lead to an impasse in the management of degenerative disease. Too little attention is often paid to the damaging effect of an unhealthy lifestyle. We should ask why some degenative diseases are endemic in Western culture and are absent in some ethnic and other racial groups having a healthier lifestyle: such people may only develop our degenerative diseases when they adopt the Western way of life. Such studies could be more fruitful than the mere study of pathology as a guide to health. Health education and preventive medicine should be given scientific priority.

Holistic medicine recognises the body's innate ability to repair and heal itself, and all therapeutic intervention should aid and support this life sustaining process. This challenges those medical interventions which can be damaging to the body's systems, thwarting healing and even putting health and life in danger. It is recognised that iatrogenic disease is on the increase. The harm that can be done by such toxic interventions as chemotherapy and radiotherapy need greater critical scrutiny.

Light and colour, fresh air, a balanced diet, exercise, rest, relaxation techniques, love, creative hobbies and interests: all may do more to enhance health and healing than toxic drugs and other harmful treatments.

The importance of the unique nature of the patient determines the need for the treatment programme to suit the individual and his requirements. Treating the whole patient is more important than merely treating symptoms and pathology. No two people have the same history or biochemistry, nor will the outcome of their treatments be identical. With the concept of the "dynamic whole" in mind, time to take a comprehensive history is essential if a practitioner is to plan a therapeutic programme suited to the patient's needs and capacities. Insight is gained from taking time to enquire into the patient's lifestyle, habits of diet, emotional and mental profile.

Hertha Larive is a transpersonal therapist specialising in spiritual and cancer counselling.

Spiritual Healing and Medical Care.

Dr. Craig K Brown

Many individuals, irrespective of medical knowledge, have the gift of bringing a healing power to others, whose innate self-healing is thereby enhanced. Probably we all potentially have this gift in some degree. It is something which can be nurtured and cultivated, but not commanded or produced to order as it originates from a higher source

There are probably more practising healers in the UK than there are practitioners of other complementary therapies. The medical profession's attitude to them has changed considerably over the past 50 years, moving from outright rejection to acceptance and, increasingly, cooperation. An important factor here has been the creation of a healers' organisation and the provision of a code of conduct for healers, as explained here by Dr Craig Brown, himself a practising GP.

Introduction

In this paper I will give a definition of healing. I will describe how healing is organised in the United Kingdom and look to the future. Finally I will outline how healing can bring spirituality into health care.

Definition of Spiritual Healing

Spiritual healing is restoring the balance of body, mind, emotion and spirit by means of contact or at a distance. It is stilling oneself to find the inner peaceful core then connecting with the universal source of all Love and Peace with the intention of channelling that healing power through oneself for the benefit of another.

It is a natural, non invasive approach that has the aim of promoting self healing to bring a sense of well-being to the recipient. Healing is strictly non-denominational and follows no creeds or rituals. Healers do not diagnose disease or offer any prescribed treatment.

124

Healing Organisations

In the United Kingdom healing, as a complementary therapy, is considered well organised. The umbrella body, the Confederation of Healing Organisations (CHO), acts as a networking and representative group. With 12,000 members healers comprise the greatest number of complementary practitioners in the United Kingdom (Mills & Peacock 1997). The most active healing organisation is the National Federation of Spiritual Healers (NFSH). It was established as a charity in 1955 and currently has 6,000 members. The NFSH is a model of self regulation having membership criteria, a code of practice and disciplinary procedure, a training programme and more recently a research group.

Membership

 Individuals come to healing through a variety of routes but generally begin to realise that they have some aptitude to healing through helping others. They may wish to learn more to develop their knowledge and skills, and generally they will attend some introductory meetings of an organisation such as the NFSH. As probationary healers they will have to complete a two year period before they can then apply to join as a full healer member. Finally to become full healer members they are tested on the code of conduct and their knowledge of healing in an interview before a membership panel of experienced healers.

Code of Conduct

Healers have always had a strict published code of practice. Recently the NFSH has been rewriting their constitution and has taken the opportunity to revise their code of conduct. This was an innovative project where through their membership and regional groups they created a healer's promise. It is essentially a statement of values which forms the bases of the code of conduct.

The Healer's Promise

All who come to me for healing I shall treat with compassion
Regardless of colour, creed, or race.
My attitude shall be non judgmental and caring.
 I shall be honest in my dealings,
And all that is said to me shall be confidential
I shall act with integrity and kindness.
I shall consider my own well-being to be important,
And I shall endeavour to be true to myself.
 I shall attune with the source of Peace and Love.

Training

The training to become a full healer is mainly by working alongside an experienced healer for a minimum of two years and joining in activities of a healing group. There are four courses each over three days that need to be attended to become a full healer member. These cover basic first aid, counselling, professional standards and theory and practice of healing. The tutors have to attend presentation courses and are accredited. Training helps to set a basic proficiency in healing and create standards. However there are no post membership courses for personal development or work in specialist areas. In the future if healers do wish to work in medical care such courses will be needed. The NFSH does have considerable experience and skill within their own ranks to develop such courses, but at present lack resources to co-ordinate a strategy. There is also a growing interest amongst other health care professionals and ways of integrating healing will have to be developed.

Research

The research groups initial task will be to collect and collate all relevant publications and act as an information resource. They will then need to set up workshops and conferences to define and explore future areas of research. Specific research projects can then be undertaken.

The main limiting factor at present is lack of funding. All complementary therapies have this problem of attracting funding for research from government, charities or other sources. Although widely supported by the public they are perceived as having little effect on disease by the medical establishment. It then becomes difficult to present the right quality of clinical evidence to support their claims to health care providers who are reluctant to fund them when resources are limited. It will require some bold initiatives to break this dead-lock. However doors are opening not only in people's hearts but in the corridors of power (Foundation of Integrated Medicine 1997). In my own general practice we have a healing clinic and have demonstrated that healing does improve the quality of life in patients referred for healing and statistically these improvements are maintained after six months (Brown C 1995). Other centres are doing similar work, and hope to show that healing not only is of benefit but is cost effective. Therapeutic touch which is similar to spiritual healing is widely taught to nurses in the USA (Kreiger 1982), and has been established in this country.

Integration of Healing and the Development of the Healer-Physician

How can we integrate these two seemingly opposite philosophies to produce a creative new paradigm? The conventional medical approach is mainly diagnostic and aimed at cure. In contrast the healing approach is non judgmental and detached from outcomes. Doctors work rationally and healers intuitively, yet both see compassion as central to their work. I believe several key concepts from healing can help integrate spirituality into healthcare.

> –   By not making a diagnosis or suggesting interventions and being fionjudgemental, healers develop an accepting attitude towards the suffering they come into contact with. This attitude of caring' detachment can be adopted by doctors, and can run alongside their diagnostic and therapy skills. It is not a matter of either one or the other approach, but both.

–   With healing the desired outcome is the development of spirituality and when practising holistically this needs to be stated explicitly. This could be helpful in the care of the dying and the chronically ill both for patients and carers as it gives them achievable goals.

–   Healers consider their own health and spirituality to be important in their work. If physicians could accept that they are as vulnerable to suffering as their patients I believe there would develop a different and improved therapeutic relationship. Physicians could be more honest and perhaps patients could be more tolerant of doctor's shortcomings.

–   Learning to channel compassion. The empathetic connection brings in the feeling aspect of the dialogue between doctor and patient, but it can leave the physician emotionally tired and drained. Healing is channelling of compassion from a universal source through the healer. After making the empathetic connection the healer visualises bringing that energy of love through them, rather than coming from them. This is a critical change in conceptualising. Besides preventing the physician feeling drained, channelling leaves him or her feeling vitalised.

We may then have a new physician-healer. By physician I mean any health care worker, doctor, nurse or complementary therapist where therapy is secondary to healing. Patients are encouraged to understand their illness and find meaning and purpose. The goal of the physician healer is to facilitate spirituality. They will identify underlying negative attributes and help patients face up to life's challenges, and for their part they accept that they are vulnerable and require healing too. That changes the relationship, empowering both parties. When the physician healer works in this way he or she receives benefit, feeling energised and enthusiastic about their work.. They appreciate that they arc being of service to another and their work is a sacred act.

Summary

Healing as a therapy in health care has every prospect of success if healers keep their vigilance in maintaining standards, and developing their training programs. Further research will provide a relevant foundation for the place of spiritual healing in medical care. When health care professionals learn about healing we may not only have a new paradigm of health but a new type of physician healer.

Dr. Craig Brown is a general practitioner who is president of the National Federation of Spiritual Healers and author of 'Optimum Health'.

References

Brown, C. *(1995). Spiritual healing in a general practice: using a quality of life questionnaire to measure outcome.* Complementary Therapies in Medicine 3, 230-233

Foundation of Integrated Medicine (1997). Integrated Healthcare. *A Way Forward for the Next Five Years,* on behalf of the steering committee for The Prince of Wale's Initiative on Integrated Medicine. (16 - 16A Baldwin Gardens, London EC IN 7RJ.) London. Foundation for Integrated Medicine.

Kneger, D.(1986). The Therapeutic Touch. New York; Prentice Hall Mills, S.,& Peacock. W. (1997). *Professional Organisation of Complementary and Alternative Medicine in the United Kingdom. A report to the department of health.* The Centre for Complementary health Studies University of Exeter.

Spiritual Healing
- Research and Practice

Daniel J. Benor., M.D.

Historically the place of the healer in all civilisations and in all ages has been an honoured one. Those most revered have been spiritual leaders, the greatest healer being Christ Himself. Subsequently, up to the present time, the Church and its organisations have had a prominent place in the provision of medical care and healing. Similarly in other religions and civilisations the healer or shaman is a powerful figure. There have been many published studies testifying to the effects of healing, whether given directly or from a distance as prayer or "absent healing". Dan Benor has fully reviewed the subject.

Introduction

> "Spiritual healing is the systematic, purposeful intervention by one or more persons aiming to help (an)other living being (person, animal, plant or other living system) or beings by means of focused intention, by touch, or by holding the hands near the other being, without application of physical, chemical, or conventional energetic means of intervention."

While uncounted healers and healees attest to the benefits of healing for every ailment known to man and beast, western science has been sceptical that spiritual healing could be anything more than suggestion or placebo effects.

A growing body of research confirms that healing is, indeed a potent intervention.

Historical Notes

Spiritual healing is one of the oldest known therapies. Practiced in every known culture, it has been given many different names:

shamanism, pranic or bioenergy healing, qigong, Reiki, Therapeutic Touch, mental healing, faith healing, paranormal healing and more. Its many names reflect the many theories of how it works, revealing our basic ignorance about this potent form of therapy.

I prefer the term spiritual healing, which acknowledges that healing opens healers and healees to awarenesses of spirituality, a participation of aspects of Self extending beyond the physical body, reaching towards the Divine, or the Infinite Source.

In the UK healing has been seen by many to be within the province of the Church. Many Christians are concerned that healing outside their church may be the work of the devil. They assume that God speaks only to those of the true faith. Such assumptions are difficult to maintain in today's global village, and in view of the evidence that healing works in many settings and for all living things - not only for humans - and this bias is shifting.

The UK is a world leader in the integration of spiritual healing with conventional medical care. The Confederation of Healing Organizations has campaigned successfully for acceptance of healing. Healers have been allowed into National Health Service hospitals at the request of patients since the 1970s. Some healers now work in doctors' surgeries and in hospital pain, cancer, arthritis, and cardiac rehabilitation centres. A few of these healers are paid by the NHS. Doctors have received Continuing Medical Education credits for workshops in which they develop their own healing gifts.

Healing Treatments

Spiritual healing is given in two major ways: 1. with a *laying-on of hands,* with the hands lightly touching or held near the body but not touching it for about 5-30 minutes; or 2. As *absent (distant)* healing, by wish, meditation or prayer, which may be sent from any distance, even from many miles away. Healers say they must focus their minds on the intent to heal in order to bring about healing effects. Many healers believe they are channeling healing energies from a natural, universal source, from Christ, Buddha, God, or some other outside agency.

131

During healing treatments, healers and healees often report sensations of heat, tingling, electrical sensations, or cold at the sites on the body that are in need of treatment. This is usually taken as confirmation that an exchange of healing energy is occurring between healer and healee.

Many healers do not diagnose at all, but 'turn the problems over to a higher power for healing'. Other healers may get intuitive impressions of what is wrong with a person and direct their healing to parts of the person they feel are in need of attention. Some healers are gifted with an ability to diagnose problems and can sometimes clarify problems intuitively when conventional medicine has failed to identify the source of a problem.

A word of caution regarding intuitive diagnosis: Healers often perceive part of the diagnostic picture but not all of it. I did two pilot studies of intuitive diagnosis with the help of Dr. Jean Roberton, a GP. The first was with a group of eight average healers and the second with a group of four very experienced healers who see auras. Each group simultaneously observed a series of individuals with known diagnoses. Each drew a picture and wrote down their diagnostic impressions of what they observed in their auras. Then each, in turn, reported to the person they observed what their impressions were. No one was more surprised than the healers when each of their reports was as different from the others' as those of the blind men and the elephant. The next surprise was when the people who had been given the intuitive diagnostic impressions indicated that they agreed with all but one of the 'readings'. It appears that all but one of the healers resonated accurately with a different facet of the problems of the people they were observing. (One healer clearly seemed to be projecting her impressions, reporting she sensed depression in most of the people she observed.) Prior to these studies most of the healers had believed that they were perceiving the whole problem when they were giving intuitive diagnostic readings.

Choosing a healer is a delicate matter, very much like choosing a psychotherapist. There are no formal tests of healing abilities, so one is reliant on word of mouth recommendations. A helpful approach is to ask whether the healer has had success with the sort of problem needing treatment.

Spiritual awareness may be awakened during healings. This brings people into contact with a vast source of inspiration which can help them deal with their dis-eases and diseases.

Spiritual healing views a peaceful death as a good healing and finds that healing often eases this transition between worlds.

There are no known deleterious effects to healing treatments, other than those due to injudicious discontinuation of other therapies (such as taking insulin) in the mistaken belief that healing could replace these.

Healing is an excellent *complement* to most other therapies, whether conventional or unconventional. In Britain, the Confederation of Healing Organizations has a code of conduct which requires that before healers give treatments they must ask prospective healees whether they have seen a doctor for their problems.

It is sad that healing has been viewed by many as a treatment of last resort, when all conventional approaches have been exhausted. Healers report that they can help much more when treatments are given early in the course of an illness.

Research

I have identified over 200 controlled studies of healing. They include studies of humans, animals, plants, bacteria, yeasts, cells in laboratory culture, enzymes and more. There are more controlled studies published on spiritual healing than on any of the other complementary therapies. Publication biases of most medical journals have excluded articles on spiritual healing. The lack of articles published in major medical journals has been used by sceptics as a reason to reject the possibility that healing may be a potent intervention. Many of the studies prior to 1990 were published in peer-reviewed parapsychology journals. Lately, many studies have appeared in nursing journals. About 30 doctoral dissertations and master's theses are available through University Microfilms International.

Distant healing is an excellent therapy for controlled, double-blind studies because it can be given with absolutely no physical or social contact between healers and healees. This makes it easy to maintain the blinds in the study, as no one but the experimenter assigning the patients for distant healing and the healers sending the healing will know which patients are being given the treatment. For example, Randolph C. Byrd, M.D. studied the effects of intercessory prayer healing on patients hospitalized in a coronary care unit (CCU). In a prospective, double-blind, randomized study, 192 patients were sent distant healing and 201 patients served as controls. There were no significant differences between groups on admission in degree of severity of myocardial infarction or in numerous other pertinent variables. "Significantly fewer patients in the prayer group required incubation/ ventilation ($p < .002$) or antibiotics ($p < .005$), had cardiopulmonary arrests ($p < .02$), developed pneumonia ($p < .03$) or required diuretics ($p < .05$). A multivariate analysis showed a very highly significant difference between the groups ($p < .0001$).

Despite the differences between groups, the mean times in CCU and durations of hospitalization between groups were nearly identical. Healing appeared to reduce the severity of cardiac pathology while not shortening duration of hospitalization.

This exceptionally good study is an exception in yet another way. It was published in the respected Southern Medical Journal.

Other studies of distant healing have confirmed effects in altering electrodermal responses in humans, wakening mice from anesthesia, and enhancing growth of plants, bacteria, and yeasts.

Healing by the laying-on of hands has demonstrated significant effects in humans for enhancing wound healing, recuperation from surgery, decreasing pain, and dealing with anxiety and depression. Out of 166 controlled studies of healing, 74 (44.6 per cent) demonstrate effects at statistically significant levels that could occur by chance only one time in a hundred or less ($p < .01$); and another 37 (22.3 per cent) at levels that could occur between two and five times out of a hundred ($p < .02-.05$). In other words, two-thirds of the studies demonstrate significant effects. Other studies are suggestive but leave questions because of flaws in design or deficiencies in reporting.

Many of the studies have been replicated, confirming that the effects are real and not just chance occurrences.

Theories

Western, reductionistic science finds it difficult to understand how spiritual healing could work. I believe a simple explanation can be found in Einstein's theory, $E = mc^2$, which has been amply validated by quantum physics. This states that matter and energy are interconvertible. Newtonian medicine has been slow to assimilate the idea that the body may be addressed as matter (as is done in conventional medicine) *or as energy* (as healers have been saying for many years).

Science remains sceptical when it cannot measure alleged energies on any instrument. This has been a problem, because no consistent electromagnetic (EM) or other energies have been identified which correlate with healing treatments, although varied reports have claimed that changes in ultraviolet light and minute EM fields were measured around healers or healees.

Healers say that there are energy fields surrounding and interpenetrating the body. These fields can be palpated by healers (and by many sensitive people who have no known healing abilities). Some people see auras of colour around and within every living thing, which they say are the energy fields identified by healers. I believe these reports are credible, because many healers and healees have reported them, and I have myself experienced such sensations both as healee and healer. Human beings are very sensitive instruments for the detection of healing energies. The difficulty with sensitive instruments is that they are subject to extraneous 'noise'. This, plus the confounding factors of experimenters' and subjects' biases and beliefs, has made it difficult to confirm healing energies through the use of human 'instruments'.

Summary

Spiritual healing is a therapy with vast potential for enhancing health care. Clinical experience and research confirm it is a potent intervention.

Daniel Benor M.D. is a psychiatrist who was founder of the Doctor-Healer Network and is author of the four-volume work 'Healing Research: Energy Medicine and Spirituality'.

Resources

Benor, D. J.,(1992), *Healing Research*, Volume I, Oxford/ Munich: Helix Books ; Revised edition Southfield, MI: Vision Publications (in press).

Benor, DJ, (1993) Healing Research, Volume II, Holistic Energy Medicine and the Energy Body, Oxford/ Munich: Helix Books; Revised edition: Southfield, MI: Vision Publications (in press)

.

Benor, DJ, *Healing Research*, Volume III, Science, Spir;t, and the Etenial Soul, Southfield, MI: Vision Publications (in press)

Benor, DJ, *Healing Research*, Volume IV: *Theory and Practice of Spiritual Healing*, Southfield, MI: Vision Publications (in press).

Dossey, L.(1993): *Healing Words*, HarperSanFrancisco.

Gerber, R, (1988), *Vibrational Medicine,* Santa Fe, NM: Bear & Co.
LeShan, L, (1974), *Clairvoyant Reality*, Wellingborough: Thorsons

The Healing Effect - Complementary Medicine's Unifying Principle.

David Hodges, Ph.D. and Tony Scofield, Ph.D

The power that comes through a healer is real, mysterious and unquantifiable. It can best be understood as an aspect of compassionate love or agape. It does not originate in the healer himself but is from a higher source for which the healer acts as a channel. David Hodges and Tony Scofield propose a unifying concept of healing energy underlying all forms of therapy, whether given by healer, therapist, nurse or doctor. Their proposal is also set out, rather more fully, in the Network Newsletter for August 1995 (No.58, 3 - 8).

Introduction

Complementary medicine is increasingly being used by lay people and, to a lesser extent, by doctors. It is also a rapidly-developing field, with apparently new treatments appearing regularly. In spite of these trends complementary therapies have been largely ignored by mainstream science and medicine because of the apparent lack of any rational principle or theoretical basis by which their effects might be explained. Similarly, the user public is presented with a bewildering array of therapies to choose from with little guidance as to their efficacy or suitability.

Although many therapies are organising the training and regulation of their members so that they are seen to be developing a more professional approach, the lack of any generally-acceptable theoretical framework suggests that complementary therapies could remain on the fringes of mainstream science and medicine. Thus it is important that, at its present stage of evolution, complementary medicine should be seeking to develop a theoretical basis which can begin to describe the mechanisms underlying the therapies and which can show what common ground there may be across the wide range of complementary health care.

Our own experiences have lead us to believe that there is a common underlying mechanism running through the whole spectrum of complementary therapies. This mechanism may be able to unify complementary therapies within a single, straightforward theoretical basis and provide, also, a basis for much of the success of nursing and conventional medical practice.

There are at *least* three levels at which both conventional medical and complementary therapies can work. These are:

1.   The physical/physiological/pharmacological level; the level of the physical body where medical science considers most treatments operate and where many procedures such as surgery, drugs and herbal treatments can have an important effect. The value of the direct physical and/or chemical effects of therapies in any system *must always be recognised.*

2.   The psychological/mental level. Medical science recognises that this level does play some part in health care, mainly through such mechanisms as the placebo effect, psychoneuroimmunology and similar psychosomatic processes. Good therapists will be effective in eliciting the placebo response.

3.   The higher mental/spiritual levels. Much of mainstream medicine does not recognise the existence of these levels. However, levels 2 and 3 are the most important levels from the point of view of complementary therapies; and it is at level 3 that we consider many complementary therapies, and especially healing, operate.

Healing, usually called spiritual, mental or paranormal healing, is the most simple and straightforward of all the complimentary therapies. It relies for its effectiveness on the transmission of 'healing energy between healer and patient; both individuals being frequently aware of the flow of what is best described as energy. Thus spiritual healers seek to channel a healing energy which, interacting with the patient's own energy systems, helps to re-establish a balance and thus to reverse the disease process [1]. This 'energetic interaction' can be termed the healing effect.

Healing as a Common Therapeutic Factor

We consider that the healing effect is a unifying principle underlying the whole range of complementary therapies, even those generally perceived as having a direct physico-chemical influence on the patient, which goes beyond the placebo and similar psychosomatic effects. We also consider that this principle similarly underlies the activities of conventional medicine. This principle can be stated as follows:

> All therapies, whether they are included in the range of conventional approaches - medical, surgical or psychiatric - or whether they are complementary, essentially involve the process of healing. In this process the doctor/therapist utilises the healing effect to a greater or lesser extent to balance the patient's energy systems and to activate the natural healing processes of the body to seek to overcome the health problem. All therapies, conventional or complementary, are only models of treatment through which the therapist manifests these healing processes, although the more obvious aspects of the therapy may also have a direct effect upon the physical body and the therapist may not be consciously aware of the involvement of the healing effect.

We suggest that all health care professionals utilize the healing effect as a primary aspect of their treatment of patients whether they are aware of it or not. In some therapies the healing effect operating at Level 3 of the patient may be more important than in others, and the balance between the healing effect operating at the higher level and the physical aspects of the therapy operating at Level 1 will vary widely depending on the individual therapy. Nevertheless, we consider that the transmission of a healing energy by the therapist to the patient and the use of this energy to stimulate the patient's innate healing power, the *vis medicatrix naturae*, may frequently be the most important, if often underlying, aspect of any health care treatment [1]. We use the term healing energy here within a healing context; in other contexts the synonymous terms subtle or spiritual energies are often used.

Some practitioners harness the healing energy more effectively than others. Some people have this ability from birth; others develop their innate healing ability later in life, or can be trained to do so. Also, if we are correct, most people working in the health care field are utilising this energy effectively, although subconsciously. With doctors and surgeons, for example, some seem to obtain consistently positive results beyond their general levels of knowledge and competence. Some surgeons have high success rates, low morbidity and more rapid patient recovery; the traditional good 'bed-side manner' was often reflected in a doctor's ability to help patients in the days before pharmaceutical medicine. Nursing in particular is a field where healing, although often done unconsciously, plays an important part in patient recovery.

So how does the healing effect operate as a 'common denominator' across this wide spectrum of therapies? It seems likely that healing stimulates the body to heal itself. As Fritjof Capra has said "health is an experience of well-being resulting from a dynamic balance that involves the physical and psychological aspects of the organism...", and many practitioners believe that healing stimulates the body to optimise this balance. However, if the underlying causes which lead to the illness are not removed, the balance may once again tilt towards dis-ease.

It is not possible at present to say what the healing energy is. Although many therapists have their own personal views, there is little objective evidence to support them. There have been reports that healing energy can be measured; but the experiments that give rise to such suggestions have rarely been repeated. Because of these shortcomings in the healing literature, our own research was intended to demonstrate the existence of healing using a simple model of salt stressed seeds. Our experiments demonstrated conclusively that a healer could effect a stressed organism and hence harness, by definition, a healing energy.[2]

The Importance of the Therapist's World View

An important aspect of healing concerns the 'world-view' of the therapist. All therapies, including conventional medicine, exist within their own coherent world-view. These views have changed throughout history and the practice of medicine is merely a reflection of the prevailing world-view. Whereas conventional medicine is grounded in the Cartesian/Newtonian mechanistic view of the universe, many complementary therapies claim to look elsewhere for a rationale of their more 'holistic' approaches. However, instead of seeking an explanation within a spiritual context, ideas which they mainly espouse, complementary practitioners often attempt to fit their therapies into the world-view of conventional society, promoting explanations based on quasi-scientific ideas or poorly-understood principles gleaned from quantum physics. These explanations are sometimes based on the belief that therapies are practised according to 'the book'. For example many homoeopaths use radionically-produced preparations, yet hypotheses regarding the mechanisms for homoeopathic action concentrate solely on changes in the structure of water induced by the process of succussion. Ultimately we will have to go beyond these more superficial explanations to find the root of healing, but many therapies are not yet at that stage.

Although we believe that the ultimate source of healing is spiritual in nature and not yet understood, it is still useful to propose a world-view which can encompass all healing phenomena, regardless of the validity of the current explanation of the underlying mechanism. Therapists and, to a certain extent, patients ideally work within a shared world-view, in which they can all believe. The long training of many therapists, whether in conventional or complementary systems, instils in the practitioners a belief in that discipline, enabling them to operate successfully within it. It also provides a rationale for why the failures of other systems of medicine may be successes within their own. Each system has its own characteristics which marks it out from others; homoeopathy uses dynamised preparations, acupuncture manipulates meridian lines, others use magnets, crystals, or lasers.

The Significance of Healing Ritual

Among the diagnostic techniques used by complementary therapists are dowsing, radionic cameras, Kirlian cameras, radial artery pulse tension, Boyd's emanometer, Vegatest and similar devices. Many of the instruments are visually impressive and form part of the world-view of the therapy. We believe them to be essential to the *ritual* of healing, but we doubt whether many have a significant *technological* function. Our experience suggests that many of these devices only provide a means for the therapist to enter the healing situation, to understand the problem within their own world-view, and to enact a ritual to harness the healing energy. This is not a new idea. Many other authors believe that healing devices release the patient's healing potential and it is the patient rather than the properties of the remedies that should be examined to gain a better understanding of healing mechanisms.

The emotional investment of the therapist in a particular ritual is, we believe, crucial to its effectiveness and may explain why therapies come and go. Throughout history many therapies have had an ephemeral existence whilst others like homoeopathy enjoy a more lasting vogue. There is a famous saying attributed to many people: "... we should use new remedies quickly, while they are still efficacious." A new treatment is exciting, inspiring hope where all else has failed. Therapies are often more successful in the hands of the founders than in those of the disciples. The founders generate the world-view in which the treatment operates and their authority arouses patients' hopes and expectations. Their greater belief in the system undoubtedly makes the harnessing of natural healing energies more effective. The emotional investment and belief of those who come after is likely to be less than that of the founders and may explain those cases where effectiveness diminishes with time.

The diversity of techniques of complementary medicine and the different explanations of how they may rebalance energies and stimulate the *vis medicatrix naturae*, may be a source of difficulty when any therapy is proposed for acceptance by government regulatory bodies. A particular problem is likely to be the diversity of equipment that often accompanies therapies. Although this equipment is probably only part of the ritual necessary to focus the therapist's consciousness on the task in order to harness healing energy, because it is often physical in nature, involving the giving of pills or tinctures or physical manipulations, the therapist is left more vulnerable to legislative sanction. The problems are compounded by the inadequacies of most of the explanations given for their effect. We believe that if most complementary therapists were to recognise that they primarily harnessed healing energy and that the techniques and instruments they used were largely part of the ritual for achieving this, then complementary medicine would be in a much stronger position to defend itself from criticisms by conventionally trained scientists.

Concluding Remarks

Although there is a significant body of research work already published in support of spiritual healing, experiments designed to look for statistically significant effects from this and other complementary therapies are urgently needed, and may well support our contention that the ritual itself is but a means to harness the same energy of healing. In putting forward these ideas we are not seeking to denigrate the whole range of complementary therapies which are available. The fact that we are proposing a simple healing model as the primary mechanism underlying these and conventional therapies does not mean that we are seeking to devalue them. On the contrary, as already stated the confidence imparted by a belief in some of the more complex therapies may enable the therapist to harness the underlying mechanism more effectively and thus become a more powerful therapeutic agent.

The concept described in this and in our earlier, 1995, paper is not new. We initially described it in outline in 1989 [3J and 1994 [4] and intimations of a similar nature were also found in Benor (1994) [5]. However, prior to this other authors had approached the idea in various ways (see references in Scofield, 1989) [3]; but it was not until the 1995 Scientific & Medical Network paper that the concept of healing as the major mechanism underlying all therapies was precisely formulated. These ideas appear to be gaining currency as other authors develop the concept either as the broad theory presented here (Benor, 1995) [6], or related to more specific areas of healing or complementary medicine, e.g. Achterberg (1996) [7].

Dr. David Hodges is a retired senior lecturer in animal physiology at Wye College. University of London. Dr. Tony Scofield is a senior lecturer in animal physiology at Wye College. University of London

References

1. Hodges, R.D., Scofield, A.M. (1995). *J. Roy. Soc. Med.,* 88:203-

2. Scofield, A.M., Hodges, R.D. (199i). j. *Soc. Psvcl~icul Res.,* *57,* 321-343.

3. Scofield, A.M. (1989). J. *Brit. Soc. Dowsers,* 33:423-483.

4. Hodges, R.D., Scofield, A.M. (1994). J. *Roy. Soc. Med.,* 87:432.

5. Benor, D.J. (1994). *Healing Research. Holistic Energy Medicine and Spirituality.* Vol.2. Deddington, Oxon.; Helix Editions.

6. Benor, D.J. (1995). *Comp. Therap. Med.,* 3:234-238.

7. Achterberg, J. (1996). *Alt. Therap. Health Med.,* 2(3):58-61.

Anthroposophical Medicine

Dr Michael Evans

Rudolf Steiner's philosophy embraces the nature of man and his relationship with the world about him, animate and inanimate. His teaching reaches into every aspect of human activity including the meaning of health, the significance of illness and the practice of medicine. The practical results of his philosophy are well shown in the examples of education (Waldorf schools) and the long term care of the mentally disabled (Camphill communities). A brief report on the work of the small hospital at Park Attwood, which follows Steiner's principles, appeared in Network Newsletter No.66 (April 1998, p 40). Dr Michael Evans was a cofounder of Park Attwood, and now works as a GP at the St Luke's Medical and Therapy Centre in Stroud.

Its Principles

Anthroposophical medicine represents a remarkable attempt to integrate the spiritual view of the human being with the conventional scientific view. It offers a way of integrating what can be known of the spiritual, psychological, vital and physical aspects of the human being. Putting these insights into practice leads into an inner spiritual path of training for the physician, with repercussions not only for the doctor/patient relationship but also for the relationship between the doctor and the kingdom of nature from which his medicinal substances are drawn. It widens the palette of therapeutic possibilities beyond but including conventional medication to medicines with a more herbal or homoeopathic character. It prescribes a range of arts developed as therapies and a number of innovative techniques in the realm of hydrotherapy and massage. It is practised in Britain in a number of NHS group practices, one of them as part of an in-patient facility at Park Attwood, and, in continental Europe, in district general hospitals and a university teaching hospital, Witten/Herdecke in Germany.

Like other great spiritual teachers, Steiner gives a spiritually orientated description of the human being and the universe. However, his description has a number of special features in that it extends into a spiritual physiology of the organs and a spiritual understanding of pathology. Unlike many other spiritual teachings anthroposophy has many of the qualities that we find in science rather than religion, in that it presents its methods of research as well as its results In this spirit Steiner discourages his readers from accepting what he says as dogma, and hopes they will regard them more as hypotheses that can be tested through life for their validity and usefulness.

The hypotheses of anthroposophy or spiritual science as it is also called, can help intellectually bridge the gap between an approach that treats the human being as an object and passive recipient of external intervention and the human being as a self-conscious individual able to exercise freedom and responsibility. Or put another way, it helps bridge the mind/body split. Part of the way Steiner does this is by describing two intermediate levels of existence between the physical/ mechanical aspects of the human being and the self-conscious spiritual aspect of our being which carries the possibility for freedom and morality. At the level nearer to the physical aspects of the human body, he describes the organisation of biological form-giving principles, the realm of life that distinguishes plants, animals and human beings from the inorganic world. Although deeply unconscious this realm has both the power and wisdom in it that we see expressed in the processes of growth and development as well as in the healing of wounds. The other level of being that he describes is closer to consciousness and is that realm of psychological existence that we have in common with the animal kingdom and can be described as conscious but not self-conscious. It is the realm of passions, instincts, drives and emotion, which at times we can be very conscious of, and others less so. He characterises this realm as one from which most illnesses have their origin.

Its Practice

This four tiered description of the human being gives a framework for both understanding existing forms of treatment such as homoeopathy as well as providing the impetus to develop a rational form of medicine that can do greater justice to the patient as a whole human being. The aim of having therapeutic effects via any of the four levels of existence has been a spur to develop new forms of treatment, as well as giving a new perspective for existing treatment methods.

This means that while in practice anthroposophical doctors prescribe conventional drugs or advise conventional surgery, they are aware that when doing so they are working primarily on the physical/ chemical level of existence. They are conscious that this may be doing little to develop the patient's own restorative forces, which have their source in the realm of the organisation giving life and biological form. Homoeopathic medicines in contrast do not work at a physical or chemical level, but when appropriately prescribed are able to work by influencing the healing capacity within this second level of existence. This is also the case for those physical treatments whose effectiveness is more dependent on the response they evoke rather than their direct mechanical effects. For example, Massage which works on the soft tissues of the body, can evoke a response from muscle and from tissue fluids and can have a vitalising effect in addition to relaxation. This vital level of existence is understood as having a particular kinship to the liquid or watery element. Anthroposophical medicine inspired the development of a rhythmic form of massage. This is based on an attempt to relate forms and movements of the massage to the form and movements inherent in this life realm. A form of hydrotherapy which has some similarity to aromatherapy has been developed. Here aromatic oils are finely dispersed in the water of a bath. After the bath the patient is wrapped up and time is allowed for the oils on the skin to work on and through the skin to stimulate a range of desired responses. The most common is a generalised warmth response of the body and a heightened sense of wellbeing.

The third level of existence may be loosely described as a level of "animal soul". This is understood as having a primarily catabolic physiological effect, and is the prime source of physical depletion and illness. This is a level of existence we share with the animal kingdom but not the plant kingdom and is the spiritual reason for the differences between plant and animal physiology [1]. The animal kingdom itself also illustrates the inverse relationship between sentience or what might be loosely called awakeness and vitality".[fig 2,3]

Our conventional medical science which aims to restrict itself to the weighable and measureable, recognises the reality of the psychosomatic causation of a growing range of physical illnesses. It also acknowledges the major role of mental stress as a cause of physical ill health. If we take seriously the importance of this psychosomatic basis of many illnesses then psychological treatment or in other words treatment via the soul, should have a major role in the treatment of physical illness. To this end a range of arts have been further developed to create various forms of therapy. They encompass therapeutic painting, drawing, modelling, sculpture, music and a special form of artistic movement called Eurythmy. The way any individual expresses himself in an artistic medium can be seen as an expression of his uniqueness and of his or her one-sidedness and is often more extreme in the states of emotional turmoil which generate physical illness. The main thrust of anthroposophical art therapy is to take this one-sidedness as a starting point and to generate a series of exercises which can step by step move towards a more balanced artistic creation. It is experienced that this process can work back powerfully on the individual's feelings and sense of themselves, in a centring and harmonising manner. When achieved this can address something of the deeper causes of illness and contribute to physical healing.

Anthroposophy distinguishes between those aspects of conscious life in which we share the animal kingdom, and those aspects which are uniquely human. It uses the term spirit or ego to describe the unique aspects and the term soul (and astral) to indicate that which we have in common with the animals.

Even without the help of spiritual science, one of the qualities that can be most easily distinguished (at least outside an approach which limits itself to natural science) is the notion of freedom and responsibility. which we can attribute to human beings in a way that is more difficult to apply to animals. In so far as we have the idea that the human being is capable of good and evil, moral and immoral deeds, ethical and unethical actions, this presupposes an element of freedom in human nature.

Another quality of the uniquely human aspect of the human being is our possibility for further development. Most of us have only achieved a small part of our potential. This possibility of individual development is connected both with moral development and a development of consciousness. This could also be described as a development of love and wisdom and is the meaning of human life. Every aspect of human life, both joy and suffering, health and illness, are potential catalysts for this development, but not its cause, as the essence of human development is freedom rather than causality. Forms of training, learning or programming which do not recognise and revere this quality in the human being risk addressing only the animal nature of the human being, and are likely to have a dehumanising danger for our culture.

Conclusion

At the heart of anthoposophical medicine is the acknowledgement of the human being as having a free spiritual potential, and that the experience of illness can have meaning. True healing of an illness is a realisation of its latent aid for the individual's development. A still wider spiritual perspective is introduced with a description of reincarnation which extends the field of potential development beyond one earth life and makes it more possible to see meaning for development also in terminal illness.

While acknowledging the essential spiritual nature of the human being, anthroposophical medicine equally acknowledges his animal/ soul nature, his vital nature and his physical bodily nature. Such recognition is fundamental to a fuller understanding of illness in general as well as particular illnesses. Such an understanding can generate new treatment possibilities, and it provides a rational basis for the prescription of treatments as diverse as surgery, conventional drug treatment, medicines with a herbal or homoeopathic quality, massage, hydrotherapy, a range of artistic therapies and spiritually based counselling.

The anthroposophical approach to medicine offers the possibility of an integrated medicine able to recognise and use what is of value in conventional medicine while also addressing the patient's unconscious healing forces, psychological life and his essential humanity.

Dr. Michael Evans is medical director of Partk Attwood Therapeutic Centre and secretary of the Anthroposophical Medical Association.

Footnotes

1.   Essentially plants possess only the first two levels of existence, i.e. a physical body and a body of life forces, have a primarily anabolic physiology and are the prime generators of living substance. In contrast the animal kingdom has a more catabolic metabolism, and are the consumers of nutrition. Plants are the only form of life capable of transforming inorganic substance i.e. water, carbon dioxide and minerals into living substances, initially simple sugars then complex

carbohydrates, fats and proteins, whereas animals are dependent on these substances as their starting point.

2.　　　Anthroposophy acknowledges that vitality, instincts, feelings, sentience, thoughts and self-consciousness, though not sense perceptible and not weighable or measureable, are realities not abstractions. By definition they are supersensible realities and thereby require a science of the supersensible, in other words, a spiritual science, which is what anthroposophy claims to be.

3.　　　Without the development of higher faculties of perception we cannot directly perceive the different levels of consciousness possessed by different animals. However, many people will not have difficulty intuiting that cold blooded animals such as earthworms may have a less well developed form of consciousness than mammals and primates. Broadly speaking the more complex forms of animal life are able to support higher degrees of sentience or wakefulness than more primitive forms of animal life and this corresponds inversely with the animals level of regenerative capacity. For example, planarians with their ability to generate two individual organisms when bisected and earthworms able to generate the hind end of their body when cut in two contrast strongly with primates' regenerative capacities being almost limited to healing wounds and being unable even to regenerate a small part of a limb.

The Changing Face of Science and Medicine

Dr. Alan Watkins

We readily accept a connection between our state of mind and our bodily health , usually in a negative sense, e.g. stress predisposing to coronary disease, bereavement predisposing to many kinds of illness, including cancer. An attempt to put this on a quantitative basis was the Holmes and Rahe scale of over 40 different stressful life events. This gives a maximum score of 100 for death of spouse, ranging down, for example, to 63 for a gaol sentence, and to 12 for the stresses of the Christmas season. It was shown that a person scoring over 300 in the course of a year was far more likely to fall ill than one whose score was under 200 (See "Getting Well Again[1] by Simonton and others). Proof that emotional stress adversely affected the immune system came from the work of the Glasers on student volunteers at exam time. Psychoneuroimmunology (PNI) began to be a serious study. The physiological basis for the mind-body connection was clarified by the discovery of numbers of neuropeptides, as described by Candace Pert in her book "Molecules of Emotion[11] An account of PNI and its relevance in different body systems is given in the book "Mind-Body Medicine", edited by Alan Watkins, who reviews the situation here.

We are all living through an amazing period of history, the technological revolution and rapid access to information is transforming all sections of society In particular medical science is undergoing very rapid change - a significant paradigm shift.

For much of this century medical science has been involved a painstaking and detailed investigation of how each bodily system works. But this reductionist approach required science to refute or ignore whole swathes of evidence in order to construct a comprehensible model of the world. Medical science is now emerging from over 500 years of unquestioned belief and faith in the laws of the universe. An increasing number of scientists and clinicians have begun to realize that the very assumptions on which science and medicine are based are incomplete. Consequently a new paradigm is emerging, one that embraces the existing view but is also a significant evolution from it. The new view is more comprehensive, more inclusive and more advanced [1].

The reductionist approach generated huge amounts of information and necessitated the evolution of numerous medical sub-specialties. But in recent years scientists have been forced to review this drive towards micro-specialisation and separation of the systems of the body. Numerous scientific studies demonstrated, often without intending to, that the traditional lines of demarcation between one system and the next were arbitrary [2]. These studies clearly demonstrated that each system in the body interacted with many other systems in a very sophisticated manner. For example, endocrinologists discovered one of the most powerfull regulators of the immune system and immunologists discovered one of the most powerfull activators of the hormonal system. It thus became clear that an individual system could not be understood in isolation, each system had to be viewed in the context of the whole if all the complex and sophisticated regulating and counter-regulating forces at play were to be fully understood [3]. The evidence has been driving science towards a systems approach to human health.

A Systems Approach

Systems theory evolved in response to increasing micro-specialisation and out of a need to manage the very rapid accumulation of a substantial amount of information. Systems thinking aims to integrate and to create wholes out of parts. It is a framework for seeing the interrelationships between parts rather than the parts themselves, for seeing dynamic patterns rather than static "snapshots". It is the science of wholeness.

The adoption of a systems approach by medicine has its modern roots in the 1970's when George Engel, Professor of Psychiatry at Rochester University advocated the adoption of a biopsychosocial model of health in place of the biomedical model [4,5]. Seeing human existence as more than a biological experience set the stage for a much broader concept of health and opened the flood gates for many more systems-based models. These models have not just integrated biological and psychosocial dimensions but have also integrated the different physiological systems in addition to different therapeutic models. The increasing integration of different physiological systems has been one of the most significant trends in medical science in the last twenty years and holds very substantial promise for the future.

This integration has been built on the increasing awareness, amongst scientists and clinicians, of how the breakdown in co-operation between different bodily systems can set the stage for the development and progression of disease. Thus science has witnessed the development of numerous inter-disciplinary approaches such as neurocardiology, immuno-endocrinology, neuroimmunology, neurogastrology, psychophysiology, immunopsychiatry and psychoneuroimmunology.

Psychoneuroimmunology (PNI)

Some of the most compelling support for a system-based approach to health and disease has come from the field of Psycho-neuro-immunology (PNI). This field evolved out of a number of discoveries in the 1970s demonstrating that behaviour (psycho) and brain function (neuro) had a significant effect on the body's natural defense mechanisms (immunology). There were two crucial "parent discoveries" to this field. Firstly, researchers at Engel's own University in Rochester noticed that the immune system could be trained to respond to certain perceptions in much the same way as Pavlov had trained his dogs [6]. This observation in addition to reports from scientists as far apart as Alabama and Germany that cells of the immune system could synthesize, from scratch, hormones normally only produced by the hormonal system demonstrated that the brain and immune system were intimately entwined [7].

Such discoveries radically challenged the existing belief that the immune system was autonomous. Since these early discoveries a wealth of hard scientific data has provided irrefutable evidence to demonstrate that virtually all arms of the immune system are under the direct control of the central nervous system (CNS) [8]. It is now well known that the CNS directly innervates the bone marrow and thymus where immune cells are generated, the lymph nodes and spleen where immune cells mature and become active, and the mucosal surfaces where infective agents gain access to the body [9,10].

Having demonstrated that immune cells were in direct physical contact with nerves scientists then demonstrated that these nerves released relevant neurotransmitters in close proximity to the immune cells [11], and that immune cells had the relevant receptors for these chemical messengers [12]. The final piece of the jigsaw dropped into place with the demonstration that transmission of messages from these nerves altered immune function [8]. To understand the biological significance of the complex interaction between the CNS and the immune system it is necessary to refer to reviews of how the brain alters immunity in specific clinical conditions [13].

Not only are there direct connections between the brain and the immune system but there is also substantial evidence to indicate that the immune system can be inhibited or stimulated by hormonal system. Such modulation of immune function is achieved through the high and low affinity receptors that exist on all immune cells for virtually all the major hormones [14]. Thus growth hormone, thyrotropin releasing hormone, thyroid stimulating hormone, human chorionic gonadotrophin, arginine vasopressin, gonadotrophin releasing hormone, androgens and prolactin have all been shown to produce immunoregulation [15,16].

Some of this research has lead scientists to question the very assumptions on which modern medicine is based. For example, the amount of growth hormone releasing hormone (GHRH) produced by immune cells in the rat spleen is 20% of that produced by the hormonal system [17]. When the number spleen cells synthesizing GHRH is taken into account the spleen can produce roughly the same amount of this hormone as the hormonal system itself. This calls into question which organ is regulating the production of growth hormone and suggests that the spleen may actually function like a fully blown hormonal gland.

The brain and the hormonal system not only regulate the immune system but they also regulate each other's function in a very sophisticated interaction on a number of levels [18]. Activation of one system tends to activate the other. For example, the application of hormonal releasing factors to nerve fibres markedly increases their firing rate [19], and chemicals released by nerve fibres are a potent stimulus for hormone production [20]. Not only does the CNS and the hormonal system modulate immune function but chemical messengers released by immune cells have been shown to profoundly affect brain and hormonal function as well as behaviour [21].

Over the last twenty years PNI has continued to break down the barriers separating the CNS, the hormonal system and the immune system. For example, recent studies demonstrated that immune cells altered pain perception [22,23], and produced molecules that were previously thought to be entirely confined to the nervous system[24].

The Future

Thus is there is now very extensive evidence to indicate that studying each bodily system in isolation fails to address their interactive complexity. Science and medicine must adopt an integrated model, since all the systems regulate each other often using the same chemical messengers to do so. Exactly how the body integrates the function of all its complex systems to provide a coordinated response to internal and external threats will be a source of considerable research over the next twenty years. This study of systems integration and systems communication will be vital if we are to truly understand how to maintain health, prevent disease and provide the optimum environment for healing.

Since bodily systems are in constant communication with each other the crucial factor is the frequency of the signaling process. Therefore in order to unravel the complexity of coordination science will need to pay more attention to the frequency domain and the mathematics of communication [18].

Evidence is beginning to accumulate showing that the frequency and coherence of messages flowing between the different systems in the body is central to health. Chaotic, incoherent messages flowing between systems promote disequilibrium, disorder, imbalance and disease. In contrast, coherent messages enhance efficiency and the functioning of the entire system [25-27].

In this regard, there is evidence to suggest that the heart plays a key role in promoting coherence within the entire human system. The electrical power generated by the heart is 50-60 times greater than that generated by the brain and the electromagnetic power generated by the heart is 1,000-5,000 greater than the brain [28]. It is through its powerful electrical and electromagnetic signaling that the human heart has the capacity to coordinate the function of all other organs including the brain and the immune system [27,29,30].

Specifically in positive emotional states the heart generates a much more coherent electrical signal which it transmits to the brain via the baroreceptor network [27,31]. Because of the power of this signal it can help promote physiological synchronization or "entrainment" all

155

other bodily systems. This entrained state has significant health benefits [25-30]. Learning to generate coherent physiological states offers significant promise for promoting health, improving quality of life and for healing [32,33].

Dr. Alan Watkins is Founder and Chairman of the Brain-Immune Network Group and editor of 'Mind-Body Medicine: The Clinician's Guide to Psychoneuroimmunology'.

References

1.   Watkins A, Dacher ES. *The Future of Health Care - Who Is Responsible?* Chapter 1 in Effective Interventions for Health and Disease Prevention. In the series: Biobehavioural Perspective on Health & Disease Prevention (ed Lydia Temeshok)(1998.)

2.   Blalcok JE *Neuroimmunoendocrinology.* Chemical Immunology vol 69 (1997). Karger Press.

3.   Dacher ES. *The Whole Healing System.* Dutton Press (1996)

4.   Engel G. *The Biopsychosocial Model and Medical Education.* The New England Journal of Medicine. 1982: 306:802-805.

5.   Engel G. *The Clinical Application of the Biopsychosocial Model.* The American Journal of Psychiatry. 1980:137:535-544.

6.   Ader R, Cohen N. *Behaviourally conditioned immunosuppression.* Psychom Med 1975.37: 333-40.

7   Blalock JE, Smith EM. *Human leukocyte interferon: Structural and biological relatedness to adreno-corticotrophic hormone and endorphins.* Proc Natl Acad Scin USA 1980.77: 5972-5974

8.   Ader R' Felten DL, Cohen N. *Psychoneuroimmunology* 2nd ed. San Diego Calif: Academic Press, (1991).

9.   Calvo W. *Innervation of the bone marrow in laboratory animals.* Am J Anat (1968). 123: 315.

10.   Williams JW, Peterson RG, Shea PA' Schmedtje JF, Bauer DC, Felten DL. *Sympathetic innervation of mouse thymus and spleen: Evidence for a functional link between nervous and immune systems.* Brain Res Bull 1980.6: 83.

11. Stevens-Felten SY, Bellinger DL. *Noradrenergic and peptidergic innervation of lymphoid organs.* In Blalock JE (ed): Neuroimmunoendocrinology, 3rd rev ed. Chem Immunol. Basel Karger (1997) 69: pp 99-131.

12. Bellinger DL, Lorton D, Romano T, Olschowka JA' Felten SY, Felten DL. *Neuropeptide innervation of lymphoid organs.* Ann NY Acad Sci (1990) 594:17-33.

13. Watkins AD. *Neuropharmacology.* Chapter 28, p501-513 In Allergy and Allergic Diseases. Kay AB (ed) Blackwell Scientific Publications Ltd (1996).

14. Ader R, Felten D, Cohen N. *Interactions between the brain and the immune system.* Annu Rev Pharmacol Toxicol (1990).30: 561-602.

15. Blalock JE. *The immune system: Our sixth sense.* Immunologist (1994).2:8-15.

16. Reichlin S. *Neuroendocrine-immune interactions.* New Eng J Med (1993). Oct 21 1246-53

17. Weigent DA' Blalock JE. *Immunoreactive growth hormone releasing hormone in rat leukocytes.* J Neuroimmunol (1990)29:1-13.

18. Watkins AD, Pert C. *The Human System. Intelligence, Emotions and Cellular Function.* Chapter 3 in Effective Interventions for Health and Disease Prevention. In the series: Biobehavioural Perspective on Health & Disease Prevention (ed Lydia Temeshok)(1998).

19. Valentino RI, Foote SL, Aston-Jones G. *Corticotropin-releasing hormone activates noradrenergic neurons of the locus coeruleus.* Brain Res (1983).270: 363-367.

20. Cunningham ET Jr, Bohn MC, Sawchenko PE. *The organisation of adrenergic inputs to the paraventricular and supraoptic nuclei of the rat hypothalamus.* J Comp Neurol (1990.292): 651-667

21. Watkins AD. *Perceptions, Emotions and Immunity: An integrated homoeostatic network.* Quarterly Journal Medicine April (1995).88:283-294.

22. Stein C, Hassan AHS, Przewlocki R, Gramsch C, Peter K, Herz A. *Opiods from immunocytes interact with receptors on sensory nerves to inhibit nociception in inflammation.* Proc Natl Acad Sci USA (1990).87: 5935-5939.

23.   Schafer M, Mousa SA' Zhang Q, Carter L, Stein C. *Expression of corticotrophin releasing factor in inflamed tissue is required for intrinsic peripheral opioid analgesia.* Proc Natl Acad Sci USA (1996).93: 6096-6100.

24   Musso NR, Brenci S, Setti M, Indiveri F, Lotti 0. *Catecholamine content and in vitro catecholamine synthesis in peripheral human lymphocytes.* J Clin Endocrinol Metab (1996).81:1-5.

25.   McCraty R, Barrios-Choplin B, Rozman D, Atkinson M, Watkins A. *The impact of a new emotional self-management program on stress, emotions, heart rate variability, DHEA and cortisol. Integrative Physiological and Behavioral Science* (1998) vol 33 (2) (in press).

26.   McCraty R, Atkinson M, Tiller WA' Rein G, Watkins AD. *The effects of emotions on the short term power spectral analysis of heart rate variability.* Am J Cardiol (1995): 76(14): 1089-1093.

27.   Tiller WA, McCraty R, Atkinson M. *Cardiac coherence: A new non-invasive measure of autonomic nervous system order. Alternative Therapies in Health and Medicine* (1996.)2: 52-65.

28.   Clarke 3. SQUIDS. *Scientific American* p46-53, Aug (1994).

29.   McCraty R, Atkinson M, Rein G, Watkins AD. *Music Enhances the Effects of Positive Emotional States on Salivary IgA. Stress Medicine* (1996) 12:167-175.

30.   Song LZYX, Schwartz GER, Russek LOS. *Heart-focused attention and heart-brain synchronisation: energetic and physiological mechanisms. Altern Ther Health Med* (1998) 4(5):44-62.

31.   Armour JA. (1994). *Peripheral Autonomic Neuronal Interactions in Cardiac Regulation.* Chapter 10, pp219-244 In Neurocardiology. Armour JA' Ardell JL (eds) Oxford University Press.

32.   Childre DL. (1994). *Freeze-Frame.* Boulder Creek: Planetary Publications.

33.   Childre DL. (1996). *Cut-Thru.* Boulder Creek: Planetary Publications.

Whatever Happened to Healers?

Dr. Larry Dossey

Does the medical curriculum unintentionally crush the wish to learn about healing that motivates most medical students? Larry Dossey certainly thinks so, and describes some schemes designed to improve matters. Robert Louis Stevenson marvelled at the change from riotous drunken students in a few short years to sober respectable medical men. But that was last century and things have changed. In spite of the resilience of youth, the pressures of the curriculum and the gruelling years of internship today induce a significant dropout rate.

> Medicine men aren't horses
> *You don't breed them*
> > > Lame Deer, Sioux medicine man.

When I began to explore the world of alternative medicine nearly three decades ago, I discovered I would have to expand my vocabulary considerably if I wanted to communicate with therapists. For example, they often used the word "healer", which was not part of the lexicon of medical school. In fact, I do not recall the term ever being used in my medical training. I had no feel for this expression and thought it quaint. If my medical colleagues and I had been called healers, we would not have known whether we were being praised or damned. We were training to become surgeons, internists, and pathologists, not healers.

I realised also that alternative therapists used "healing" differently than we did in medical school. We'd learned that healing was something that occurred automatically in wounds and incisions, whereas my alternative therapy friends believed healing had something to do with consciousness. They furthermore differentiated healing from curing and they mysteriously maintained that "a healing" could occur even in the event of death.

Not much has changed since my encounter with these ideas. The concept of the healer remains virtually absent in medical training, and "healing"[1] continues to be used in a narrow physiologic sense.

Whatever happened to healers? Have we simply run out of them? Surely not; all cultures seem to have produced them in abundance. They continue to abound - those passionate, idealistic young persons whose desire to be involved in healing is mysterious, powerful, and often inexplicable. They simply "know" they must become healers and they will do almost anything to fulfill their calling. Hearkening to a deep and primal drive they often migrate to medical schools, the healing path that currently enjoys the most emphatic social sanction. Yet, this can be a painful, suffocating experience for many of them, because most medical schools have a completely different view of the nature of healers and healing than that of the natural-born healers themselves. Thus we encounter a paradox: our medical schools, which of all our institutions should be most attuned to nourishing and developing the natural healing talents of gifted young people, seem adept at extinguishing them.

These problems are not restricted to the United States. The enormous strain and dissatisfaction experienced by British medical students have recently been emphasised by a BBC television series. Because of the stresses, an estimated 18% to 25% of newly qualified British physicians never enter medical practice, or leave medicine shortly after qualifying.

How can we expect medical students to emerge as compassionate physicians when they are treated so uncompassionately in their training? If one wanted to snuff out the healing instinct and the idealism that students often bring to medical school, one could hardly imagine a more efficient method,

Becoming a Healer: Transformation

Our profession's discomfort with healers, healing, and healing power is a historical aberration. For 50,000 years shamans and native healers of every variety have believed they possess the power to heal and that they were meant to be healers, convictions shared by their cultures. This same inchoate drive lies latent in many medical students, and it beckons them toward medicine. Learning how actually to use this power was never considered just an exercise of the intellect, as it is now regarded. Becoming a healer exercised every aspect of one's being - a process that is vividly captured in the words of an Iglulik Eskimo shaman:

> "I endeavored to become a shaman by the help of others; but in this I did not succeed. I visited many famous shamans, and gave them great gifts... .1 sought solitude, and here I soon became very melancholy. I would sometimes fall to weeping and feel unhappy without knowing why. Then, for no reason, all would suddenly be changed, and I felt a great, inexplicable joy, a joy so powerful that I could not restrain it, but had to break into song, a mighty song, with only room for the one word, joy, joy! And I had to use the full strength of my voice. And then in the midst of such a fit of mysterious and overwhelming delight I became a shaman, not knowing myself how it came about. But I was a shaman. I could see and hear in a totally different way. I had gained my *qaumanEq,* my enlightenment, the shaman-light of brain and body, and this in such a manner that it was not only I who could see through the darkness of life, but the same light also shone out of me, imperceptible to human beings, but visible to all the spirits of earth and sky and sea, and these now came to me and became my helping spirits."

If a single word could describe the process of becoming a shaman, it might be *transformation.* The transformative experiences described by the Iglulik shaman would cause a modern psychiatrist to shudder, and most faculty members entrusted with the education of medical students would consider them bizarre and pathological. If a student were to report such a transformation, he would almost certainly be scheduled for an appointment in the department of psychiatry.

In modern medical education "transformation" has been supplanted by "information". The result is the production of counterfeits-physicians who cannot heal and who regard "healing power" as a quaint anachronism.

Wounded Healers

Chiron, the centaur in Greek mythology who taught the art of healing, was wounded by a poisoned arrow. Although he extracted the arrow, he could not remove the poison, which he carried for ever in his body. Chiron is immortal and cannot die, but neither can he be entirely healthy. He is the exemplar of the wounded healer, one who paradoxically heals and is in need of healing.

We are collectively wounded - healer, medical schools and the culture that spawns them. Can we extract the arrow? Can we rid ourselves of at least some of the poisons?

Ecologist Paul Ehrlich observes, "The first rule of intelligent tinkering is to save all the parts. Our medical schools have tinkered with young healers for generations. I believe they have saved the parts - *vision, soul* and *spirit* in medicine have never really died -and can summon the courage required to put them back together in a pattern resembling a healer.

There are signs of healthy change. For example, approximately 30 medical schools have developed courses in alternative medicine. Researcher Helene Smith offers a hopeful view of medicine's ability to meet these challenges. "The medical establishment actually is much better at changing than many other institutions" she says.

If our medical schools are to produce healers they must first stop destroying them. This will require reducing or eliminating the many ways the medical school experience has become dehumanising. An exemplary step in this direction is the Health Awareness Workshop for first-year medical students, which has been available at the University of Louisville Medical School since 1981. The course was developed by Joel Elkes MD. professor emeritus of psychiatry and Leah Dickstein MD professor in the Department of Psychiatry and Behavioral Sciences, and associate dean for faculty and student advocacy.

The Health Awareness Workshop rests on the recognition that "the medical student is a person at risk", that "some of these risks are avoidable" and that "other-care is best begun with self-care". This 4-day course is offered to entering medical students prior to enrollment and commencement of studies. Although it is voluntary, more than

90% of freshmen elect to participate. Topics include mode of life as a factor in illness and disability, the psychobiology of human adaptation, stress and the stress response, the physiology of nutrition, exercise and relaxation;   the psychology of time management and study skills; listening and the give-and-take of relationships; substance abuse and the impaired physician; gender issues in medicine; and introduction to the ethics of medical practice and the place of belief in healing. In addition to the didactic presentation of scientific data, an experiental, participatory "fun" approach to learning is included in the workshop through involvement in music, art, acting, film, singing and chanting; a "nutritional picnic" and pizza supper;   aerobic exercise, softball and a "fun run"; and a river cruise on the *Belle of Louisville.* The students learn of the history of the city of Louisville and the University of: Louisville School of Medicine.

　　Second year students volunteer to be "health tutors" to groups of 16 freshmen. They share their anxieties, coping styles, and lessons learned and even serve as chefs in preparing healthy foods for the incoming students.   Faculty members, usually selected by the sophomore students play a similar role. Workshop sessions are also held for the spouses, children and significant others of the incoming students. As a result of these interactions, a social network forms between student and student₁ and between student and faculty. The resulting message delivered by the medical school to the incoming students is clear and unmistakable. We *care* about you - your physical, psychological and spiritual wellbeing - and we will go to great lengths to help you become a skilled physician and a fulfilled human being. But in our enthusiasm for change, let us not deceive ourselves. It would be a mistake to suppose that there is a formula for generating healers. There never has been. Becoming a healer remains largely a mysterious process not amenable to manipulation and control, as the above experience of the Iglulik shaman illustrates, and as Lame Deer, the Sioux medicine man, warns in the epigraph. We note the 1932 report by the Commission on Medical Education: "The medical course cannot produce a physician" Neither can it produce a healer.

Dr. Larry Dossey is Executive Editor of 'Alternative Therapies in Health and Medicine and author of many best selling books on holistic and mind-body medicine.

Conclusion

Dr John Cosh

For the great majority of bodily ills conventional medicine and surgery serve us well. Complementary medicine helps too, and many of us on an everyday level make use of herbal or homoeopathic remedies, or may turn to the acupuncturist or osteopath for help. But healing in its fullest sense can only be achieved by recognising man as a multilevel being. Sometimes conventional medicine is not enough, and a holistic therapist may help in ways described by Hertha Larive with therapies such as yoga, meditation or healing.

Patient care may then have to be shared between conventional and complementary practitioners, and cooperation between them may be uncertain or even nonexistent   The aims and energies of the Foundation for Integration in Medicine are seeking ways of overcoming such a division. One solution may be in a form of general practice in which conventional doctors and complementary practitioners work in partnership. Or it may be possible to broaden the role of physician into that of physician-healer in the manner envisaged by Dr Craig Brown. The well established principles and methods of the doctor practising Anthroposophical medicine, as presented here by Dr Michael Evans, also offer a model that could be developed.

The clinical results of healing, whether given directly or as absent healing have been confirmed in a number of studies, which have been reviewed by Dan Benor. The healing effects that come through a healer, therapist or practitioner are probably all manifestations of the same power, in different guises and settings, as David Hodges and Tony Scofield propose. They have demonstrated something of the same effect transmitted from themselves to seeds; a similar effect surely passes

164

between humans and plants, which must be why some of us talk to them. Furthermore, there are healers who hold clinics for animals, and we have cause to be grateful for the reciprocal healing effect that much loved animals can bring to humans. This is particularly beneficial to those who are ill, lonely, isolated or even in gaol.

Just how does this healing power have its effect? Whether received consciously or unconsciously, it would appear to enhance the self healing power of the recipient. We can conceive it as a form of compassionate love being accepted at some level in the mind, and through that having an effect on the body. After all, no one can doubt the effect that love in more popular form can have on our endocrines and hormones, to say nothing of its stimulating effect on most other bodily systems.

Our insight into the mind-body connection has been revolutionised by the identification of the complex web of communications linking our nervous system with all other systems through relatively simple chemical messengers, neuropeptides, An intriguing aspect of PNI mentioned here by Alan Watkins is the observation that the heart itself may initiate its own influence through neuropeptides quite apart from its direct power over the circulation.

In spite of the vast growth in our knowledge since the days of Ambrose Pare we can still echo his sense of wonder at the healing powers of the human body. We realise how limited is our appreciation of these powers when we learn of the work and results of people like Meir Schneider (see his book "Self Healing") and, even more, the accounts of "Remarkable Recovery" described by Caryl Hirshberg in her book of that title. The inner transformation, at emotional and spiritual levels, which took place in the patients she describes produced healing and recovery in clinical situations clearly regarded as hopelessly terminal.

We cannot prescribe or engineer such transformations any more than we can make a healer, as Larry Dossey says. But we believe we can point the way.

The continuing public interest in complementary medicine, combined with appreciation of the advances in medical science provide the drive towards some form of practical integration. Such a combination would greatly enrich the healing services available to us.

Dr. John Cosh is a retired consultant physician and rheumatologist.

References

Hirshberg, Caryle and Marc Ian Barasch, *Remarkable Recovery*, Headline Books (Putnam Berkley Group) NY

Schneider, Meir, *Self Healing. My Life and Vision*, 1989 Arkana Books, London

Simonton, 0 Carl, Stephanie Matthews-Simonton and James Creighton *Getting Well Again*, 1986 Bantam Books, London

Watkins, Alan (Ed) *Mind-Body Medicine: A Clinician's Guide to PNI* 1997 Churchill Livingstone, NY

Chapter 4
Towards an Integral Science of Consciousness

Edited by David Lorimer

Introduction

T he past decade has seen such a renaissance of interest in 'consciousness studies', that it may come as something of a surprise to be reminded by Peter Fenwick that he could not find the word 'consciousness' properly indexed at the outset of his research career. Yet twenty years ago, few people mentioned the word consciousness. On looking back through the annals of the Mystics and Scientists conferences, now in their 22nd year, one notes that the third conference – in 1980 – was entitled 'A Science of Consciousness' at a time when the words were not often heard in conjunction. Peter Fenwick's annual mind and brain symposia at the Institute of Psychiatry date from 1989. Going further back, The Religious Experience Research Unit was founded in Oxford in 1969 by zoologist Sir Alister Hardy. The Centre has over 5,000 records of spiritual and religious experiences in its archives, representing a rich mine of unusual conscious experiences.

Hardy was strongly influenced by William James, whose classic *Varieties of Religious Experience* dates from 1903, being the text of his Gifford Lectures delivered in the University of Edinburgh in 1901-2 – just about a hundred years ago. William James was at once a philosopher, psychologist and psychical researcher and coined the term 'radical empiricism', signifying that science should take account of the whole range of human experience. A recent book by Eugene Taylor – *William James on Consciousness Beyond the Margin* – traces how James lost out to the experimental mode of psychology imported from Germany. After his death, Harvard refused an endowment for a chair of psychical research and psychology embarked on its behaviourist agenda that arguably set consciousness studies back decades. It is only in the 1990s that we are once again picking up the threads that James was weaving a hundred years ago. James realised, as did Edwin Burtt in his classic 1924 *Metaphysical Foundations of Modern Science* that all science was undergirded by a metaphysical system, whether or not acknowledged: 'the juices of metaphysical assumptions leak in at every joint'. Burtt contends that the assumptions of Newton, shorn of their Deism and reduced to mechanistic materialism, were passed on implicitly and unconsciously down succeeding generations of scientists.

Among those currently involved in consciousness studies there are two basic orientations: those who follow the traditional Western method of looking from the outside in as detached observers – the third person perspective. Then there are those who look from the inside out – the first person perspective – and who are interested in exploring the nature of their own consciousness. The Eastern meditative traditions fall into this latter category, but, as Ravi Ravindra points out, yoga has its own form of objectivity through rigorous self-observation and training of the mind. It can readily be appreciated that proponents of these two perspectives mean something rather different when they use the term 'science of consciousness'. This chapter presents a wide range of perspectives on the field.

It begins with an essay by Emilios Bouratinos arguing that consciousness studies have an importance far greater than is generally realised. As he puts it: 'there can be no science of consciousness without a consciousness of the science thus created'. His call for a critical analysis of science's foundations reflects similar points made in Max Payne's chapter below. We have reached a point where self-awareness and an understanding of understanding itself is crucial, given that civilisation itself is ultimately the outpicturing of mind with its beliefs and values. The process leads in turn to questions governing the quality of our exchange, to work with dialogue explored both by traditional societies and creative thinkers like David Bohm.

Inter-disciplinary Consciousness Studies: What Science and Society Stand to Gain

Emilios Bouratinos

This text outlines an initiative for the establishment of inter-disciplinary consciousness studies, which will mediate both a more rewarding scientific endeavour and a more sanguine human existence. The new discipline will differ from the older ones in a fundamental respect: It will bridge the deep conceptual gap between feeling and mental abstraction, specificity and intuition, locality and non-locality. Above all it will attempt to bring together the seemingly polar opposites of subjectivity and objectivity.

Almost by definition consciousness cannot become an object of study without the investigator asking himself in the same breath what he invests in his study and why. If consciousness studies are to become a source of guidance for science in particular and for society in general, they must start from themselves. The scientific claim to objectivity demands it. There can be no science of consciousness without a consciousness of the science thus created. Criteria, qualities and methods of operation all need to be scrutinised to the same extent as goals, quantities and applications. Common sense and the path-breaking new advances in both science and theory demand it.

Compelling Reasons for a Science of Consciousness

Four particular reasons — all of them compelling — mitigate for the establishment of the proposed new field.

The first is to protect science against erosion from business interests, political agendas, self-reference, institutional prejudice, career considerations, paradigmatic bias, revitalisation, scientism, conceptual stagnation, funding pressures and subconscious conditioning. No ultimate evaluation of theories, hypotheses, experimental projects or research results is possible without taking into account the blank spots, values, expectations, school of thought, educational background, bend of mind, personal conditioning and other factors influencing the practising scientist or research institution.

Increased awareness of what goes into science will allow the scientific community to serve both knowledge and society better than seems currently possible. More objective science will make for more humanity, not less. Becoming an integral part of the overall scientific enterprise, interdisciplinary consciousness studies will contribute to the drafting of a new epistemology and social charter by necessity. These will reflect not only the major scientific breakthroughs of the 20th century. They will reflect the important new ways of thinking these breakthroughs invite.

As currently practised, science doesn't guarantee more objectivity. It guarantees less. The reason is that the one thing science hasn't yet been able to be objective about is objectivity itself. It has considered adherence to it so self-evident that it has not questioned the premises on which its understanding of the subject rests. A science of consciousness must critically examine these premises.

The second compelling reason for creating an interdisciplinary science of consciousness is the multi-levelled, trans-qualitative, cross-functional and inter-dimensional understanding of reality, which has resulted from recent science — particularly its non-linear branch. Because involved with sensitive conceptual issues, this dynamic new picture doesn't depend only on objective observation. It depends equally on the observer as a qualifying agent - and on the forces that qualify him.

Unless we understand how we understand, we cannot understand much else. Neither can we understand why we should avoid getting trapped in what we do in fact understand; how we can remain open to what as yet we don't; and why new understanding depends as much on new aspects of reality being brought to light as on new ways of looking at the old. Objectivity requires subjectivity, subjectivity requires direct personal experience and direct personal experience requires a willing reduction of the investigator to the ultimate inclinations of his sociobiological substratum - plus the ultimate intimations of the unique persona that has emerged from it.

The third compelling reason mitigating for the creation of the new study field is to meet in a radical manner the present ills of civilisation. Most of these originate in (and from) the mind. We cannot hope to understand them without studying it. More importantly, we cannot hope to solve them without being willing to act on what we discover there. Inter-disciplinary consciousness studies are also necessary for helping to plan a new self-regulating development, free from the type of current short term planning which undermines the prospects of long-term social and individual well being.

Finally, the fourth major reason for creating the new science is technology. Mechanical constructs should once again be experienced as mere extensions of natural human abilities, not as autonomous entities. This doesn't only demand greater familiarity with the defining traits of human nature. It demands in-depth knowledge of the particular quality woven into these traits.

It also demands protection against the ever-present danger of identifying with the mechanical constructs — and thus removing their use from human criteria. Unwitting identification with the ways in which technology works and the principles underpinning it is the principal cause of the current malaise. The more we develop technologically the more must we develop as human beings — and especially the more must we be willing to develop.

What a Science of Consciousness Will Do

Informed by the above four compelling reasons, the proposed new field of studies will engage in five inter-connected activities. The first (and most important) will be to catalogue and correlate information about which aspects of consciousness are being researched by the major sciences today - and which aspects of it influence the sciences in turn. Among the specific disciplines falling into this category are physics, neurophysiology, psychology, medicine, sociology, mathematics, anthropology, formal logic, information science, linguistics, philosophy, history of art and ideas, epistemology, comparative religion, biology and the meditative traditions.

Correlating information from the above very different areas and finding which is really important for consciousness studies will require the development of special "translation" and facilitation techniques — in the sense of making the data obtained in one discipline both scientifically intelligible and psychologically accessible to the practitioners of another.

The second activity for an interdisciplinary science of consciousness will be to research, formulate, test and apply an information assessment system for use by scientists in all disciplines. The fact that there is today so much information that it has become difficult to disseminate or assimilate, means that the disciplines thus inundated must learn how to weed out irrelevant material quickly and easily. Qualitative weighing of information needs to become the hallmark not only of the proposed new field, but of science in general and of information science in particular.

The third activity for consciousness studies will be to encourage new research into consciousness, once the pertinent information from the above disciplines has been properly assessed, correlated, catalogued and digested. This will be done in the same self-critical spirit outlined for activity No 1 - that dealing with how consciousness influences work in the other branches of science. Awareness of what goes into our research on consciousness (including the reasons for it) cannot prove less important than its content.

The fourth activity will be to investigate the antiquity, awareness and influence of the component 'consciousness' in the creation of civilisation itself. We need to know not only how we developed culturally, where and when. We need to know why. We also need to know how it happened that we established the habit of cultural identification to begin with. Establishing and then blindly following such a habit is by no means self-evident for a species that is supposed to be both above instinctual compulsion and highly intelligent.

Finally the fifth and last activity is to use the knowledge obtained from the previous four for wisely informing science and society. The role played by the consciousness component in public affairs - and the extent to which people are aware of it - is a huge subject with serious ramifications. These cannot (and should not) be outlined in a text by one person. They should, in good time, become the subject of a carefully planned trans-disciplinary conference.

Practical Steps

Some practical assistance and collaboration is needed for stimulating an initial interest in such a type of self-referring inter-disciplinary consciousness studies as outlined in this text. An attractive brochure, video and e-mail feeler - all produced by top professionals - must be sent to scientists, professionals, business people, academics, artists, intellectuals, doctors, cultural institutions, meditation teachers, select young people and private foundations. To the extent that sufficient intellectual support and funding interest is expressed among these, an institute can then be established which will undertake to promote the proposed discipline in the spirit described above.

This institute will have four successive goals, which it will pursue when (and as) it acquires the means to do so.

–   The first goal will be to create an open-ended theoretical framework for the new field. It could be based on the understanding that consciousness constitutes a defining articulation of wholeness in and through fragmentation.

–   The second goal will be to advance the introduction of inter-disciplinary consciousness studies in universities. It could entail special presentations to and private meetings with faculty members.

–   The third goal will be to make the educated public aware of the need to incorporate the consciousness component into future major decision making. It could materialise through articles, videos, TV programmes documentaries and talk shows.

– Finally the institute must try to create an electronic data bank on consciousness, which will be accessible to researchers.

Interpersonal Dialogue in the Service of Consciousness Studies

Both the proposed new study field and the institute acting as its mid-wife must operate on the highest qualitative level. To secure this, the institute (and hopefully the faculty members of future consciousness departments in universities) will be well advised to consider their tasks, assess their findings and grow institutionally in the light of inter-personal dialogue. This is a technique being practised by traditional societies throughout the globe for thousands of years, with the aim of getting collectively to the bottom of any issue of importance. It works on the principle that how a conclusion is reached matters as much (if not more) as what the conclusion is.

Inter-personal dialogue sees to it that interlocutors manage to tap into the particular information field in which both their topic and its potential are rooted. This is achieved by way of mobilising their interest in obtaining the best possible answer; their love of the truth; their need for self-respect; and above all, their willingness (and ability) to keep ego and career preoccupations out of the discussions.

Inter-personal dialogue (now adapted for modern use by the late David Bohm) isn't only capable of accessing hitherto unformulated knowledge. It is capable of maintaining high standards in assessing it, of drawing out its less obvious parameters, of refining it and finally of determining its theoretical and practical implications. (The Dialogue Project at MIT has collected impressive evidence for this.)

Back to Being Alert

The need for consciousness to be investigated by a science finely tuned is matched by a need for science to be assessed by a consciousness fully alert. How consciousness treats science and society tomorrow will depend on how science and society treat consciousness today.

174

If the goal is quality of life, as everybody claims, then the above con-clusion becomes inescapable. A collective existence not consciously mediated is unworthy of a species priding itself on being not only conscious, but self-conscious.

Emilios Bouratiinos is an essayist and former adviser on cultural affairs, US Embassy, Athens.

An Integral Science of Consciousness

Ken Wilber

The next piece, by Ken Wilber, further delineates the elements of what could truly be called an integral science of consciousness. In his extensive writings he has underlined the centrality of consciousness as a vital element in an integral world-view. Here he shows, like Bouratinos, that a future science of consciousness must be both self-aware and trans-disciplinary. He also points out that some forms of consciousness studies imply a transformation of the knower, a qualitative shift from an outside-in to an inside-out view. Similar versions of this article have appeared in the Journal of Consciousness Studies and Noetic Sciences Review.

      Consciousness, interiority, and awareness in the broadest sense - and science - empirical investigation based on reproducible evidence - are arguably the two most important branches of the human knowledge quest. How has the integral quest coming along? How close are we to what David Chalmers has called "a theory of everything" - that is, a theory that would unite the hard realities of empirical science with the soft but irrefutable realities of the interior and conscious domain.

Pieces of the Puzzle

Looking over the field of consciousness studies in the last decade, it becomes obvious that we have our task cut out for us. There are now at least a dozen major schools of consciousness studies and, far from moving toward a convergence, they are often opposed, contradictory, and dramatically conflicting. Here is a very brief summary of some of the major contenders:

1.   **Cognitive Science**, which tends to view consciousness as anchored in functional schemas of the brain-mind, either in a simple representational fashion or in the more complex emergent-connectionist models, which view consciousness in terms of hierarchically integrated networks, The emergent- connectionist is perhaps the dominant model of cognitive science at this point, and is nicely summarized in Alwyn Scott's *Stairway to the Mind,* the "stairway" being the hierarchy of emergent factors culminating in consciousness.

2.   **Introspectionism** maintains that consciousness is best understood in terms of intentionality, anchored in first-person accounts - the inspection and interpretation of immediate awareness and lived experience. This approach contrasts sharply with third-person (objective) accounts, no matter how "scientific" they might appear. Without denying their significant differences, this broad category includes everything from philosophical intentionality to introspective psychology, existentialism, and phenomenology.

3.   **Neuropsychology** views consciousness as anchored in neural systems, neurotransmitters, and organic brain mechanisms, Unlike cognitive science, which is often based on computer science and is consequently vague about how consciousness is actually related to organic brain structures, neuropsychology is a more biologically based approach. Anchored in neuroscience more than computer science, it views consciousness as intrinsically residing in organic neural systems of sufficient complexity.

4.   **Individual Psychotherapy** uses introspective and interpretive psychology to treat distressing symptoms and emotional problems; it thus tends to view consciousness as primarily anchored in an individual organism's adaptive capacities. Most major schools of psychotherapy embody a theory of consciousness precisely because they must account for a human being's need to create meaning and significance, the disruption of which results in painful symptoms of mental and emotional distress. In its more avant-garde forms, such as the Jungian,

this approach postulates collective or archetypal structures of intentionality (and thus consciousness)-the fragmentation of which contributes to psychopathology.

5.   **Social Psychology** views consciousness as embedded in networks of cultural meaning or, alternatively, as being largely a by-product of the social system itself, This includes approaches as varied as ecological Marxist, constructivist, and cultural hermeneutics, all of which maintain that the nexus of consciousness is not located merely or even principally in the individual.

6.   **Clinical Psychiatry** focuses on the relation of psychopathology, behavioural patterns, and psychopharmacology. For the last half century, psychiatry was largely anchored in a Freudian metapsychology, but the field increasingly tends to view consciousness in strictly neurophysiological and biological terms, verging on a clinical identity theory: consciousness is the neuronal system, so that a presenting problem in the former is actually an imbalance in the latter, correctable with medication.

7.   **Developmental Psychology** views consciousness not as a single entity but as a developmentally unfolding process with a substantially different architecture at each of its stages of growth. Thus an understanding of consciousness demands an investigation of the architecture at each of its levels of unfolding. In its more inclusive forms, this approach covers higher stages of exceptional development and well-being, and the study of gifted, extraordinary, and supranormal capacities, viewed as higher developmental potentials latent in all humans. This includes higher stages of cognitive, affective, somatic, moral and spiritual development.

8.   **Psychosomatic Medicine** views consciousness as strongly and intrinsically interactive with organic bodily processes, evidenced in such fields as psychoneuroimmunology and biofeedback. In its more challenging and controversial forms, this approach includes consciousness and miraculous healing, the effects of prayer on remarkable recoveries, light, sound and healing, spontaneous remission, and so on. It also includes any of the approaches that investigate the effects of intentionality on healing, from art therapy to visualisation to psychotherapy and meditation.

9.   **Nonordinary States of Consciousness,** from dreams to psychedelics, constitute a field of study that, its advocates believe, is crucial to a grasp of consciousness in general. Although some of the effects of psychedelics - to take a controversial example - are undoubtedly due to toxic side-effects, the consensus in this area of research is that they also act as a "nonspecific amplifier of experience," and thus they can be instrumental in disclosing and amplifying aspects of consciousness that might otherwise go unstudied.

10.   **Eastern and Contemplative Traditions** maintain that ordinary consciousness is but a narrow and restricted version of deeper or higher modes of awareness, and that specific injunctions (yoga, meditation) are necessary to evoke these higher and exceptional potentials. Moreover, they all maintain that the essentials of consciousness itself can only be grasped in these higher, postformal and nondual states of consciousness.

11.   **Quantum Consciousness,** as it may be called, views consciousness as being intrinsically capable of interacting with, and altering, the physical world, generally through quantum interactions, both in the human body at the intracellular level (for example, microtubules), and in the material world at large (psi). This approach also includes the many and various attempts to plug consciousness into the physical world according to various avant-garde physical theories (bootstrapping, hyperspace, strings).

12.   **Subtle Energies Research** has postulated that there exist subtler types of bioenergies beyond the four recognised forces of physics (strong and weak nuclear, electromagnetic, gravitational), and that these subtler energies play an intrinsic role in consciousness and its activity. Known in the traditions by such terms as *prana, ki,* and *chi* – and said to be responsible for the effectiveness of acupuncture, to give only one example-these energies are often held to be the missing link" between intentional mind and physical body. For the Great Chain theorists, both East and West, this bioenergy acts as a two-way conveyor belt, transferring the impact of matter to the mind and imposing the intentionality of the mind on matter.

Premature Cognitive Commitment

What I have observed in the field of consciousness studies (as elsewhere) is that researchers tend to choose one or two of those approaches very early in their careers, usually under the influence of a significant mentor, organisation, or academic department. And, human nature being what it is, it is then extremely difficult for them to embrace, or sometimes even acknowledge, the existence of the other approaches. Evidence that supports their position is avidly accumulated; evidence that does not is ignored, devalued, or explained away.

But what if, instead, we make the following assumption: the human mind is incapable of producing 100 percent error. In other words, nobody is smart enough to be wrong all the time. That would mean, very simply, that each of those dozen approaches cannot contain only error; put positively, each of them has something extremely important and valuable to say. And that means, inescapably, *that we will measure our progress toward a truly integral orientation based precisely on our capacity to include, synthesise, and integrate* all *twelve of those important approaches.* It is clearly a daunting challenge; but it is equally clear that anything less than that simply cannot claim the adjective "integral."

How, then, are we actually doing? How far down this integral path are we? And, just as important, what are some of the steps we might take in the immediate future in order to further this noble quest?

The Hard-Headed and the Softhearted

From the view of empirical science, we might note that the dozen approaches span the spectrum from the very hard to the very soft. At one end are the "harder" approaches, approaches that attempt vigorously to ground themselves in empirical observables, These include cognitive science, neuropsychology, and clinical psychiatry. These "harder" views shade into a softer range of approaches that begin to give a substantial weight to inferiority and consciousness-including psychosomatic medicine, quantum approaches, individual psychotherapy, developmental psychology, and social psychology. And these shade into the very soft" approaches that stress the fundamental priority of consciousness itself, especially as disclosed in subtle energies, nonordinary states, and contemplative endeavours.

Surveying the various directions in consciousness studies in the past decade, several strong trends stand out. To begin with, substantial strides have been made by all three "camps." At the harder end of the spectrum, cognitive science (and its many offshoots and affiliates) has come to define the mainstream of the "science of consciousness studies," at least in Anglo-Saxon countries. While advocates of the other approaches might feel that cognitive science and neuropsychology take much too narrow a stance, nonetheless the strides these fields have made are indeed most impressive - starting with the simple fact that they have at least begun to introduce the study of consciousness as a "respectable" and "scientific" endeavour, after what amounted to several decades of positivistic and behaviouristic denial that consciousness even existed! This feat alone is something of a historical breakthrough that has especially come to fruition in the last decade.

The intermediate range approaches - exemplified by developmental psychology and social psychology - have also made substantial (and in some cases paradigmatic) breakthroughs. Following in the wake of the Piagetian revolution (which I believe will be ranked as one of the two or three greatest psychological revolutions of the modern era), the notion *of higher stages of consciousness unfolding* has been given strong empirical and phenomenological grounding, and has been backed by cross-cultural studies in social psychology. Abraham Maslow, the cofounder of both Third Force (humanistic) and Fourth Force (transpersonal) psychologies, stands here in an absolutely pivotal role, and numerous studies in the past decade have continued and greatly refined this Piaget/Maslow line of research.

The approaches at the tenderest end of the spectrum have likewise reported equally impressive advances, At this moment, we have more access to more contemplative traditions than at any time in history. Beginning roughly two or three decades ago, an unprecedented number of young Americans took up advanced contemplative studies, ranging from Zen to contemplative prayer, from *kundalini* yoga to *vipassana*, from Vajrayana to Sufism, from Vedanta to Kabalah. Many of these students have now "graduated" and are themselves gifted and inspiring teachers, calling us all to recognise the primordial and sacred nature of consciousness itself, by whatever name.

In addition to the individual advances in each of the camps, we might note two important overall trends or "megatrends" in consciousness studies as a whole. On the one hand, there has occurred something of a consolidation and entrenchment of the "harder" approaches: In the Anglo-Saxon mainstream view, cognitive science, neuroscience, neuropsychology, and clinical psychiatry are the "real" approaches to consciousness, with everything else relegated to "unscientific" (translation: not real) status. Compared to the softer approaches, this hegemony of the hard-headed is perhaps unfortunate; but let us remember that, compared with positivism and behaviorism, this is a major and massive advance! Some of us might even like to see this as an evolutionary or developmental advance, but a step up from positivistic flatland it is indeed.

The other megatrend simply leans into this advance even further: although the harder views have become the institutional mainstream, nonetheless the intermediate and softer approaches are making substantial headway. There has been, in the last decade, a general, subtle, but unmistakable "softening" toward the tender end of the spectrum.

Perhaps this softening is due to a general evolution of consciousness itself. Perhaps it is due to the massive accumulation of data that gives very hard evidence for very soft realities. (One major but often overlooked reason for this softening? The college kids who did inhale and who are now department heads of psychology and psychiatry know from first-hand experience that there are softer realities than are dreamt of in hard-headed science.)

But whatever the reason, this second megatrend - a drift toward the tender - seems undeniable. Indeed, "noetic studies" has come to mean something of an emphasis on the softer end of the spectrum, grounding itself in introspectionism and contemplative studies to complement the harder approaches. Of course, how much impact this second megatrend will have (a shift towards the noetic) remains to seen. Indeed, one of the items we will want to examine is how to further this particular avenue of research-the uniting of the hard-headed and the soft-hearted, which is simply another way to think of the integral approach (I will return to this notion in a moment).

The Pieces Prevail

Thus, in surveying the field of consciousness studies in the last decade, I am both heartened and saddened. There has been an unprecedented explosion of interest in consciousness studies on the whole. We have witnessed the publication of numerous and quite significant books on consciousness itself, and they come not merely from "alternative" education centers or publishers, but rather from the likes of Oxford University Press, MIT, Praeger, and Harvard. We have seen increasing empirical research on everything from the effects of meditation on psychological health to the effects of prayer on heart patients. Combined with the wealth of information from Eastern and contemplative approaches, we very likely possess, in these closing years of the second millennium, more sheer data on consciousness studies than at any time in humankind's history.

And yet, and yet... the pieces prevail. Although there are numerous important exceptions, for the most part the research remains "one-approach" bound. Daniel Dennett takes a functionalist cognitive stance (#1); John Searle stresses intentionality (#2). Systems theorists (#5) resort to a holistic view, but it is an exterior holism only, grounded in monological and process it-language, devoid of an "I" or a "we." Neuropsychology (#3) races toward the day when the beauty of a sunset will be described in chemical terms such as "dopamine," "serotonin," and "synaptic re-uptake." Quantum consciousness (#11) breathlessly announces that human free will resides in the collapse of the Schrödinger wave equation. Exceptional healing (#8) looks for consciousness in the display of the miraculous, while social constructivism (#5) maintains that the entire show is a facade of ideology and power parading as knowledge itself.

Thus, even though each of these approaches has made impressive advances in the last decade, and even though an important megatrend has been the softening and more inclusive stance of various tender approaches, and even though there is a concerted effort on the part of some researchers to create inter-disciplinary dialogue, I still find that this is by far the weakest link in the chain of consciousness studies. In other words, I find that there is a palpable absence of a concerted effort to study and advance not just the dozen or so major approaches but the ways in which they all without exception, *intrinsically* fit together as part of the unbroken Kosmos. And so perhaps I might close with a few thoughts on just that topic.

The Challenge

Given the above factors, I believe that three major steps, in particular, are necessary for the future of consciousness studies:

> 1. *Continue research on the various particular approaches.* That is, continue to refine our understanding of the many pieces of the puzzle of consciousness. The twelve approaches I briefly outlined are twelve significant pieces of this extraordinary enigma; each is profoundly important; each deserves continued and vigorous research and development.
> 2. *Confront the simple fact that, in some cases, a change in consciousness on the part of the researchers themselves is mandatory for the investigation of consciousness itself.* Some aspects of consciousness can indeed be accessed by conventional, empirical scientific methodology. But, as numerous approaches (for example, #7, #9, #10) have pointed out, the higher or postformal stages of consciousness development can only be accessed by those who have themselves developed to a postformal level. You can master systems theory without necessarily developing postformal awareness; you absolutely cannot master Zen without doing so. You can understand Dennett without transforming consciousness; you cannot understand Plotinus without doing so. If you are therefore investigating postformal domains, then postformal injunctions are mandatory.

Thus, some consciousness studies can indeed be continued by doing "business as usual" and it is important to acknowledge that. But some of the pieces of the puzzle of consciousness cannot be grasped without postformal development on the part of participant-observers. This deepest of taboos and deepest of myths-namely, the sanctity of the detached observer-does not ensure objectivity in postformal studies: It insures failure to grasp the data at the very start.

Given the two megatrends that we noted (the entrenchment of the harder cognitive sciences, and yet a discernible shift toward the softer and noetic end of the spectrum), this would specifically mean: Let us continue to work especially to advance noetic studies as a counterbalance to the harder mainstream views, Not anti-mainstream, not against, not denying, not denigrating, not deconstructing, but rather complementing, supplementing, completing, and fulfilling: *transcend* and *include* mainstream, not transcend and deny.

> 3.   *Continue to grope our way toward a genuinely integral theory of consciousness itself.* The mere claim to be "integral," as we have seen, is virtually meaningless, since most of the various approaches sincerely believe they are covering all the really important bases, and thus most of them implicitly claim to be as integral as one can be. In the last decade, although there have been some significant exceptions, we have mostly had twelve pieces all claiming to be the whole pie.

In a series of books (including *Sex, Ecology, Spirituality; A Brief History of Everything;* and *The Eye of Spirit: An Integral Vision for a World Gone Slightly Mad),* I have attempted to outline one version of an integral theory of consciousness that explicitly includes those twelve major approaches. In this short space I cannot even begin to give an adequate summary, and I don't think it would be appropriate to do so in an essay surveying consciousness studies as a whole. What is important is not, I think, my particular version of an integral view, but rather that we all begin to enter into this extraordinary dialogue about the possibility of an integral approach in general, an approach that - we can say this in several different ways - integrates the hard-headed with the softhearted, the natural sciences with the noetic sciences, objective realities with subjective realities, the empirical with the transcendent.

Let us hope that a decade from now somebody might spot a third great megatrend in consciousness studies-namely, the truly integral - and let it start right now with all of us who share this concern for holism, for embrace, for synthesising, for integrating: let this outreach start with us, right here, right now,

Is a genuinely integral theory of consciousness even possible? That would be my question, and my challenge. How big is our umbrella? How wide and how deep can we throw our net of good will? How many voices will we allow in this chorus of consciousness? How many faces of the divine will smile on our endeavour? How many colours will we genuinely acknowledge in our rainbow coalition?

And when we pause from all this research, and put theory temporarily to rest, and when we relax into the primordial ground of our own intrinsic awareness, what will we find therein? When the joy of the robin sings on a clear morning dawn, where is our consciousness then? When the sunlight beams from the glory of a snow-capped mountain, where is consciousness then? In the place that time forgot, in this eternal moment without date or duration, in the secret cave of the heart where time touches eternity and space cries out for infinity, when the raindrop pulses on the temple roof and announces the beauty of the divine with every single beat, when the moonlight reflects in a simple dewdrop to remind us who and what we are, and when in the entire universe there is nothing but the sound of a lonely waterfall somewhere in the mists, gently calling your name - where is consciousness then?

Ken Wilber is the author of more than a dozen hooks, including 'No Boundary'; 'Transformations of Consciousness'; 'Grace and Grit'; 'Sex, Ecology, Spirituality'; and 'A Brief History of Everything'. His own suggestions for an integral theory of consciousness can he found in 'The Eye of Spirit - An Integral Vision for a World Gone Slightly Mad' (Shambhala Publications)

Yoga and the Future Science of Consciousness

Ravi Ravindra

Ravi Ravindra now considers the potential contribution of yoga traditions to a future science of consciousness. He reminds us that the most important question we can ask ourselves is 'Who Am I?' When pursued assiduously, the path leads to what he calls 'knowledge by identity' or realisation of the first person universal, the ultimate nature of mind or consciousness in which we all participate.

Knowing through the Mind

Koham kathamidam cheti samsaramalamatatam
pravicharyam prayatnena prajñena sahasadhuna

Who am I? Whence is this widespread cosmic flux?
These, the wise should inquire into diligently,
    Soon — nay, now.
                                    —*Mahopanishad IV, 21*

Am I primarily a body that has, in response to accidental material forces and laws, produced a mind and a sense of self which can think and which has both self-consciousness and consciousness of other people and things? Or am I essentially something else –variously called spirit, soul, self, Brahman, God, the Buddha Mind, the Very Person– who has taken on a body (including the mind) as an instrument for the purpose of action, love and delight in the world? Does the body have the consciousness or does consciousness have the body? Can the body exist without consciousness, and can consciousness exist without bodily functions?

It is quite clear on which side of these questions lie the responses of yoga and all other spiritual disciplines. The responses of our contemporary science are on the other side. This should hardly come as surprise, for the very basic assumptions and procedures of modern science preclude knowing anything which is above the level of the mind in the hierarchy of the levels of consciousness.[1]

One of the fundamental assertions in the theory and discipline of yoga is that the true knower is not the mind. The real knower – called *Purusha*, the Very Person– knows *through* the mind, not *with* the mind.[2] It is useful to recall a remark of William Blake in this context: "I see not with the eyes but through the eyes." What is at issue is a hierarchy of levels of being and therefore of consciousness within a person, and a question about the nature of the person. It is for this reason that in every spiritual tradition, the question 'Who am I?,' or some variant on it, is considered the fundamental human question. As a contemporary Zen master in Korea, Chulwoong Sunim, simply said to me, 'Who am I ?' is the most essential and comprehensive *koan* It is also a basic question about the nature of the cosmos for we are not apart from it, nor can we have any certainty about the nature and validity of what we know about the cosmos without having some clarity of what in us knows and how. The Psalmist asks in the Bible (*Psalm* 8):

> When I consider thy heavens, the work of thy fingers,
> The moon and the stars, which thou hast ordained;
> What is man, that thou art mindful of him?

A very important heuristic principle in modern science interferes with the knowledge of a radically different and higher level. This principle enters as the Copernican Principle in Astronomy and Cosmology and as the Principle of Uniformitarianism in Geology and Biology, one to do with space and the other with time. According to the former, any point in the universe can be taken to be the centre, for in each direction the universe on the large is homogeneous and isotropic. The latter principle says essentially that the same laws and forces have operated in the past as in the present. Neither of these principles have anything to say about levels of consciousness. But in practice one consequence of these principles has been a denial of a radical difference not only in terms of regions of space and time, but also in terms of levels of being among humans. One of the important aspects of modern science, starting with the great scientific revolution of the sixteenth and seventeenth centuries, has been a scientifically very successful idea that the materials and laws on other planets and galaxies, and in the past and future times, can be studied in terms of the laws, materials and forces available to us now on the earth. But, almost by implication and quite subtly, this notion has done away with the analogical and symbolic modes of thinking according to which a fully developed person could mirror internally the various levels of the external cosmos.

A Science of Consciousness Requires Transformed Scientists

When the ancients and even the medieval thinkers in Europe, China or India –in their sciences of alchemy, astronomy and cosmology– spoke of different planets having different materials and different laws, at least in part it meant that various levels of being or consciousness have different laws. From this perspective higher consciousness cannot be understood in terms of, or by, a lower consciousness. The subtler and higher aspects of the cosmos can be understood only by the subtler and higher levels within humans. True knowledge is obtained by participation and fusion of the knower with the object of study, and the scientist is required to become higher in order to understand higher things. As St. Paul said, things of the mind can be understood by the mind; things of the spirit by the spirit. The ancient Indian texts say that only by becoming Brahman can one know Brahman. The *Gandharva Tantra* says that "no one who is not himself divine can successfully worship divinity." For Parmenides and for Plotinus "to be and to know are one and the same."[3]

   This has implications for any future science of higher consciousness which would hope to relate with what is real. Such a science would have to be *esoteric*, not in the sense of being an exclusive possession of some privileged group, but because it would speak of qualities which are more subtle and less obvious, such a science would demand and assist the preparation, integration and attunement of the body, mind and heart of the scientists so that they would be able to

188

participate in the vision revealed by higher consciousness. In the felicitous phrase of Meister Eckhart, one needs to be 'fused and not confused.' *Tatra prajña ritambhara* (there insight is naturally truth-bearing), says Patanjali's *Yoga Sutra* (1.48-49; 2.15; 3.54). This preparation is needed in order to open the third eye, for the two usual eyes do not correspond to the higher vision. It is only the third that can see the hidden Sun, for as Plotinus says, "to any vision must be brought an eye adapted to what is to be seen, and having some likeness to it. Never did the eye see the sun unless it had first become sun-like, and never can the soul have vision of the First Beauty unless itself be beautiful."[4]

The important lesson here from the perspective of any future science of consciousness is the importance of knowledge by identity. We cannot remain separate and detached if we wish to understand. We need to participate in and be one with what we wish to understand. Thus Meister Eckhart: "Why does my eye recognize the sky, and why do not my feet recognize it? Because my eye is more akin to heaven than my feet. Therefore my soul must be divine if it is to recognize God."[5] Similarly Goethe:

> Waer' nicht das Auge sonnenhaft,
> Die Sonne koennt' es nie erblicken.
> Laeg' nicht in uns des Gottes eigene Kraft,
> Wie koennt' uns Goettliches entzuecken?

> If the eye were not sensitive to the sun,
> It could not perceive the sun.
> If God's own power did not lie within us,
> How could the divine enchant us?

In the well nigh universal traditional idea of a correspondence between a human being and the cosmos, the microcosmos-macrocosmos homology, it is easily forgotten is that this idea does not apply to every human being. It is only the fully developed person (*mahapurusha*) who is said to mirror the whole cosmos. Such developed persons are quite rare. The idea of inner levels of being (or of consciousness) is absolutely central, as is the question of 'What is a person?' It is difficult to convince oneself that the various spiritual disciplines for the purpose of transformation of human consciousness can be dispensed with by developing concepts or instruments from relatively lower levels of consciousness. But unwillingness to accept the need for radical transformation and to subject oneself to a spiritual discipline is ubiquitous. Even when the idea of transformation has an appeal, one wishes to be transformed without changing –without a renunciation of what one now is and with an attitude of saying, "Lord, save me while I stay as I am."

It is important to remark that it is not possible to come to a higher state of consciousness without coming to a higher state of conscience. The general scholarly bias tends to be towards a study of various levels of consciousness – which are much more often spoken of in the Indic traditions– and not so much towards various levels of conscience which are more frequently elaborated in the Biblical traditions. It would be difficult to make much sense of Dante's *Divine Comedy* without an appreciation of levels of conscience. In many languages, such as Spanish, French and Sanskrit, the word for both conscience and consciousness is the same. This fact alone should alert us to the possibility of an intimate connection between the two. The awakening of conscience is the feeling preparation for an enhancement of consciousness.

The Future Was and Is

Time has a different sense and meaning in different states of consciousness, and an essential feature of high levels of consciousness is a sense of timelessness or a simultaneity of all time. The remark of Jesus Christ, "the lamb slain from the foundation of the world," (*Revelation* 13:8) that "Before Abraham was, I AM" (*John* 8:58) indicates the freedom from time sequence which is a characteristic of high states of consciousness. Such states correspond to levels that are 'eternal' (which is not the same as 'everlasting').[6] According to the *Yoga Sutra* (4:33), the sense of time as sequence enters when the level of consciousness falls from the highest. The highest state –that of *kaivalya*– is that of freedom precisely because it is free of the constraints of time. All our scientific measurements quite rightly are in the realm of time. Otherwise, there can be no measurement. One of the root meanings of the word 'maya' in Sanskrit is to measure. Thus that which can be measured cannot possibly be real; the Real practically by definition being that which is perceived in the highest state of consciousness. The Real is immeasurable; but It can be tasted, experienced, delighted in.

An important concept related with time is that of 'progress'. It is silly to deny certain kinds of progress brought about by science and technology. But when it comes to an understanding of higher consciousness, what the great traditions have revealed does not pertain only to the past. Of necessity, the documents and the heroes of the traditions are from the past. But strictly speaking, the major concern of the traditions is the Real, eternally and forever, neither in the past nor in the future.

The First Person Universal

In our attempts to find objective knowledge, which is the great aspiration of science, the yoga of the West, we cannot eliminate the person. What is needed in fact is an enlargement of the person – freed from the merely personal and subjective – to be inclusive. In order to comprehend one needs to be comprehensive – not as a horizontal extension of more and more knowledge, but as a vertical transformation in order to participate in the universal mind.

Reverting to the opening idea in this paper, although it is true that we humans know and think, the question is what or who thinks. During a conversation with the author, J. Krishnamurti said quite simply, "You know, sir, it occurs to me that K does not *think* at all. That's strange. He just *looks*."[7] We know from association that *K* was a short form of *Krishnamurti*. But what is *Krishnamurti* a short form of? Of the entire cosmos? Not him alone, potentially so each one of us. If so, what looks and knows through thought rather than with thought?

The yoga of the East is towards the realization of the First Person Universal. Only such a person can know without opposition and separation, freed from any desire to control or to manipulate. Then one loves what one knows.

191

Prof. Ravi Ravindra is professor of comparative religion and physics at Dalhousie University, Canada.

Notes:

[1] Please see R. Ravindra, "Experience and Experiment: A Critique of Modern Scientific Knowing," *Dalhousie Review,* vol. 55, 1975-76, pp. 655-674. Reprinted as chapter 7 in *Science and Spirit,* ed. R. Ravindra; Paragon House, New York, 1991.

[2] In this connection, please see R. Ravindra, "Yoga: the Royal Path to Freedom," in *Hindu Spirituality: Vedas Through Vedanta;* ed. K. Sivaraman; New York, Crossroad Publishers, 1989, 177-191. [Volume 6 of *World Spirituality: An Encyclopedic History of the Religious Quest*]. Also included in R. Ravindra: *Yoga and the Teaching of Krishna,* Theosophical Publishing House, Adyar, India, 1997.

[3] Parmenides, *Diels, Fr.* 185; Plotinus, *Enneads* vi. 9.

[4] Plotinus, *Enneads* I. 6.9.

[5] Quoted by Klaus K. Klostermaier in his *A Survey of Hinduism,* State University of New York Press, second edition, 1994, footnote no. 20, p. 533.

[6] Please see R. Ravindra and P. Murray, "Is the Eternal Everlasting?," *The Theosophist,* v. 117, 140-146, 1996. Also included in R. Ravindra: *Yoga and the Teaching of Krishna,* Theosophical Publishing House, Adyar, India, 1997.
[7] See R. Ravindra, *Krishnamurti: Two Birds on One Tree,* Quest Books, Wheaton, Illinois, U.S.A., 1995, p. 77.

Eastern Ideas and Western Thought

David Fontana

David Fontana follows on from Ravi Ravindra with a Westerner's view on some of the same issues. He points out the radical distinction between Western or outer-directed views of consciousness as secondary and Eastern or mystical views upholding the primacy of consciousness and the importance of immediate experience. He goes on to draw parallels between this unitive understanding of consciousness and analagous models emerging from quantum physics and parapsychology. These point towards a convergence of understanding not heralded by older more atomistic theories.

The Western World-View: Consciousness as Secondary

One of the problems of a culture as sophisticated and as materially powerful as our own is that it conditions us from an early age into a particular way of thinking. There is nothing remarkable about such a statement. Commentators have been saying something similar for a century and more. But I have in mind a deeper issue than the self-centred, materialistic thinking to which most of these commentators refer. I have in mind the way of thinking that regards the external world as primary, paramount, and ultimately objectively knowable, and sees the inner world of consciousness as secondary. Such a way of thinking, with its naive realism, forms an integral part of the education we offer our children, and their academic progress from early schooling to university depends in large measure upon their success in incorporating it into their world view. Their life goals are thus formulated and pursued in terms of it, and failure to subscribe to it risks exclusion from the mainstream of thought and progress, and consequent professional and even social isolation.

The Eastern World View:
Consciousness as Primary

Nevertheless, there is an alternative way of looking at life. We tend to associate it particularly with Eastern thought, and it is in the context of Eastern thought that I want principally to refer to it. But it has been present from early times in the West as well, mainly as a persecuted undercurrent to more orthodox thinking. We find it in the Greek and Chaldean mystery traditions. There are important elements of it in Platonic idealism, and later in the gnostic traditions within Christianity which were ruthlessly repressed in the 13th Century. There are echoes of it in the ideas of such Western philosophers as Berkeley, Bergson, William James and A. N. Whitehead. Aldous Huxley spoke of it as forming part of what he termed the *perennial wisdom*, the esoteric strand of thought and practice that underlies and unites the mystical elements in all the great spiritual traditions. And it influenced the work of many poets and creative artists such as Blake, Goethe, Shelley, Wordsworth, and more recently T. S. Eliot.

Orthodoxies of Church and Science

Space does not allow me to present all the reasons why this alternative world view largely failed to influence Western thinking, but one of the most important has to do with the Western insistence that intellectual orthodoxy and obedience to temporal authority are necessary corollaries of each other. Such insistence had its genesis in the adoption by the Emperor Constantine in the 4th Century CE of Christianity as the official religion of the Roman empire, and was greatly augmented in succeeding centuries as the church, in its role as guardian of literacy and learning, came to provide temporal rulers with increasingly necessary clerical and administrative support. In the process, the church gained widespread control over what could and could not be thought and expressed, and was thus able further to assist the state by serving as a formidable engine for social and political control. As a result it grew rich and powerful, and when threatened by gnostic heresies which taught that men and women could find God for themselves and had no need of a priesthood, it reacted with excommunications and the authorised brutalities of the Albigensian crusades and of the Inquisition.

When science in due course dethroned the church, it inherited its hold over people's minds. The Western world was conditioned to look to external authority rather than to inner experience for direction on what to believe about the universe and human nature. In the East however, things were very different. The great spiritual traditions of Hinduism, Buddhism, Jainism and Taoism never became bent to the service of secular rulers, and remained essentially inward-looking and self-reflective. Even in Tibetan Buddhism, where spiritual and temporal authority were combined in the same individuals and institutions, there was little despotism over thought, as from the start Buddhism emphasised not salvation through the actions of gods and priests, but enlightenment through the activities of one's own mind.

Two Ways of Knowing

We thus historically have two separate ways of knowing, one directed primarily outwards as in the West, and the other directed primarily inwards as in the East.   In contrast to the Western view that consciousness is secondary and merely an epiphenomenon acted upon and arising out of the material world, the East sees it as primary, a spiritual reality which creates the illusory material world by the act of experiencing it. Our Western conditioning assures us that the former way of seeing is self-evidently the correct one, but Eastern sages remind us that consciousness, as the direct knowledge of our inner world, is of necessity more 'real' than the second-hand representations which are all we can know of external phenomena. (If we ask what is meant by 'real' in this context, the Eastern sage would probably tell us we have already missed the point).

Essentially then, Eastern psycho-spiritual systems see us as responsible for the creation of the outer world of appearances. It is the action of our consciousness upon the infinite potential of the energy flux outside our heads that brings the outer world into being. The universe indeed plays out its existence within our own minds.   And since our own consciousness thus contains - and therefore also pervades - the universe, inner and outer worlds are recognised as fundamentally one. This leads to another concept of Eastern thought, namely that all things, ultimately, are part of the same unity. It is not difficult to arrive at some aspects of this concept for ourselves simply by acknowledging the interdependence of all things, but the Eastern mind goes beyond mere logic, and directly experiences this awareness of unity. Probably we did so ourselves as small children, but the sense of separateness, of individual identity, of opposition between subject and object is quickly instilled into us by prevailing cultural forces. And as Buddhism puts it, 'when the opposites arise, the Buddha-mind (i.e. the mind that directly perceives reality) is lost'.

A unified world-view may not only be more accurate than a fragmented one, it leads almost inevitably to a greater respect for all existence, as all existence is recognised as a part of oneself. The *ahimsa* (non-violence) doctrine, seen at its most remarkable in Jainism, is one outcome of this respect, as is the *wu-wei* (non-interference) doctrine of Taoism. It would be unrealistic to suppose that the growing interest shown by the West in the Eastern world-view has as yet made much impression upon our models of reality, far less that it has percolated sufficiently into our consciousness to change the way in which we see ourselves. But it would be equally unrealistic to suggest it has had no effect at all. The increasing disenchantment of many Westerners with prevailing materialist-reductionist philosophies, coupled with a growing interest in techniques for mind development such as meditation and creative visualisation, has meant that Eastern psycho-spiritual philosophies do now have a small but significant presence in the West.

Quantum Physics and Eastern Thought

However, the most important boost to future interest in Eastern thought is likely to arise from those developments within Western scientific thinking which lead increasingly to the conclusion that consciousness may indeed be primary rather than secondary, and that an all-prevailing unity does in fact appear to underlie the apparent diversity of the visible world. These conclusions depend particularly upon the discovery by physicists that the presence of an observer is necessary if the quantum wave function is to collapse into a particle and become manifest in space-time reality (i.e. if the subtle energy which is now regarded as the constituent of all matter is to become stabilised into the world of form). Further, as the material brain is itself a quantum system, it must also require the awareness of an 'observer', an 'observer' suggested by some physicists to be a kind of unitive consciousness which acts as the underlying process of mind, but of whose existence we are normally unaware (e.g. Goswami 1993). And it is precisely because we are normally unaware of it that we trick ourselves into our illusory sense of separateness. (Other aspects of the parallels between Eastern thought and quantum physics were discussed some years ago in popular texts by Capra 1975 and Zukav 1979, and are touched on more recently by Bohm 1980, Zohar 1990, Laszlo e.g. 1993, Robertson 1995 and others.)

This of course is by no means the end of the story, for it raises the question how is it possible for our transitory brain-mind consciousness to become directly aware of this unitive consciousness apparently responsible for bringing it into existence? The answer is by *becoming* it, an experience in which the distinction between observer and observed disappears and is replaced by the oceanic state reported by mystics of all traditions and incorporated into coherent and accepted models of mind in the East. Thus, just as the distinction between observed and observer disappears when the brain-mind awareness of the latter leads to the collapse of the wave function, so the distinction between observed and observer disappears when the experience of unitive consciousness leads to the collapse of individual consciousness. Note, however, that just as the collapse of the wave function transforms rather than annihilates the energy of the wave, so the collapse of individual consciousness transforms rather than annihilates the energy of individuality.

The Importance of Parapsychology

It may seem extraordinary that Western physics, by a very different route, now appears to be moving towards a confirmation of Eastern views of the primacy and unitive nature of consciousness, but further support for this confirmation comes from the findings of modern para-psychology. During the last decade and a half, the use of meta-analysis (a technique increasingly employed in the behavioural, social and life sciences which combines data from a number of similar individual experiments) has confirmed that the experimental evidence establishes beyond reasonable doubt the reality of psychic abilities (see e.g. Radin 1997 for an excellent survey). And if psychic abilities do exist, and manifest themselves in such things as telepathy and psycho-kinesis, they demonstrate the direct action of consciousness both on the brains of other people and also on inanimate objects. Research has failed to find any material 'force' operating between minds in telepathy, or be-tween mind and object in psychokinesis, so whatever the energy or energies involved, they certainly do not appear to be physical.

In addition, as psychic effects frequently do not show attenuation over distance, and appear even to operate on occasions precognitively, they strongly suggest that consciousness can operate outside the bounds of the space-time continuum. Among other things, the existence of psychic abilities thus supports the idea of consciousness as primary and as non-physical in that it can operate directly upon matter and is not limited by the parameters defining the material world. Turning Eastwards again, we find that under the title of the *siddhis*, psychic abilities have long been accepted by all the great traditions, and are moreover held to arise as a direct consequence of the refinement and expansion of consciousness developed through mind-training techniques such as meditation and mindfulness.

Conclusion

For the reasons summarised in this chapter, Eastern thought, quan-tum physics and parapsychology combine to demonstrate how ill-ad-vised Western science has been in ignoring consciousness for the greater part of the present century. Not only do all three sources point to-wards consciousness as primary and unitive, they may also, by suggest-ing it is capable of acting outside space and time, provide support for its continuing existence after the death of the physical body. It may not be too over-optimistic to suggest that the coming century could see consciousness, in its various facets, as constituting a major focus for research. If so, we can expect an even closer rapprochement between Eastern thought and Western science, to the great potential benefit of both.

Professor David Fontana is professor of educational psychology, Universities of Minho and Algarve, Portugal, Chair of the British Psychological Society Transpersonal Section and author of over twenty books.

References

Bohm, D. (1980) *Wholeness and the Implicate Order.* London: Routledge.

Capra, F. (1975) *The Tao of Physics.* London: Wildwood House.

Goswami, A. (1993) *The Self-Aware Universe: How Consciousness Creates the Material World.* London: Simon & Schuster.

Laszlo, E. (1993) *The Creative Cosmos: A Unified Science of Matter, Life and Mind.* Edinburgh: Floris Books.

Radin, D. (1997) *The Conscious Universe: The Scientific Truth of Psychic Phenomena.* San Francisco: Harper.

Roberston, G. (1995) *Unity Consciousness and the Perfect Observer: Quantum Understanding Beyond Reason and Reality.* Basingstoke, Hants.: Robertson Publishing.

Zohar, D. (1990) *The Quantum Self.* London: Bloomsbury.

Zukav, G. (1979) *The Dancing Wu Li Masters.* London: Rider.

A Model of the Individual

Geoffrey Leytham

After these broad surveys, the next piece proposes a concrete model of consciousness drawing mainly upon various Western transpersonal traditions.

Einstein said that: 'The object of all science, whether natural science or psychology, is to coordinate our experiences and to bring them into a logical system.' As far as psychology is concerned, it will obviously depend upon one's personal experiences just what has to be brought into a logical system. As my experiences include both spiritual and paranormal events, my system will be more comprehensive than that of a person who denies that such experiences can take place. Hence the following system will appeal most to others who have had experiences similar to my own, but I hope that it will be sufficiently inclusive to cover all other experiences as well.

It seemed to me that the most appropriate unit for a comprehensive human psychology would be 'the individual'. This fits in with the units of other sciences, and forms part of a chain of physical, biological and psychological sciences: atoms, molecules, cells, individuals, groups, and societies. There are models of all these units, so I would like to propose a model of 'the individual' as a fitting logical system for comprehending the vast range of human experiences.

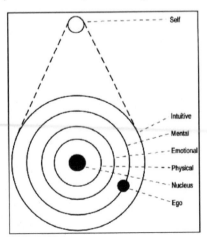

The various aspects of the model are shown in the diagram, and in the following brief description of these, I will suggest possible links with similar components in other psychological theories.

Nucleus - transforms neural impulses into potential ego experiences in one direction (sensory input), and converts ego stimuli into neural impulses for action or response in the opposite airec-ion (motor output). (cf. Freud's *das Es*, and the lowest level of Maslow's hierarchy of needs - the physiological drives.)

Ego - immediate experience, and the perceptual world from which the physical, biological and social worlds are inferred. It functions and becomes conscious on any of the four levels of awareness, and may be focussed or diffused. Energy can be directed inwardly (introversion) or outwardly (extraversion). (cf. many theories of personality, including Jung's ego and Freud's *das Ich*)

Levels of Awareness

Physical - Ego becomes conscious of sensory input. (cf. Jung's sensation function, and Maslow's safety needs.)
Emotional - Ego becomes conscious of feelings. (cf. Jung's feeling function, and Maslow's belongingness and love needs.)

Mental - Ego becomes conscious of language and thoughts, and may be occupied with reasoning and logical analysis. (cf. Jung's thinking function, and Maslow's esteem needs.)
Intuitive - Ego becomes conscious of supra-rational information, often involving synthesis and a more global conception. Probably a key aspect of creativity. (cf. Jung's intuition function, and Maslow's need for self-actualization.)

Self - the centre of highest consciousness. (cf. Assagioli's Higher Self, Brunton's Overself, Jung's Self, and Freud's *Uber-Ich*.)

I regard the Self as being outside time and space, and as animating the whole individual through an all-embracing *Psychofield*. This is not unlike Jung's concept of the collective unconscious. Finally, I regard all individuals as being immersed in sea of Divine Energy, or Cosmic Consciousness, which I call the *Theofield*. Spiritual and paranormal

201

experiences, such as telepathy, would seem to follow quite logically on this assumption of such a universal system of consciousness.

The successive levels of awareness round the nucleus, relate to successive stages of psychological development, and represent increasing spatial and temporal awareness. Thus, each level has a longer 'specious present', and at the intuitive level this could cover a period before and after the actual event; much as an aeroplane could see what was behind and ahead of a car travelling on a twisty road. This would apply especially in dreams, and could account for precognitive experiences.

Few actual people would have such a harmonious psychological development as shown in the diagram, where the rings are equally spaced. Often, the mental level will be developed at the expense of the emotional; a state which is sometimes brought about by the relative emphases of our educational system, and by parental ambition for their children. These individual differences can be represented diagrammatically by varying the respective spaces between the levels to fit the particular person.

Geoffrey Leytham was director of communications in the department of pscyhology, University of Liverpool.

Neuropsychiatric Difficulties in Explaining Consciousness

Peter Fenwick

Peter Fenwick describes the options for explaining consciousness and brain function as he understands them. He rejects materialistic approaches, specifies the explanatory variables of a comprehensive theory, and opts for a hypothesis advanced by Amit Goswami that combines philosophical idealism with a grasp of modern quantum mechanics.

Introduction

At the age of 15, recognising that I needed to know about consciousness, I hurried to the biology library to look it up in the largest text book I could find. To my surprise, it wasn't even mentioned in the index; unconsciousness was the closest I could get. Nowhere was consciousness, as an entity, mentioned. Levels of alertness yes, consciousness, no. There were good descriptions of the neurone and how it fired but no mention of consciousness. Clearly nothing had progressed since the 1920s when Sherrington had said in his Gifford Lectures (Man on His Nature) that the energy scheme describes how the light from a star strikes the eye, sets up an electrochemical reaction and is conducted to the cortex; but as to the way consciousness arises, in Sherrington's words, "It puts its finger to its lips and is silent."

The Modern Dilemma

As a practising neuropsychiatrist, the situation now is in some respects very much better than it was when my interest in consciousness was first aroused in the 1950s. Current functional neuroimaging techniques have led to a much better understanding of the brain in action and have revealed a new phrenology of the mind. The brain appears to work as a set of interlocking modules, each one with a defined location on the cortex, and each with a specific function, all joined together in a magical way (the binding problem) to produce the unified world view of conscious experience.

It has become clear that a purely mechanistic view of the brain can lead to a fuller understanding of mind and the modification of mind by an alteration of its chemical and structural components. Nowhere within this picture does consciousness appear. It is worth pausing for a moment to examine why this is the case.

Our science is based on the rationalism of Descartes, Galileo, Locke, Bacon and Newton. Galileo defined a two-stuff universe: matter and energy. These stuffs, he said, had primary and secondary qualities. The primary qualities were those aspects of nature that could be measured, such as velocity, acceleration, weight, mass etc. There were also secondary qualities, the qualities of subjective experience, such as smell, vision, truth, beauty, love etc. Galileo maintained that the domain of science was the domain of primary qualities. Secondary qualities were non-scientific. "To excite in us tastes, odours and sounds I believe that nothing is required in external bodies except shapes, numbers, and slow or rapid movements. I think that if ears, tongues and noses were removed, shapes and numbers and motions would remain but not odours or tastes or sounds."

Clearly, our primary quality science has been outstandingly successful in examining and quantifying the world around us, and in producing our current technology, but it still puts its fingers to its lips and is silent when the question of consciousness arises. The reason for this is that consciousness, the view from the observer, is a secondary quality and it has been removed, by definition. This leaves our science very lopsided, as only the physical aspects of any phenomenon - a view from nowhere as it has been described - can be investigated by the scientific method. Yet a moment's thought, as Max Velmans has pointed out (shows that that all phenomena are essentially psychological entities). It is the way that the evidence is obtained that makes the difference between objective and subjective qualities. Objective qualities are tested by asking individuals if their psychological concepts match, e.g. do we all see the same pointer readings when we do the same experiment? In the West the secondary science has yet to be evolved, which would ask whether we all have the same psychological state in the same circumstances. This form of science is very much an Eastern perspective used to investigate mind.

Two major philosophical schools currently attempt to explain brain function and tackle the nature of consciousness. Dennett's neurophilosophy characterises one extreme. He argues that consciousness and subjective experience are just the functions of neural nets. Nothing is required to explain personal experience and wider states of consciousness except a detailed knowledge of neural nets. This is clearly a reductionist approach, Galilean primary quality, equating subjective experience with neural mechanisms (Dennett 1991). The other extreme is characterised by the philosophy of Nagel (1974) who argues that it is never possible to learn from an objective third-person point of view what it is like to have a first-person experience. Subjective experience is not available to the scientific method, a it is not in the third person and cannot be validated in the public domain. Nagel argues that however much we understand about the neurophysiology of the functioning of a bat's brain, we will never know what is it like to be a bat. This view suggests that the explanation of subjective experience requires a new principle which is beyond neural nets.

Searle (1992) argues from an intermediate position. He regards subjective experience as being a property of neural nets, but he does not agree with Dennett that a full understanding of neural net functioning is sufficient to explain subjective experience. Searle's view is that we need a Newton of neurophysiology to produce an entirely new principle - a synthesis between first- and third-person experience.

Downward Causation

Another major difficulty relates to the question of control within the central nervous system. As an experiencing human being, within limits I feel that I can control my movements, attend to a specific sensory input, and to some extent control my thinking. However, the main thrust of reductionist science is that upward causation (neuronal functioning) is the prime cause of experiential control. If that was so we would have to take a mechanistic view of man and there would be no question of free will, or of creativity.

Science has been concerned with upward causation for so long that it finds difficulty in seeing that macroscopic events within a biological system (in this case mind and meaning) may play a major part in the organisation of, and may direct the physics, chemistry and biology of, lower order systems.

This control by higher order systems of lower order systems within the body is called downward causation. Control is thought to go from mind (including social and cultural meaning) through the central nervous system to bodily function. Roger Sperry has pointed out that downward causation within the central nervous system is a common property "things are controlled not only from below upwards but also from above downwards by mental .. and other macro properties (furthermore) primacy is given to the highest level control rather than the lowest." (Sperry 1987).

This new mentalistic view, giving prominence to downward causation, helps to redress the balance and allows the driver of the brain, in certain spheres, to be the conscious individual. But again, without a theory of consciousness which links brain directly to the possibilities of conscious experience, we remain immersed in a reductionist trap.

The Role of Anomalies

The current scientific view is that psychological processes are generated entirely within the brain and limited to the brain and the organism. Over the last 50 years large numbers of parapsychological experiments have been carried out which suggest that mind is not limited to the brain and that it is possible to demonstrate directly the effect of mind on other minds (telepathy) and the effect of mind on matter (psychokinesis). For those interested in a more comprehensive review of this subject, the recent book by Dean Radin *The Conscious Universe* (see Dean's piece below) provides a wide range of references to the studies and examines some of the meta-analyses which have demonstrated these effects.

The Current Position

In my view, a satisfactory explanation of consciousness must include a detailed role for brain mechanisms, an explanation for the action of mind outside the brain, and an explanation of free will, meaning and purpose. It should also give an explanation of wide mental states, including mystical experience and near-death experiences, when the experiencer sees through into the structure of the universe. Finally, it should provide a clear explanation for apparent downward causation (purpose) throughout the universe and in the brain, as well as some solution to the question raised, particularly in Eastern cultures, of the survival of aspects of consciousness after death.

The study of quantum mechanical effects suggests that the universe is highly interconnected and that particles interact with each other at a distance. Thus the idea that mind could also be interactive outside the skull is theoretically possible. The quantum mechanical theories of Chris Clarke and Michael Lockwood, and the quantum gravitational theories of Roger Penrose and Stuart Hameroff are all possibilities. However, to my mind, the current most likely contender to link consciousness with brain function, as it has a wider explanatory power and leads to several testable predictions is a theory by Amit Gotswami (1993). He argues that consciousness is a basic stuff of the universe and exists like energy. When a choice is involved, an observation made, the wave function is collapsed in consciousness and matter arises, the standard wave/particle duality theory. His contribution (akin to Schrödinger) is that there is only one observer: a universal, undivided consciousness. He argues that brains have evolved a special mechanism for trapping consciousness, so that when consciousness interacts with brain processes the probability wave collapses, on the one hand producing the external object, and on the other, subjective experience of that object.

This theory has significant explanatory power, as it will link together the binding problem within the brain, parapsychological phenomena, and more particularly for the neuropsychiatrist, a possible explanation of the wide mental states when the individual sees through into the structure of the universe. Of further interest, in arguing for a field of possibilities (consciousness), the theory suggests a mechanism for creativity, as the consciousness field can be tapped directly by brain processes. This theory does not displace current neuroscience but leaves it as a valuable basis on which consciousness acts through the brain. Both are required. Of more importance, however, this view heals science, adds meaning and purpose to life again, and links us to the primary creative force of the universe.

Dr. Peter Fenwick is emeritus consultant neuropsychiatrist at the Maudsley Hospital, London, Senior Lecturer at the Institute of Psychiatry and chairman of the Scientific and Medical Network Council.

References

Dennett, D.C. (1991) *Consciousness Explained*, London, Penguin.

Nagel, T (1974) *What is it like to b e a bat?* Philosophical Review 83: 435-50

Rabin, D. (1997) *The Conscious Universe*, Harper Edge, San Francisco.

Searle, J. (1993) *The problem of consciousness.* In P. Nagel (ed) CIBA Foundation symposium no 174 *Experimental and Theoretical Studies of Consciousness*, Chichester: John Wiley pp 61-80

Sperry R.W. (1987) *Structure and significance of the consciousness revolution.* The Journal of Mind and Behaviour 8,1
Velmans, M., *A reflexive science of consciousness* In P. Nagel (ed) CIBA Foundation symposium no 174 *Experimental and Theoretical Studies of Consciousness*, Chichester: John Wiley pp 81-100.

Taking Psi Seriously [1]

Dean I. Radin

Peter Fenwick referred above to the role of anomalies in opening up the possibilities of a genuinely comprehensive science of consciousness. Dean Radin's landmark 1997 book sets out the case for scientific psi research in a rigorous fashion and makes it abundantly clear not only that there is a wealth of scientific data, but also that continuing dismissal of such evidence can only be explained by a combination of wilful ignorance and unscientific a priori prejudice. The book was awarded the Network Book Prize for 1997.

"The only solid piece of scientific truth about which I feel totally confident is that we are profoundly ignorant about nature .... It is this sudden confrontation with the depth and scope of ignorance that represents the most significant contribution of twentieth-century science to the human intellect."

Lewis Thomas, The Medusa
and the Snail

For nearly a century, doubts about the existence of psychic phenomena were so engrained that few scientists imagined the "psi hypothesis" would ever need to be taken seriously. During the last decade of the 20th century, these doubts began to slowly and then briskly erode under the weight of valid, replicable experiments. Today, even informed skeptics have begun to concede that something interesting is going on. The time has come seriously to ponder what psi implies about who and what we are, and what scientific and technological changes it may stimulate in the coming millennium.

What is "psi?" It's a common human experience, given many names over the centuries, suggesting something like a deep interconnectedness among all things. The most remarkable aspect of psi, and the most perplexing, is that psi-type interconnections appear to transcend not only the limitations of the human sensory system, but also the boundaries of space and time as we presently understand them. It is the transcendence of time that has made theoretical understanding of psi particularly difficult.

Now I must introduce an important caveat. When revolutionary ideas are placed on the table for serious discussion, it is predictable that the Law of Unintended Consequences is clapping its hands with glee, often in the guise of a table-tipping Trickster. While we can fruitfully interpolate today's leading-edge science and technology perhaps ten years into the future, we cannot go much beyond that with any confidence. Trying then to pin down the implications of psi pushes our forecasting confidence into the realm of near-fantasy. So please understand that I can only offer speculations.

Another reason for exercising caution is that we know a fair amount about what psi is not, but precious little about what it is. We have good reason to believe that psi as observed in the laboratory is not mediated by electromagnetic signals, it is not due to experimental design artifacts, nor subject or experimenter fraud, nor selective reporting practices, nor sensory leakage, nor randomization problems .... But if not these, then what? At this stage, we are restricted to

209

phrases like "unexpected correlations" and "deep interconnectedness" to provide an inkling about what it is. This is not a satisfying state of affairs, but it is to be expected for empirical observations that are ahead of their time.

So for the moment let's set aside concerns about the depth of our ignorance, and instead wonder what might happen when psi phenomena become accepted by the broader scientific community. One possibility is that psi may be viewed as little more than a cosmic oddity, perhaps as a psychological reflection of the quantum interconnectedness of the universe. Another possibility is that psi will be explained with a theory that carries revolutionary conceptual impact, but little practical import, like Einstein's General Relativity. Perhaps it will go no further than that.

Perhaps Not

I suspect that a breakthrough in understanding psi will usher in an era of science and technology that, from today's perspective, would look like pure magic. Psi-based "manipulations" of the fundamental properties of space, time, matter and energy could lead to unimaginable revisions of reality. On the other hand, while it is probably true that some fundamentals may have to be radically revised, I think it unlikely that a psi breakthrough will significantly alter the world that most people experience in their everyday lives. In other words, the sun will still shine and the oceans will still wave with or without psi. Initially at least, theorists will be positively giddy or bewildered, but we will still have grocery stores and Christmas. Larger-scale societal and world-view changes will take many generations to percolate throughout the world.

What PSI Implies

With the above caveats in mind, what does psi imply? At minimum, it implies four things:

(1)   what science presently knows about the nature of the universe
        is incomplete,

(2)   the capabilities and limitations of human potential have been
        vastly underestimated,

(3)   beliefs about the strict separation of objective and subjective
        have been overly simplistic, and

(4)   some "miracles" previously attributed to religious or
        supernatural sources may be due to extraordinary capabilities
        of human consciousness.

Together, these implications suggest that on the spectrum of mere oddity to revolutionary, psi probably lies in the realm of revolutionary. Any one of these implications could lead to major scientific, technological, psychological or theological breakthroughs, with reverberations throughout society. Now let's consider these implications focused more by discipline.

Physics

> "It is almost an absurd prejudice to suppose that existence can only be physical. As a matter of fact, the only form of existence of which we have immediate knowledge is psychic [i.e., in the mind]. We might as well say, on the contrary, that physical existence is a mere inference, since we know of matter only in so far as we perceive psychic images mediated by the senses."
>
> Carl Jung

Physicists who have retained some humility in the face of Nature's mysteries are interested in psi because it implies that we have overlooked essential properties of space, time, energy and information, and their interactions with mind. Theoretical notions like advanced waves in electrodynamics, time symmetry, closed time-like loops in General Relativity, and quantum nonlocality - all of which were thought of at one time to be mere mathematical abstractions - may not only exist, but be directly experienced.

Overlooking fundamental physical properties is more serious than it sounds. Many basic scientific models and experimental techniques are anchored on assumptions that the fundamentals are in fact fundamental. If an important assumption begins to crack, like the independence of the flow of time, this immediately threatens the entire network of scientific assumptions that defines the scientific worldview. It may be that just as we were shocked to learn at the dawn of the 20th century that matter and energy were essentially the same, perhaps at the dawn of the 21st century we are about to discover that mind and matter are essentially the same. This is assumed in various forms by both materialistic and transcendental monism, and of course by Eastern philosophies, but here I refer to something new, a "complementary monism." This would allow such distinctive entities as mind, matter, space, time, and energy to arise out of a common ground, enjoy deeply intimate interactions, and also retain some degree of autonomy.

Psi effects on random number generators (RNG) suggest a particularly perilous heresy for physics: quantum theory may not be complete. Psi experiments on RNGs indicate, as physicist Helmut Schmidt put it, that

> "... the outcome of quantum jumps, which quantum theory attributes to nothing but chance, can be influenced by a person's mental effort. This implies that quantum theory is wrong when experimentally applied to systems that include human subjects. It remains to be seen whether the quantum formalism can be modified to include psi effects, and perhaps even to clarify the still somewhat puzzling role of the human observer in the theory."[1]

Quantum theory has been one of the most successful physical theories in history, but like any theory it is an approximation of the world, not the world itself. If a decade from now psi research convincingly demonstrates that quantum theory is a special case of a more comprehensive theory, then life-long quantum mechanics may be upset, and will no doubt furiously try to put the omelette back into the egg, but it will come as no great surprise to historians of science. Incidentally, clairvoyance is ordinarily thought of as the ability to perceive across vast distances. We can imagine a future "Clairvoyant Space Corps" tasked with exploring distant galaxies. Likewise, we ordinarily think of precognition and retrocognition as seeing across vast gulfs of time, and may envision teams of Indiana Jones-like "Time Historians," who explore ancient and future civilizations. It is easy to imagine that mind-matter effects may some day be used to push atoms around, operate television sets by psychic remote control, and operate wheelchairs. Of course, it is equally likely that clairvoyance will allow us to see across infinitesimally tiny distances, that precognition will allow us to perceive infinitesimally brief times, and that mind-matter effects can allow us to push entire planets around. These extremes may seem outlandish, but given that we know almost nothing about the limits of psi, setting any limits at this point would be a mistake.

And besides, there already is a fascinating bit of evidence that clairvoyance can be used to see the infinitesimally tiny. An article by physicist Stephen Phillips provides evidence that a century ago, two Theosophists used psi to examine atomic and subatomic states. Their descriptions didn't make much sense at the time, or for many decades afterwards. Today their descriptions bear a remarkable resemblance to the quark model of particle physics and to aspects of superstring theory. Perhaps the next greatest advancements in our explorations of space, time and energy will be through such psi-enhanced methods.

Biology

Psi raises far more questions than provides answers for the biological realm. How does psi information get into a living organism? Are there hidden senses we have overlooked? What are the limits of distant mental interactions in living systems? Is psi an invisible carrier of information among living systems? Is psi interconnectedness related to the unitary sense of self in human beings, or the oneness sometimes felt by groups engaged in the same activity? Does hive behaviour in some animals reflect psi-like connections?

Does psi imply the existence of an even larger unity among human beings, among all sentient creatures, or among all life? Does it serve any evolutionary purpose? Is it an ability, a talent, a throwback to a more primitive sense, a glimpse of our future? Or is it merely a biological reflection of the nonlocal nature of physical matter? Whatever the answers, an improved understanding of psi has the potential of significantly altering some prevailing views about biology.

Psychology

Our understanding of human perception, memory, and communication will be deeply affected by an improved understanding of psi. Is unconscious psi more prevalent than previously thought (I believe it is), and if so, what role might it play in ordinary human behaviour? If we are not as separate from one Another as commonly believed, does psi play a role in understanding the mass behaviour of groups, crowds, and society?

Psychological interest in psi is often predicated on the observation that magical thinking lies close to the veneer of the sophisticated modern mind. Magical thinking in this context refers to the tendency to attribute meaning to things based on an organic world-view. This world-view, strongly reminiscent of the world-view implied by psi phenomena, is permeated with deep, meaningful interconnections among all things. In contrast, much of modern science has supported a world-view permeated with "nothing but" meaningless isolation. Clinical psychologists know that the feeling of being fundamentally alone often leads to anxiety, declining health, and depression. To maintain mental and physical health, not only as individuals but as societies, we must believe and act as though we live in a world that does have deep meaning and personal value.

Psi supports the concept of an interconnected "conscious universe," not merely as a psychological coping mechanism, but as reality. As science shifts towards a reality that supports our deepest psychological needs rather than denies them, we may expect significant beneficial influences on individual and societal mental health.

Sociology

We know that air, land and sea pollution spread out and affect the global ecology in many ways. Recent studies of the effects of mass-consciousness on physical systems suggest, as farfetched as it may sound, that there may be a mental analogy to environmental ecology - something like an "ecology of thought" that invisibly interweaves through the fabric of society. It suggests that disruptive, scattered or violent thoughts may pollute the social fabric in ways extending far beyond local influences. That is, a single individual harbouring malevolent thoughts may directly affect those around him because of his destructive or antisocial behaviour. Beyond this, his intent may also spread out and indirectly "infect" and disrupt others at a distance. Those disruptions may in turn spread out, like a multiplying "psi virus," until the infection encircles the globe. Perhaps periods of widespread madness, such as wars, are indicators of mass-mind infections.

There may also be the equivalent of a mass-mind "immune system" that helps to fight off psi viruses. These are those brief, shining moments when intensely nurturing thoughts from a single individual, or groups of like-minded individuals, spread out and quite literally heal the world-mind. Perhaps periods of widespread lucidity, like the period preceding the fall of the Berlin Wall, are indicators of mass-mind healings. In general, the mass-mind studies suggest that thoughts may be less ephemeral or private than we normally think. One wonders what role the "mind of the world" plays in shaping the evolution of global interconnectedness.

Philosophy

Psi research has empirically addressed the core of many age-old philosophical questions, especially the "mind-body" debate, the nature of causality, the ontological reality of the objective versus the subjective, and the nature of free will versus determinism. I believe it likely that psi will eventually force a fundamental re-examination of these basic philosophical concepts. A survey of contemporary ideas about the nature of mind reveals that none are entirely satisfactory. Orthodox materialism helped spawn the nonsensical notion that the mind is a meaningless illusion. Functionalism argues that it does not matter what mind is made of, all that matters is what it does. This is a pragmatic approach, but it doesn't help us understand what the mind actually is. Classic dualism is haunted by the spectre of disembodied minds. Other philosophical approaches to mind are equally ambiguous, which is why the nature of the mind persists as a perennial topic of debate. Philosopher David Chalmers provides a pithy summary of the four

215

common approaches used to explain consciousness. He says that they either "explain something else, or deny the phenomenon, or simply declare victory, or find a neatly ambiguous metaphor which sounds for an instant as if it might bridge mind and matter."

While consciousness is still a complete mystery, each approach to understanding it has offered a glimpse at what might be going on. The behaviourist camp showed that the mind is less private than previously supposed, because much of the inner workings can be inferred through careful observation of behaviour. The functionalists proposed that some aspects of mental functioning can be embodied in different ways, for example, as sophisticated computer programs. Neuroscientists have demonstrated that much of the mind's information-processing capabilities can be understood as patterns of activity in the brain. Dualists have pointed out that no comprehensive model of the mind can leave out subjective experience. Identity theorists have suggested that the workings of the brain and the mind are linked in some non-separable way.

A recent twist on identity theory, called "naturalistic panpsychism" by philosopher Michael Lockwood, suggests that a fundamental property of the universe may include a recursive, or self-reflective sense of "what it's likeness." This would allow a materialistic universe to contain the strange property of subjective mind because "what it's likeness" is built-in to the same fabric as everything else. We are aware that we are constructions of matter and energy because awareness is fundamental to matter and energy.

What psi offers to the puzzle about consciousness is the observation that information can be obtained in ways unbound by the limitations of the ordinary sensory system, and there may be ways of directly influencing the outer world by mental means alone. At first it may seem that the existence of psi immediately rejects some of the strictly materialistic and mechanistic proposals about the nature of consciousness, but this is not so. With a concept like naturalistic panpsychism, everything proposed by a hard-core, materialistic neuroscience is still perfectly compatible with psi. All that is needed is the additional assumption that some aspects of a fully interconnected universe - including interconnections through time - can be directly experienced. In any case, any future philosophical understanding of consciousness that even presumes to be comprehensive must include the sorts of interconnectedness suggested by psi.

Religion

Much of the awe underlying the traditional religions can be traced to stories of miracles, which are used to illustrate the wonders of divine power. From a psi perspective, the great religious scriptures are encyclopedic repositories of stories about psi effects - telepathy, clairvoyance, precognition, mental healing, and mind-matter interactions. For some people, the scientific confirmation that psi is genuine may strengthen their religious faith, because if psi-like miracles are true even by secular standards, then perhaps the stories in the scriptures may be true as well. For others, the scientific study of psi is blasphemous because it "tests God." This latter opinion reflects a widespread fear that some things should not be studied because there are some things we just shouldn't know.

In fact, psi may support the idea that there is something more to mind than just the mind/body system. In particular, a mind that is less tightly bound in space or time than expected by traditional scientific models might be able to communicate with persons from the past or future. If so, when a medium claims to be in contact with a departed spirit, perhaps he or she is actually in contact with someone who is alive in the past. From the "departed" person's perspective, they may find themselves communicating with someone from their future, although it is doubtful that they would understand this.

While it is not clear that psi implies anything about actual survival of consciousness after bodily death, it does imply that communications transcending time may be possible. From that viewpoint, long-departed Grandma is still very much alive, and she can be contacted, but she is alive "then" while we are alive "now." Could the occasional passing thought about a strangely familiar but unknown person be a glimmering telepathic contact from an ancestor or a descendant?

Applications

What does the future hold when breakthroughs in understanding psi are exploited? In medicine, for instance, it is likely that future experiments will continue to confirm that effects of distant mental intention on healing are not merely real, but are clinically useful in treating some physical and mental illnesses, including AIDS. Given the inertia of large organisations, it's unlikely that we'll see doctors routinely prescribing distant mental healing treatments in the near future, but we will undoubtedly see subgroups of mainstream medical and psychiatric associations showing increasing interest in the therapeutic effects of psi-based healing intention, psi-based medical diagnosis, and possibly even secular forms of prayer.

Over the longer term, the practice of medicine must change, independent of psi. Economic pressures assure this. But once we understand more of the factors underlying distant healing effects, and how to enhance psi-based diagnostic methods, it is possible that new specialities will form within medicine. Some physicians may opt for training in a new discipline that would today look like a mixture of ancient magical principles combined with future technologies.

What about technology? Starting in the early 1980s, it became increasingly clear (to me at least) that some psi-based high-technologies would begin to appear before the turn of the century. Progress seems to be on track, for on November 3rd 1998, the first patent for a psi-based device was issued by the US Patent Office to a team of Princeton University researchers. For economic reasons, any viable psi-based technology will have to do things that can't be done, or done very efficiently, by ordinary means. Building a psychic garage door opener may be fun, but it will not replace conventional electronic remote controls. On the other hand, using a technology-enhanced telepathic communication system to "call" a friend in a distant spacecraft, or someone in a deeply submerged submarine, does make sense, and these applications, as well as games and new human-computer interaction methods, are likely to show up first.

We may be surprised to learn that psi applications will accidentally crop up in the development of atomic-sized devices, known as nanotechnology. At this scale, even minuscule mind-matter interaction effects may have huge consequences, and what may initially be perceived as extraordinary encounters with Murphy's Law (if anything can go wrong, it will) during development of these tiny devices, may eventually be understood as these devices' inadvertent responses to the users' thoughts and wishes.

Military and intelligence communities have used and will continue to use psi because it occasionally proves to be useful. To avoid the glare of media there will be predictable periods when authorities vigorously deny that anyone is interested in psi. The same is true for psychic detective work. Public openness about this topic depends entirely on the mood of the times. If it is calmly acknowledged, without hype or hysteria, that there are some valid intelligence aspects to psi, then the large underground of police and government agents who already use psi, or wish to explore its use, will emerge.

Psi has been used to enhance decision-making in business and political arenas for many years. Combined with the best available information, even the briefest intuitive flash about future possibilities can recast a devastating loss into a gigantic profit. Likewise, violent conflicts may be deftly eased with just the right bit of political information at the right time.

Projecting to a future where psi-refined intuition is routinely used to enhance decision-making raises a curious paradox: If too many people begin to accurately peek at their possible futures, and they change their behaviours as a result, the causal loops established between the future and the past may agitate the future from a few likely outcomes into a completely undetermined probabilistic mush. By analogy, recall that in the early days of uncontrolled computer-based stock market trading, tens of thousands of independent, individually simple, mathematically-aided buy/sell decisions innocently conspired one day in 1987 to spin the New York Stock Exchange into a death spiral. Similarly, billions of independent, simple glimpses of the future, resulting in altered actions, may one day innocently spin the future into a chaotic whirlwind. This may not be all bad. A society that consciously uses precognition to guide the future is one that is realising true freedom. That is, the act of billions of people seeing and action on their own futures may result in fracturing undesirable, "fated" destinies set in motion long ago. This would allow us to create the future as we wish, rather than blindly follow a predetermined course through ignorance.

So, how can we sum up the implications of taking psi seriously? Perhaps the best way is to say that the ideas sketched here merely scratch the tip of an iceberg, which is floating in a vast ocean of possibilities. The only thing I am confident of is that we are headed towards a wonderful, shocking, astonishing future.

1. This chapter is a revision of a section from the author's book, *The Conscious Universe,* 1997, HarperEdge Publishers, San Francisco.

2. Note that I hedge on the word "manipulation" because it is not at all clear that psi works the way we ordinarily think about things "working."

3. I would be remiss if I did not point out that there are on-going, hot debates about how to properly interpret the results of successful psi-based distant healing effects. There is much disagreement over whether these effects should be thought of as causal, or as correlative, or as something else.

4. US patent number 5,830,064, "Apparatus and method for distinguishing events which collectively exceed chance expectations and thereby controlling an output."

Dean I. Radin, Ph.D. works in the Consciousness Research Laboratory, Palo Alto, CA and is author of 'The Conscious Universe'.

References

1. Schmidt, H. (1993b). *Observation of a psychokinetic effect under highly controlled conditions.* JP, 57, 351-372.

2. Phillips, S. M. (1995). *Extrasensory perception of subatomic particles. I. Historical evidence.* Journal of Scientific Exploration, 9 (4), 489-525.

3.   The Economist. (July 20, 1996). *Moreover: Science does it with feeling,* 71-73

Chalmers, D. J. (December, 1995). *The puzzle of conscious experience.* Scientific American.

4.   Lockwood, M. (1989). *Mind, brain and the quantum. The compound "I".* NewYork: B. Blackwell.

5.   Galante, M. A. (January 27, 1986*). Psychics: lawyers using seers to help select juries, find missing children.* The National Law Journal, 8, 1.

Lyons, A. & Truzzi, M. (1990). *The Blue Sense: psychic detectives and crime.* NY: Mysterious Press.

On the Scientific Study of Non-Physical Worlds

Charles T. Tart

As mentioned by Peter Fenwick above, an adequate theory of consciousness would make some sense of the evidence for survival of consciousness after bodily death. In a book of this size it is impossible to be comprehensive in this respect. Mainstream psychology pays no attention whatsoever to this kind of evidence, which I myself assessed in my book 'Survival? (1984). A great deal of research has also been carried out over the past two decades into the near-death experience (see 'The Near-Death Experience, A Reader', edited by Lee Bailey, Routledge 1996 for a good introductory overview). Brain-based approaches tell only half the story, I believe, while a dispassionate analysis points in the direction of mind or consciousness transcending the locality of the brain and extending beyond it.

Another research field pioneered by Professor Ian Stevenson is with children who remember previous lives. His book of this title (1987, University of Virginia Press) gives a rigorous introduction to the work. More recently he has compared these memories with a different, biological line of evidence by considering cases involving birth marks and birth defects.

The results of this study are published in the truly monumental 'Reincarnation and Biology' (two volumes, University of Virginia Press, 1997) and summarised in his shorter work 'Where Reincarnation and Biology Intersect' (also University of Virginia Press, 1997). Psychologists have in the meantime probed hypnotically induced memories in their patients, but these have rarely met with the same degree of evidential rigour.

The final piece in this chapter is from Professor Charles Tart, who has been at the forefront of research in both parapsychology and transpersonal psychology for three decades. It comes from the final chapter of his edited book 'Body, Mind, Spirit' (Hampton Roads 1997) and is reprinted with permission. In it he speculates about hos science might go about the study of so-called non-physical worlds.

This final piece is intended to be provocative, suggesting that a relatively objective scientific inquiry is possible in areas normally reserved for speculative thought and theology. The suggestions here may still be premature for our current stage of development: when I presented some of these ideas at the Parapsychological Association meeting in 1986 (Tart, 1987), there was very little discussion of them then or subsequently. But they are important for the future study of parapsychology and the spiritual.

A major instigating force behind the nineteenth century's psychical research movement was the desire to test the essential claims of religion. Contemporary parapsychology has almost totally abandoned such an aim in its quest for technical precision and scientific respectability. Technical excellence is fine, but we must not lose sight of what is humanly important about our research endeavour. One aspect of that is to investigate as objectively as possible the reality (or lack of it) of ostensibly independently existing "nonphysical" worlds (NPWs). The concept of personal survival of bodily death assumes the reality of at least one NPW, for example, at least insofar as we must assume that surviving spirits exist "somewhere." NPWs are not a fashionable concept in orthodox science, to put it mildly, but if they have any reality at all, they are enormously important for understanding our nature and the nature of the world.

The most common contact with ostensible NPWs is during out-of-the-body experiences (OBEs). The OBEr finds him- or herself in an experiential world which is "sensorily" or perceptibly real, vivid and usually stable, yet is clearly not our earthly physical world. The more lucid quality of OBE consciousness, its immediate clarity (compared to dream consciousness), which is typical of the OBE inclines the OBEr to take the perceived NPW reality as existing independently of their personal experience of it, in the same way we believe the physical world exists independently of our experience of it, and that, to answer a classical question, a tree falling in the woods makes a sound whether there is anyone there to hear it or not. Considering such an NPW independently real is especially likely if: (1) it is stable and not changed by arbitrary acts of will on the OBEr's part, as can happen in lucid dreams; and (2) repeated OBE visits to the NPW show it to have consistent, lawful properties.

To illustrate this, consider the following descriptions from the OBEs of Robert Monroe, an American businessman who had repeated, usually voluntary, OBEs over many years. Monroe's experiences are described in his three books (Monroe, 1971; 1985; 1994), in my one experimental study with him (Tart, 1967), and in a biography (Stockton, 1989).

> 11/5/58 Afternoon. The vibrations came quickly and easily...I tried to lift out the physical with no result. Whatever thought or combination I tried, I remained confined right where I was. I then remember the rotating trick, which operates just as if you are turning over in bed. I started to turn, and recognised that my physical was not 'turning' with me. I moved slowly after a moment I was "face down," or in direct opposition to the placement of my physical body. The moment I reached this 180° position...there was a hole. That's the only way to describe it. To my senses, it seemed to be a hole in a wall which was about two feet thick and stretched endlessly in all directions...The periphery of he hole was just precisely the shape of my physical body....I moved cautiously through the hole, holding on to its side...." (Monroe, 1971, 86-87)

During the next couple of years, over a dozen times, Monroe went through that hole. To him it was a repeatable experiment. He waited for the vibrations, did the action that created the feeling of rotating 180 degrees, a hole would appear and he would go through it. The place he went to had recognisably similar and stable characteristics each time. He called it, "Locale III." He could wander around there, invisible to the inhabitants of that apparently real world. To Monroe, the reality of Locale III would be like what any of us could experience by stepping out of our house for a few minutes, wandering around, looking at some things, and coming back. If we went out again, and looked at the same of area, it would be pretty much the same place. That's what it was like for Monroe.

He reported that Locale III had a lot of stable characteristics that were similar to those of our own, ordinary world. It was a physical matter world. There were trees, houses, people, artifacts, all the appurtenances of a reasonably civilised society. There were homes, families, businesses; people worked for a living; there were roads, vehicles travelled on the roads, and so forth. And yet it also had quite stable characteristics that were not similar to our world. For instance, he saw nothing that would suggest any kind of electrical devices. No telephones, no electric lights, no TV. He saw no internal combustion devices, nothing that looked like it ran on gasoline or oil or anything like that. But there was mechanical power in use. For example he reported:

> ....Careful examination of one of the locomotives that pulled a string of old-fashioned looking passenger cars showed it to be driven by a steam engine. The cars appeared to be made of wood, the locomotive of metal, but of a different shape than our now obsolete types. The track gauge was much smaller than our standard track spacing, smaller than our narrow-gauge mountain railways.
>
> I observed the servicing of one of the locomotives in detail. Neither wood nor coal was used as a thermal source to produce steam. Instead, large, vatlike containers were carefully slid from under the boiler, detached, and rolled by small cart into a building with massive thick walls. The containers had pipelike protuberances extending from the top. Men, working behind shields, performed the removal, casually

cautious, and did not relax their automatic vigilance until the containers were safely in the building and the door closed. The containers were "hot," either through heat or radiation. The actions of the technicians all seemed to indicate the latter.

The streets and roads are different, again principally in size. The "lane" on which vehicles travel is nearly twice as wide as ours. Their version of our automobile is much larger. Even the smallest has a single bench seat that will hold five or six people abreast....Wheels are used, but without inflated tires....Motive power is contained somewhere in the rear. Their movement is not very fast, at something like 15 to 20 miles per hour. Traffic is not heavy...." (Monroe, 1971, 94-95)

NPWs versus Lucid Dreams

The contrast with lucid dream worlds is particularly important here. When an ordinary dream becomes lucid, the state of the dreamer's consciousness changes such that she knows she is dreaming *while* she is dreaming; she has relatively full access to her waking state memories and knowledge; and she can plan actions and carry them out in a far more active way than in ordinary dreaming. The "sensorily" experienced dream world nevertheless remains real and vivid. The lucid dream world has a major difference from ordinary reality, however, in that "paranormal" (by physical world standards) events become common. By willing an object in the lucid dream world to disappear, for example, it is likely to vanish into thin air.

NPWs, compared to lucid-dream worlds, are reported to have a solidity, stability, and lawfulness that resists the OBEr's mental desires. If you want an object to disappear from the NPW scene, wishing is not enough; you will have to pick it up and carry it away, or otherwise follow the laws that appear to apply in the NPW. The possession of lawful properties in a way apparently independent of the experiencer's wishes leads to the ascription of independent reality to the world in both ordinary waking life experiences and NPW experiences.

Such experienced phenomenal independence and lawfulness of NPWs could he accounted for by retaining the hypothesis that the NPWs are still subjective creations and that there are simply more rigid psychological processes (automated habits) underlying their apparent consistency and independence. Some NPWs are probably adequately accounted for by such a hypothesis. But suppose some NPWs really are independently existing realities, not subjective creations of the experiencers' minds. How would we discriminate such NPWs from purely subjective ones?

Are Some NPWs Real?

Let's assume we develop a technology for producing consistent OBE excursions to NPWs, or have consistent meditative techniques producing similar experiences, or can locate people capable of doing this through their own natural talents. Then we may look for *consistency* of descriptions from *independent* observers as a test of particular NPWs' reality. If their descriptions of a particular NPW, NPW-A, for example, were coherent and consistent in major details and not significantly contradictory on important details we could provisionally grant at least partial independent reality status to NPW-A.

By analogy, I have never been to "Munich," and probably never will go there. I have met a number of people who claim to have travelled to "Munich," and their descriptions of what "Munich" looks like have been, in the main, consistent. Therefore I will accept the idea that "Munich" has an independent existence. I don't know if "Munich" really exists in any absolute sense, but the proof of its existence is good enough for many practical and personal purposes, such as mail ordering something from a company that is purportedly located there, for example. Similarly if several people claim to have repeatedly visited NPW-A during OBEs, and give consistent descriptions of what it is like, I am inclined provisionally to grant at least some likelihood of independent existence of NPW-A.

Weighing the Evidence for an NPW

Several factors will influence how much likelihood we will grant to NPW-A's independent existence. First, we know that interior experiences can often be strongly shaped by belief and suggestion, so we must ask: is the reported nature of NPW-A significantly different from what would be expected, given overt cultural beliefs held by our OBErs about such ostensible worlds? Second, we must consider the influence of implicit, covert cultural beliefs. If we have a control group of people from the same culture *fantasise* about having an OBE and visiting NPW-A (with minimal directions for getting there), how different are their fantasy productions from the reports given by the OBErs who claim to have actually been there? It's important to check that the people in the control group do not actually have an OBE as a result of the questioning procedure also, as some naturally talented people might have. Research in hypnosis, for example, was confused for many years because some of the people in the "control" (no formal hypnotic induction procedure) group were highly hypnotisable people who went into hypnosis as a result of the testing procedures, yet were erroneously classified as "unhypnotised."

Third, people influence each other, so we would want to establish strongly that our several OBE explorers have not been influencing each other during normal, physical-world contact. Ideally, they should not know each other's identities and never have any communications with each other. If normal contact is effectively ruled out, the more difficult problem of ruling out psychic influences on each other, influences that might lead to consistent subjective constructions, arises. This is analogous to the problem of the super-ESP hypothesis for explaining survival data. We cannot rule such possible telepathic "contamination" out at this stage of our knowledge, but such a counterhypothesis itself lends some support to the idea of the reality of NPWs, in the same way that the super-ESP hypothesis lends general support to the possibility of survival of death.

Our analogy between reports of "Munich" and of NPW-A is limited, because we have two distinct advantages in establishing the independent reality of "Munich." First, our travelers can bring back physical evidence like photographs. Second, we can potentially travel there ourselves. At present we do not have anything analogous to photographs for NPW-A, but if particular NPWs do have an independent existence, perhaps something analogous might develop. Further, as we develop our sciences of altered states of consciousness and parapsychology, we may develop training methods that are reliable and successful enough that we may indeed be able to travel to NPW-A ourselves. This latter potential development does not completely solve the problem of objectively real independent existence, but it certainly raises the stakes in the game!

The proposed lines of research into the existence of NPWs will not be easy ones, running against current scientific prejudice as they do, but it might produce data highly germane to questions about the nature of humanity, our place in the universe, and the possibility of some kind of survival of death.

Professor Charles T. Tart is emeritus professor of psychology in the University of California, Davis and author of many books and articles.

References

Monroe, R. A. (1971) *Journeys out of the Body*, Garden City, Anchor Books

Monroe, R.A. (1985) *Far Journey*, New York, Doubleday

Monroe, R.A. (1994) *Ultimate Journey*, New York, Doubleday

Stockton , B. (1989) *Catapult: The Biography of Robert Monroe*, Norfolk, VA, Donning

Tart, C.T. (1967) A second psychophysiological study of out-of-the-body experiences in a gifted subject. *International Journal of Parapsychology, 9, pp. 251-8*

Tart, C.T., (1987) On the scientific study of other worlds. In D. Weiner and R. Nelson (eds), *Research in Parapsychology 1986,* Metuchen, Scarecrow Press.

Although the field of consciousness studies is more active than ever and the elements of an integral science of consciousness are present, a great deal of work remains to be done if a unified theoretical approach is to be developed. The papers in this chapter all take a broad view and open up new avenues of thinking and research. The question of the

nature of consciousness is an immediate and essential one for any thinking human being, as is the answer to the question of how consciousness is related to the brain.

The options in this respect were set out a hundred years ago by William
James, F.C.S. Schiller and Henri Bergson, all philosophers with an
interest in psychical research (See James's Ingersoll Lecture on
Immortality, 1898 for a lucid discussion)   Put bluntly, either consciousness is actually produced by brain activity and perishes with the
death of the brain; or it is in some sense filtered by the brain and need
not perish at death.

Some form of the latter theory is required in order to makes
sense of veridical out-of-the-body experiences in NDEs and certainly
for children who remember previous lives and other well attested
evidence for survival unless, in my view, one stretches the super-ESP
hypothesis beyond plausibility. Mark Woodhouse's 'energy monism'
(see his 'Paradigm Wars' 1996 and his piece in the next chapter) is
formulated in the light of this kind of evidence as well as that from
mystical states and may be the best theory we have so far.

Chapter 5
Philosophy and Values
for Living

Foreword
Max Payne, Editor

D uring the 25 years of its existence the central concern of
Network philosophy has been metaphysical prophecy. The
archives contain many eloquent denunciations of the limits
of reductionist materialism.   But the Network spirit is not best
encapsulated in negative criticism, however acute it might be. There
have been many attempts to erect detailed alternative metaphysical
systems, but the assumption that any one system can be the final
solution to God, the universe and everything goes against the grain of
the Network commitment to open self-critical inquiry. The most typical
direction of Network thought has been a demand for a fundamental
reconstruction of the basic paradigms of scientific knowledge. If a
new world-view is the answer, what is the problem? The problem is
that the current official scientific world view is dangerously incomplete.
Nearly 100 years ago science went through a massive paradigm shift.
Newtonian mechanics was replaced by Relativity and quantum physics.
This shift has still not been properly digested. We know that the laws
of science are something we impose on the universe in order to make
sense of it.   They are not the final prescriptive commands of God.
We know that physical reality is far wider than the thin slice of it
revealed by our five senses, but official science still presumes that there
is nothing in the dimensions of consciousness which might disturb
the bored thoughts of a sceptical professor on a Monday morning.
We have known for 70 years that the observer and the thing observed
are deeply intertwined at sub-atomic level. Yet there are plenty of hard
line materialists who presume that consciousness can be totally
explained away as the by product of brain activity. This assumption
involves interesting paradoxes once hard matter is translated down into
energies on a sub-atomic level, but few reductionists seem to give this

230

much consideration. Science is the creative product of scientific inquiry, and scientific inquiry is carried out by human beings. What then is the scientific picture of man? How did science itself come about? Looked at in terms of scientific knowledge a human being is just a thing, a nexus of physical forces. Looked at in terms of the actual process of scientific inquiry, man is a centre of creative consciousness. The problem is that official science gives the first answer and ignores the second. Sir Kelvin Spencer was one of the founder members of the Network, and the extract from his writings leads right into the centre of this question. Human experience is higher, wider and deeper than official science allows us to describe. We require new paradigms of understanding.

The triumphant advance of science and its attendant technology has led the late 20th century into a crisis which neither current science, nor 20th century culture can solve. We have probed the structure of the furthest galaxies, and the innermost energies of the atom. Unravelling the DNA molecule has given us the possibility of genetic engineering and a power over human life, which theology once reserved for God. We are able to lift humanity up to undreamed of heights of achievement or we can turn this planet into a lifeless desert. And by attempting the first, we could well achieve the second by mistake. The problem is, how shall we wield these terrible powers? What moral code or vision shall guide us? What restraints, if any, stand in our way of doing anything, including acts of planetary suicide? The rise of science has discredited or undermined all traditional religions and codes of social conduct. Scriptures that start with creation in a garden 6000 years ago or social codes evolved to meet the needs of the Victorian middle class no longer appear to be universally valid. The basic unit of moral currency is the value of an individual human being. But what is the picture of man in current orthodox science - a bundle of organic chemicals worth 50p after cremation, a selfish gene, a nexus of chemical and electrical signals in the brain, or an erratic super computer? Modern science is the most successful form of knowledge the human race has ever achieved, but its meaning seems to lead us to a black hole of total nihilism. As a way out of the abyss Henryk Skolimowski makes an eloquent plea for what he calls "life-enhancing knowledge" to be given an equal status to the objective knowledge of science.

What is wrong with scientific objectivity? Skolimowski suggests that in order to get accurate predictions of physical things, we exclude too much else from our experience on the way. Objectivity is too restrictive a grid. Both Richard Dixey and Ilya Prigogine suggest that scientific thought has put into itself into a straitjacket which is too tight even by its own standards. Whatever is ultimately there may not work according to the canons of strict causality which we find so convenient to apply to it. Energy does not have to be conceived of as always being in a closed system. The second law of thermodynamics is something we impose on nature in order to understand it. The universe itself may work differently. Science thought of in terms of non-causal and open systems becomes a much more liberating insight into nature than 19th century Newtonian mechanics carried over into the late 20th century.

According to Willis Harman current science can be categorised as "separateness science", and its ontological presuppositions are objectivism, positivism, and reductionism. These assumptions are reaching the end of their useful life, and have thrown up paradoxes they cannot handle, and anomalies they cannot go on ignoring. These include non-locality in particle physics, biological life, paranormal phenomena, and the obvious fact of "downward causation" where the mind affects the body as well as the reverse effect so beloved of reductionists. He proposes that the time has come to move on to a "wholeness science" which will include matter and mind in one holistic system.

If this is to be the case, then Western thought is due for a major paradigm shift. Mark Woodhouse lists the changes which may take place. He celebrates a new openness of thought which will take civilisation forward over the horizon. He prophesies that a new vision of science will have moral and social consequences. In a holistic vision everything fits together. A deeper and more open science means a greater concern for the environment , and greater moral responsibility towards the rest of mankind. It also means a wider and more ambitious vision of human development, and wider opportunities of personal fulfilment. It also could liberate technology to discover new benign sources of energy.

Richard Tarnas shares the same vision of a new holistic science The outward knowledge of the universe must be reconciled with our inward awareness of the self. However Tarnas raises a further question. If we demand that a paradigm shift must take place, how exactly do we know we are shifting in the right direction, when we do shift? He is not convinced by Kuhn's notion that paradigm shifts are incommensurable. He rejects the arguments of the extreme sceptics like Feyerabend who suggest that scientific laws are just dogmatic statements. Tarnas proposes that the basic assumptions of science are a condensation of the total wisdom of the age, and as our age is changing its cultural concepts, so inevitably our scientific paradigms will change as well.

Another founder member of the Network, George Blaker, gives a more personal witness to the problems of the modern scientific world view.. He points out what a wise reflection on the full experience of human living must demand. We must find meaning and purpose in our existence, and we have the right to ask whether or not our highest thoughts have an echo in the workings of the whole cosmos. He recounts individual testimony to paranormal experiences which demonstrate that human consciousness can be independent of the body. Professional philosophers tend to fight shy of quoting personal experience in support of their metaphysical ideas, but then that may account for the sterile irrelevance of most academic philosophy. In requiring an understanding which goes beyond the conventional framework of scientific and religious belief, George Blaker is demanding that we go beyond intellectual theory and seek total wisdom.

The final extract is from another founder member of the Network, D.M.A. Leggett, (always known to his friends as Peter). This is an optimistic survey of the direction in which Network thought is pointing. If all things can be seen to fit together into one holistic system, then the result is a vision of cosmic interconnectedness. The cells of the body, the atoms that compose them, the individual person, the whole human race, the planet, the cosmos are all one of another in one skein of mutual responsibility. If we liberate our view of consciousness from narrow materialism, then existence has a spiritual dimension, and the question of life before birth and after death becomes a real issue. The result is a profoundly spiritual vision that is quite independent of the authority of any particular religious system.

"My Last Words".

Sir Kelvin Spencer

I've pondered much on how to respond to the invitation to imagine that I am now writing my last words on Earth   that I am trying to state what in my old age I consider worth passing on as a testimony to the world and to the future. To do this, as instructed, in not more than about 1,000 words is a challenging compression.

Schopenhauer is recorded as saying: "Were an Asiatic to ask me for a definition of Europe, I should be forced to answer him: it is a part of the world which is haunted by the incredible illusion that man was created out of nothing and that his present birth is his first entrance into life". It is still a fact that most people think we first came into existence at birth and decisively end at death. Most such folk, though, would soon get tangled up if pressed to define what they meant by "we", that is, by the essential "I" of each and every one of us.

Looking back some eighty years to my first stirrings of thoughtfulness, I can remember no time when I thought as Schopenhauer alleges most Europeans do. Up to my early teens I deferred to the conventions absorbed from my parents and others, and so kept quiet about my embryo thoughts on what and where I was before birth. Then, when aged fifteen, I took the London Matric examination. One of the questions in the English paper was to paraphrase Wordsworth's famous stanza:-

> Our birth is but a sleep and a forgetting:
> The Soul that rises with us, our life's Star,
> Hath had elsewhere its setting,
> And cometh from afar:
> Not in entire forgetfulness,

And not in utter nakedness,
But trailing clouds of glory do we come From God, who is our home

I still remember vividly my shock and surprise at finding expressed in words, and expressed so clearly, what my fumbling thoughts had long been trying to bring into coherence. And the lines in that stanza that follow struck home indeed. For some while I'd been vaguely feeling the shades of the prison house descending on me. What hitherto in my childish experiences had been alight with the glory and the freshness of a dream was, alas, fading into the light of common day. But that prison house has never closed completely. I admit that during much of my professional life it became ever more difficult to glimpse the glory and the freshness of this fairyland of Earth. But now, when the hurly burly of my noisy years is past I'm understanding better what that same poet elsewhere expressed – his

.... sense sublime
Of something far more deeply interfused,
Whose dwelling is the light of setting suns,
And the round ocean and the living air,
And the blue sky, and in the mind of man:
A motion and a spirit, that impels
All thinking things, all objects of all thought,
And rolls through all things.

That 'spirit that impels all thinking things , all objects of all thought , and rolls through all things" is, I think, the nearest we mortals can get to a worthy conception of God. But that word God has been used in to many contexts and stands for such vastly different concepts, that I like to avoid using it. Instead I think of "Cosmic Consciousness", by which I intend to capture a concept that has been given many other names. Among these are: an all-pervading spirit; immanent spirituality; the 'Will' of Schopenhauer; other-worldly Grades of Significance; transcendence; the scriptural 'Many Mansions'; and the Nirvana of Eastern religions. It is what, perhaps, contemporary physics might be coaxed into recognising if referred to in some such jargon as an 'all-pervading field of spirituality'. For at the heart of contemporary theoretical physics is the concept of immaterial fields (gravity, the electro-magnetic spectrum, and the strong and weak fields within the atom). So it should not be too difficult for physics to take a leap forward and postulate a spiritual field. A strong argument for doing so is that it holds promise of giving a basis for a theory on which to hang the many happenings that don't fit into the contemporary scientific paradigm and so are often ignored, denied or derided. Such a theory would meet the principle of Occam's Razor* better than any other I've heard of.

The "testimony to the world and to the future" I'm invited to set down can (inadequately) be summarised as follows.
We should all strive –

(i)   to realise how imprisoned we are in the naive philosophy that accepts as the only reality the sensory world of everyday life;

(ii)   to widen our awareness to that we recognise that far more enters into our consciousness and subconsciousness than what comes from sensory signals;

(iii)   to encourage the acceptance by the scientific establishment of the paranormal as a respectable field of research endeavour;

(iv)   to coax such scientists as respond to (iii) to realise that dramatic manifestations of paranormal happenings (precognition, psychokinesis, unorthodox healing, clairvoyance, etc.,) are but steps to knowledge of something far more deeply interfused;

(v)   to reawaken knowledge now nearly lost in the West that man is a spiritual entity which is temporarily incarnate in a transient physical body;

(vi)   to seek a philosophy by which to live arising out of the above summarised lines of thought which restores to earthly life meaning and purpose, these having been nearly smothered during the last three centuries by the disastrous and unbelievable philosophy of scientific materialism.

* *Occam's Razor* states that theories should be devised so that entities are not needlessly multiplied, i.e. the principle of parsimony of hypotheses. The learned like to quote the original latin: Entia non sunt multiplicanda.

The ideas I've tried to convey in the above six clauses will, I expect, be unintelligible to many and dismissed as the ravings of an untutored pseudo-philosopher pontificating about things he doesn't understand. Well, I make no claim to 'understand'. I go no further than to hope that the thoughts of those who are becoming disillusioned by scientific materialism may find hints, ill-expressed as they certainly are, which they will ponder over and, maybe, develop. I recognise my immaturity in these fields of thought; recognise, too, how difficult it is to give expression to them while avoiding mere emotional verbosity on the one hand and on the other religious language that would antagonise many. For what to me is religion is a far cry from theological dogmas that are often accepted as the essence of religion and, because they don't fit today's thoughts and knowledge, are dismissed by many along with everything tainted or seemingly tainted with such religion.

We are living in an age of increasing turmoil and upheaval when nearly all things that people have regarded as sacred, sacrosanct and stable, are being destroyed. Reacting to this situation by pessimism is sterile, and unworthy of man's heritage. My hope is that a philosophy of living can and will be fashioned by speculating along the lines I've tried to sketch. If sufficient people can be weaned from scientific materialism to a more worthy philosophy, there is some chance that the transition now upon us from industrial civilization to whatever kind of civilization may come after it - that such transition will come about with less agonising travail than at present seems likely.

Examining Values and The Wall Of Science

Professor Henryk Skolimowski

Unexamined life is not worth living. Unexamined values are not worth having. As we examine life and values together, we invariably stumble over the wall of science which appears so huge to us, so impenetrable, almost made of concrete. We have been so often told that science and its world view – this big wall – have nothing to do with values. If we want to entertain some values (so we were told), we may do so, but very quietly and privately. Thus in intimate corners of our private universe, we have been struggling with values. We have been asking such questions as "What to do with ethics? What to do with science? What to do with ourselves?

Yet this is the picture of the past. The big wall of science has crumbled. However something else has remained. The picture of the physical world as described by classical science is gone. The knowledge through which this picture was erected and maintained somehow stays on. Cognitive claims of science, of whatever science and however flimsy they are, are still regarded as superior to value judgements. The old mentality of science and its ethos still prevail; and also its ethics. The ethos of science and its ethics exert a great deal of influence over our minds. I shall explain in some detail what I mean by the ethics of science as we go along.

Let me start by asserting that we have not perceived so far, or at least not sufficiently, that behind what we consider to be the architecture of science, there exists an invisible scaffolding – its normative structure, or simply its ethics. We have accepted that the edifice of the world as described by science has crumbled. We have not perceived so far that something else has crumbled. The ethical system embedded in and underlying classical science and the world view that follows from it. Thus I am arguing that the collapse of its underlying cognitive structure and of its underlhing *ethical structure.*

I am going to propose that this ethical structure is the *form* underlying the ethos of the edifice. This ethos has been guiding scientists and the pursuit of science for the last three centuries. Taking the clues from ancient philosophy, I wish to propose an Aristotelian view of this form. Aristotle claimed that a substance of an object and its form are a unity. Once you break a jar, you have broken ts underlying form. This is in contrast to the Platonic position which argues that even if you break a jar, the underlying form persists because it is imperishable.

Let me observe that most philosophers, and especially scientists, are Platonists in respect to the point I have raised. They think that we may give up the edifice of the world as constructed by science and yet retain its scaffoldings, its language, its underlying cognitive structure –

with its specific criteria of validity and its hidden ethics. This to me is a mistake. Of stupendous proportions.

We treat scientific knowledge on its face value. It tell us it is value free. We believe it. It tells us that its cognitive claims are value free and furthermore that these claims are superior to values. We believe it to be som. But is it not so. Scientific knowledge is a system of values. It is based on a core of values. It perpetuates distinctive values. Cognitive claims of physical knowledge are laced with values. These claims (and the rationality underlying them) tell us "You should approach the world objectively;" "You should be rational in your approach:" (while this rationality is fashioned by science itself); "You should rely only on physical facts and reject all non-physical phenomena." And to these "You should not accept value judgements...... " while underneath, in an invisible ink, it is written "....except the value judgments which the physicalist paradigm proclaims."

We need to see it clearly that the demise of the external edifice the physical picture of the world which science had erected; and this means its underlying form, its cognitive criteria of validity; and yet – its ethics. We must clearly see the ethical plight of science. Its bold assumption – which was for far too long unexamined – was that you only need to describe the world physically. And somehow, through this description, we can create a sustainable human world. This has led to disastrous human, social and ecological consequences.

Let me express my main thesis: *cognitive strictures of science regarding human values and the normative underpinning of human lives do not have any validity any more.*

This statement immediately frees us to develop new knowledge and new ethics Our main criterion for both should be whether and to what extent it is life-enhancing, for both human life and non-human life; whether it contributes to harmony and avoids destruction, whether it contributes to the noy of life and to further self-realisation. I am aware that these are value judgements. These are new life-enhancing value judgements. And nobody from the old cognitive/empiricist paradigm should tell us that we should not make them.

Thus instead of the old ethics: it is a physical fact, a physical theory, a physical structure, a physical description, therefore it is good

239

(for such has been the unwritten ethical imperative of science); we are now asserting; it is a structure, a theory, a form of human behaviour which contributes to the fullness and blossoming of life (its life-enhancing) therefore it is good.

The difficulties in accepting this new perspective may be considerable but they are a trifle in comparison with the agony which we have experienced while trying to live with the unviable and unsustainable paradigm of knowledge/values which we have evolved in the post-Renaissance times. Once we accept that together with the broken jar the form of the jar is broken; once we understand that the assertion "cognitive claims are superior to normative judgements" is itself a *value judgement* and an expression of the intellectual tyranny, then the door to liberation is open. What I am proposing is a liberation of ethics from the cognitive grid of science, which claims to be value-neutral, while it perpetuates distinctive empiricist values of the materialist world view.

Let me draw two final conclusions. I suggest that there is no such thing as knowledge independent of and neutral with regard to values. Physical knowledge (classical science) has operated through its distinctive values through which it has attempted to suppress (with a great success as a matter of fact) other values. With the end of the physicalist paradigm, this form of ethical tyranny comes to an end.

And the final point. Every cosmology contains both ontology and its corresponding ethics. We have thought for a while that it was different with modernistic cosmology, and that it was a structure without an ethics built into it. This is simply not true. The hidden ethics of mechanistic cosmology has been a poisonous chalice which has poisoned the whole civilisation. A holistic reverential cosmology and its corresponding life-enhancing ethics are an imperative of our times and of the approaching Third Millennium.

Professor Henryk Skolimowski has been professor of philosophy in a number of universities and is author of many books including 'Living Philosophy' and 'The Participatory Mind'.

Science and Meaning

Richard Dixey

The important question is this: How is it that the role of intention and will in causation - which was perfectly clear to Socrates - seems so novel to Western science? Might there be reasons other than scientific ones involved in the issue of causation? The answer is yes, for since causes are prior to evidence, the ideas that go into the creation of causal models am as vulnerable to social and cultural influence as any other part of life. Perhaps through understanding the context in which causal concepts were formulated we might get a clearer idea of the implications involved. This seems to me to be yet another area where the Institute's Causality Project can find a fruitful area of inquiry. It would be useful to have net only a history of scientific explanations, but also an understanding of the social and other issues that have impact on the scientists of the day, as they have on all of us.

For example, Western science originated in a period of crisis, and is characterized by a wholesale rejection of naturalism - the idea that the natural order itself is meaningful. Through a series of historical developments the figures of the sixteenth and seventeenth centuries, notably Galileo, Descartes, Bacon and Newton, created a science of nature which dealt only in mathematically analyzable objects. That science explicitly denied the existence of the richness and complexity of the natural world, claiming it was merely an illusion created by the senses.

Before then, for Aristotle, and indeed for the medieval scholastics, the ultimate cause of a thing was not so much what made it in terms of its physical structure, but rather its purpose, the final cause. This was explicitly rejected in the seventeenth century by a series of arguments which have no philosophical validity but are possible to analyze in terms of the historical situation of the day. Indeed, the idea that the perceived world is something quite different from what we actually see makes the possibility of any knowledge of it a profound problem, and this "problem of knowledge" has obsessed philosophy ever since.

This type of historical approach has tremendous importance. It reveals Western science as a deeply Christian science originating from the notion that one should preserve Church authority from the attack of naturalism. In the skeptical reaction that followed the Counter Reformation at the end of the sixteenth century, the authority of the Church was under attack from all sides. For hew can the unique meaning of the communion be preserved if nature itself is a source of meaning and authority? And this was precisely what was occurring in the Neo-Platonic revival and scholastic materialism of the late sixteenth century. In the time of John Dee, Robert Fludd and Giordano Bruno natural magic and occultism were rife and the appeal of a scientific model that confined all meaning to the preserve of the mind and banished it altogether from Nature was not without its adherents in both the Church as well as the laity. The outer world was by definition meaningless to these people because all meaning came from the inner world - the world of Christendom or whatever religious belief one happened to have. This is the historical root of modern science.

The secure and stable world of the medieval, where man stood at the centre of his world, and indeed the world itself was seen as ultimately serving him and his Creator, was thrown away for an altogether more sinister conception of Nature - a world devoid of meaning, colour, taste and beauty, and ultimately in our modern times seen as created by chance. As Alexander Koyre, a famous Newtonian scholar, put it, "In solving the puzzle of the universe,Modern Man replaced it with another enigma - the enigma of himself."

So what do we do now as inheritors of that? We live in a purled where the authority of the Church is in decline, yet we have inherited a science, and indeed a view of Nature, which relies on the moral authority of the inner life to make it meaningful at all. Bet we have lost the moral sense that the originators may have had which made sense of the split between mind and body, humankind and nature, the perceiver and the perceived, subject and object. We have inherited the philosophy and the methodology of that split and, I believe, an appalling moral vacuum is the result. We now have the tragic situation in which science cannot be put to solely useful use. It must be used willy-nilly. If you discover the ultimate bomb, you've got to make it. You may discover the bomb through the reductionistic analysis of nature, but you cannot reduce the theory of not using the bomb. You cannot do that, so consequently you make the bomb.

There is almost no way we can get more out of control. And this seems to me to be the causality issue writ large - that science has become, if you like, acausal at the human level. It has ceased to relate to any reality we might experience.

Dr. Richard Dixey is a philosopher of science and chairman of Phytopharm

A (very) Brief History of Certainty

Ilya Prigogine

The title refers, of course, to Stephen Hawking's well-known (1988) book, *A Brief History of Time*. There Hawking concludes that we are close to the moment when we shall read the mind of God, close to the end of science. Once the 'complete theory' of the universe is discovered, the only remaining question would be 'why it is that we and the universe exist. If we find the answer to that, it would be the ultimate triumph of human reason.' Then we would know the mind of God.
Hawking's conclusion reflects the traditional view of what should be the ultimate goal of physics. Already, three centuries ago, W. Leibniz, one of the founders of modern science, wrote that if we knew the 'full causes' and 'entire' effect, our knowledge would become comparable with God's knowledge of the world He created. The idea of a final theory - 'a theory of everything' is quite alive today, as testified by two recent books, *Dreams of a Final Theory* by Steven Weinberg and *The God Particle* by Leon Lederman.

It is indeed a grandiose program. Again, to quote Leibniz, 'In the least of substances, eyes as piercing as those of God could read the whole course of the universe'. There would be no distinction between past present and future; we would share the certitude of God.

No doubt the claim to certainty has been at the basis of the conviction that science expresses rationality at the highest level and that progress in social and political sciences should be linked to the application of scientific laws to society; however there is today a growing doubt about the ideology of science. In his book *The Closing of the American Mind* [the late] Allan Bloom wrote: 'The idea of culture was established in an attempt to find the dignity of man within the context of modern science. That science was materialistic, hence reductionist and deterministic'.

None of these qualifications applies to the present situation in science, but before coming to this point let us put the idea of certainty into its historical perspective. In his most interesting 1990 book *Cosmopolis,* Stephen Toulmin points out the tragedy of the 17th Century, the religious wars, the political in stability. It was in the midst of this difficult situation that Rene' Descartes formulated his quest for certainty, a certainty that all humans, independently of their religion, could share. A quest for certainty in philosophy is based in his famous *'cogito '*as well as in science based on mathematical proofs. Descartes' programme proved to be immensely successful. It influenced Leibniz's concept of 'laws of nature'. It found its concrete realization in Newton's work, which has been the model for physics for more than three centuries...

For Einstein, also, science was a way to go beyond the turmoil of everyday existence. He compared scientific activity to the longing that irresistibly pulls the town-dweller away from his noisy, cramped quarters and toward the silent, high mountains'. For him, also, certainty was the supreme ideal of science. Everyone knows his saying 'God does not play dice'.

The idea of certainty, when seen in its historical perspective, is associated with a denial of time and novelty and therefore leads to a pessimistic outlook, which ultimately leads to alienation. It is often stated that science is neutral; this seems to me only partly true. How can science be neutral when it deals with our very position in nature? This feeling of alienation has not only been expressed by critics of science, philosophers and theologians, but we find it also in Weinberg's oft-quoted remark, 'The more the universe seems comprehensible, the more it seems pointless'.Indeed, the ideal of certainty forces us to give up the notion of events and eliminates novelty and creativity, with out which our own lives would indeed be pointless. The denial of time makes us foreigners in the world we try to describe. The logical consequence is dualism. According to Descartes we have on one side matter viewed as pure extension following deterministic laws, on the other side intellectual activity radically separated from matter.

In *The Emperor's New Mind* (1989), Roger Penrose wrote, It is our present lack of understanding of the fundamental laws of physics that prevents us from coming to grips with the concept of "mind" in physical or logical terms'. I think that Penrose is right. We need a reappraisal of what we mean by the 'fundamental laws of physics'.

This reappraisal is already starting. While president of the International Union of Theoretical and Applied Mechanics, Sir James Lighthill wrote in 1986 in the *Proceedings of the Royal Society:* 'We are all deeply conscious today that the enthusiasm of our forebears for the marvellous achievement of Newtonian mechanics led them to make generalizations in this area of predictability that ... we now recognize are false. We collectively want to apologize ... for spreading ideas about determinism that after 1960 were to be proven incorrect'.

This is a quite unusual confession. Here, certainty, which for three centuries appeared as the key symbol of scientific intelligibility, is put into question. Lighthill refers to what is known as the theory of 'chaos', started by Henri Poincare' at the end of the 19th Century. There can be no possibility in the framework of this short article to explain chaos. Innumerable books and articles are readily available. Chaos has many aspects, some of which we are only beginning to understand. However, I want to make a remark that arises from recent work by my groups in Austin and Brussels.

That is that chaos changes the formulation of the laws of physics. Instead of expressing certitudes, they express possibilities. At its start, the universe was like a newborn child who can become a lawyer, an astronaut or an architect - but not all at the same time. As W. Thirring has written: 'Our formulation of the laws of nature cannot contradict experience, otherwise they should be modified, but they will be far from determining everything. As the universe evolves, the circumstances create new laws'.

Giving up the ideal of certainty may appear to be a defeat of human reason. I don't believe so. Once we replace the deterministic description with a description involving probability, we can introduce the arrow of time into our basic equations. We begin, then, to be able to describe an evolutionary universe in agreement with our present picture in which evolution plays an essential role on all levels of description, from cosmology to human history...

In his 1991 book *The Passion of the Western Mind,* Richard Tarnas wrote that 'the deepest passion of the western world is to reunite with the ground of its being'. We need a science whose progress marks the solidarity of men with the world it describes.

The future is uncertain; this is true for the nature we describe and this is true on the level of our own existence. But this uncertainty is at the very heart of human creativity. Time becomes 'construction' and creativity a way to participate in this construction.

Prof. Vicomte Ilya Prigogine is Director of the Solvay Institutes in Brussels and has been awarded the Nobel Prize for Chemistry in 1977.

The Issue Before Us: Reassessment of the Metaphysical Foundations of Modern Science

Willis Harman

Michael Friedjung's paper "Modern Physics and the Nature of the World" (April 1991 Network Newsletter) exemplifies that we are still trying to patch up modern science to somehow become adequate to handling the areas of concern to the Network. I believe it to be true that this can't be done - even with quantum physics, holographic mind metaphors, chaos theory, and all such trimmings. To achieve clarity we have to get to the heart of the matter -to the metaphysical foundations considered inviolate throughout the history of modern science.

I enclose two versions of yet another attempt to make this clear - a longer one and an abbreviated one. It seems to me that if we could get the question of the metaphysical foundations accepted as a valid and important question (which it is not at present), this might do more than any one thing to further the cause of the Network.

In your own work, you urge a "new science" in the form of a "complementary" science. It seems to me this may be a tactical way-station, but in the end a truly holistic science must be an "extended" science, with conventional science as a limited special case. However that is a secondary point; the main thing is to get the question legitimated.

A recent cartoon shows a woman driver attempting to deal with a police officer who has accosted her for driving the wrong way down a one-way street. "Officer," she says, "did it ever occur to you that maybe the sign is wrong?"

The scientific and medical communities have given a rather unfriendly reception to research in psi phenomena, dissociative states, altered states of consciousness, extraordinary healings, and other areas related to consciousness in some of its non-normal forms. This has been mainly because the meaning and significance people tended to attach to these experiences seemed to clash so directly with prevailing assumptions about the nature of scientific reality. But perhaps it is our "official" concept of reality that is wrong.

The Broader Challenge to the Worldview of Modern Science

But it has not only been peoples other-states-of-consciousness and paranormal experiences that challenge the worldview of modern science. Among the areas where there are major failures of the prevailing scientific worldview to accommodate well substantiated evidence are the following:

> 1   The fundamental inquiry within physics into the **ultimate nature of things** does not appear to be convergent. The search for more fundamental particles seems to lead to still more fundamental particles; the search for the ultimate reductionist explanations seems to point to a wholeness. It is a fundamental initial assumption of physics, which has influenced every other area of science, that ultimate reality consists of fundamental particles, separate from one another interacting through mechanisms (especially fields) which can be discovered and specified. But with Bell's theorem, quantum physics now displays an inherent

contradiction; particles originally assumed separate turn out, apparently, to be connected.

2   There appears to he evidence for a fundamental **self-organising force in living systems**, from the smallest to the largest conceivable organisms, which remains unexplained by physical principles. Living systems exhibit a tendency toward self-organisation (eg homeostasis; intricate patterns in flowers, butterfly wings, etc); toward preservation of integrity (eg healing and regeneration; ontogenesis from a single fertilised egg to an adult organism); toward survival of the organism and the species (eg complex instinctual patterns for protection and reproduction). The evidences of a cumulative effect, over time, of this self-organising tendency in evolution cast doubt on the adequacy of the neo-Darwinist orthodoxy.

3   There is a persistent puzzle of "action at a distance" or **non-local causality**. This shows up, as we have already observed, in the far reaches of quantum physics. It also appears in the area which John Beloff calls **"meaningful coincidences" (1977)**, referring to two or more events where there appears to be a meaningful connection although there is no physical connection.   Here "meaningful" may refer either to the subjective judgement of the observer, or to a judgement based in historical data (as in the case of astrology or the I Ching). The term "meaningful coincidences" includes Carl Jung's "synchronicity" (Peat, 1987) and the most of the range of the "paranormal." Examples include apparently "telepathic" communication, seemingly clairvoyant "remote viewing," and the "coincidence" between the act of prayer and the occurrence of the prayed-for, such as healing. Another example is the feeling if having a "guardian angel" when a person feels warned about a danger, or provided with a particularly fortuitous circumstance in life. A host of historical and anecdotal examples fall into the categories of "miracles" and psi phenomena".

4 Our scientific knowledge about the universe appears to be incomplete in that there is no place in it for the **consciousness of the observer** - nor in general, for **volition** ("free will") or any of the other attributes of consciousness,. Nobel laureate Roger Sperry (1987) insists that no science can be complete that does not include "downward causation", from the higher level of consciousness to the lower, physico-chemical level.

5   One of the most challenging aspects of the consciousness puzzle is **the concept of the self**. The conscious self is ineluctably involved in observation; yet the science constructed from those observations contains no place for the self. Psychologist Gordon Allport wrote in 1955, in a little volume entitled *Becoming,* "For two generations, psychologists have tried every conceivable way of accounting for the integration, organisation and striving of the human person without having recourse to the postulate of a self." The battle is still going on.

6   Related, but worthy of separate mention is the area of **altered states of consciousness**, including particularly those states traditionally sought out in a spiritual or mystical context.

Reviewing the Nature of Scientific Inquiry

To understand what it means for science to be presented with such a broad challenge we need to review some basic aspects of scientific inquiry.

Quine's "theoretical network" argument. W.V.O Quine, a major figure in recent philosophy of science, argued (1962) that the scientific explanation for any phenomenon is embedded in a theoretical network which involves multitudinous assumptions, including:

assumptions involved in "observations" of the phenomenon;

hypotheses about the context of the phenomenon;

underlying theoretical hypotheses;

"basic laws" of the pertinent area of science;

the accepted nature of scientific methodology;

epistemological assumptions underlying scientific inquiry;

ontological assumptions about the basic nature of reality

When there is an "anomaly", or a failure of observations to conform to scientific expectations, it means that *somewhere* in that network there is a falsity. There is no way to tell just where in the theoretical network the falsity lies. Thus in the face of an anomaly, we must consider revising any or all elements of the network - including, possibly, basic metaphysical assumptions.

When experience contradicts science, the science must be changed, but there is no infallible logic for determining exactly what to change in one's theory. We must, says Quine, give up any idea that we can use experience *either to confirm or to falsify* particular scientific hypotheses. A consequence of Quine's view is that even our epistemological convictions about how we acquire knowledge, and about the nature of explanation, justification, and confirmation, are subject to revision and correction.

It is precisely to that point which present-day scientific paradoxes seem to have brought us. Most scientists today would assert that science has moved away from the strict determinism, reductionism, positivism, and bebaviourism of a half century ago. But it remains to be discerned what scientists are moving *toward*.

The Metaphysical Foundations of Modern Science.

Modern science is based on the metaphysical foundations of logical empiricism. The most important of these assumptions can be summarised as:

> *Objectivism:* the assumption of an objective world which the observer can hold at a distance and study separately from himself;
>
> *Positivism:* the assumption that the real world is what is physically measurable;
>
> *Reductionism:* the assumption that we come to really understand a phenomenon through studying the behaviour of its elemental parts (eg fundamental particles).

To be sure, these underlying assumptions have been modified with the advent of quantum physics, particularly by the indeterminacy principle and the inherent statistical nature of measurement of the very small. What we want to suggest here is the possibility of an even more fundamental change - change at the level of underlying ontological and epistemological assumptions.

Underlying the above (modified) classical assumptions is *an ontological assumption* of separateness - separability of observer from observed, of man from nature, of mind from matter, of science from religion; ultimate explanations in terms of interactions between separate "fundamental particles" - and an *epistemological assumption* that our sole empirical basis for constructing a science is the data from our physical senses.

Scientists typically take these ontological and epistemological assumptions to be inviolate, to be an inherent and ineluctable part of the definition of science. But it is precisely here that we are likely to find the resolution of some of the most fundamental puzzles in science.

Toward a More Holistic Science

There is increasingly widespread agreement that science must somehow develop the ability to look at things more holistically. The "separateness" assumption that underlies modern science is in a way an artifact of the history of Western civilisation. In a more holistic view, where everything, including physical and mental, is connected to everything, a change in any part affects the whole. The familiar concepts of scientific causation apply only when a part of the whole can be sufficiently isolated from the rest that reductionistic causes appear to describe adequately why things behave as they do. In general, *"causes" are limited explanations that depend upon context.* In completely holistic view there are not "cause" and "effect", only a whole system evolving.

Thus, "wholeness science" is naturally concerned with "downward causation" (Campbell, 1974; Sperry, 1987) as well as the reductionistic "upward causation" which presently dominates the scientific world. The presence of teleological factors in the biological realm presents no problem, once there is releasing of the insistence that biology be reducible to physics and chemistry. We observe teleology in ourselves; why not, then in the larger system of which we are a part?

The mistake of modern society has been to assume that ultimately, reductionistic "scientific" causes should explain everything. One should not expect reductionistic science to comprise an adequate worldview. The context of reductionistic science is the desire to gain control through manipulation of physical environment. Within that context its description of "causes" works amazingly well. Our problems arise when we change the context and attempt to elevate that kind of science to the level of a worldview. That is when we generate conflicts like "free will versus determinism" and "science versus religion."

The "wholeness science needed to deal more adequately with consciousness related phenomena would be based on (a) *an ontological assumption of oneness, wholeness,* interconnectedness of everything, and (b) *an epistemological assumption that we contact reality in not one, but two ways.* One of these is through physical sense data - which form the basis of normal science. The other is through being ourselves part of the oneness - through deep intuitive "inner knowing". In other words, our encountering of reality comprises an *objective* aspect - being aware of, and giving meaning to, the messages from our physical senses - and a *subjective* aspect in an intuitive, aesthetic, spiritual, noetic and mystical sense. (It should not escape our notice that an intuitive and aesthetic factor already enters into normal science in various ways - for example, the aesthetic factor already enters into normal science in various ways - for example, the aesthetic principle of "elegance"; the "principle of parsimony" in choosing between alternative explanations).

Once we recognise the non-necessity of the separateness assumption, there is no reason to assume the biological and cognitive sciences can be reduced to the physical sciences (materialistic, reductionistic, deterministic), let alone to physics. The biological sciences involve more holistic concepts (eg organism, function of an organ) which have no counterparts at the physical sciences level. Similarly, there is no reason to assume that the characteristics of consciousness are reducible to biology. In other words, while theory reduction (as, for example, the laws of optics explained through electromagnetic theory) will be welcomed whenever it proves to be possible, it is not a dogma of "extended" science that it must be, in general, possible.

Starting from the holistic assumption, there is no separation of observer from observed. "Action at a distance" does not pose a particular problem. Volition, other states of consciousness, teleological influences, "meaningful coincidences," etc are not "anomalous". Neither do consciousness, and the concept of the self, present any fundamental problem to the extended science.

To re-emphasise the point, within "extended" or "wholeness" science none of present "hard" science is invalidated in the limited domains where it was generated. Certain aspects of the unity that is the Whole will continue to be quite profitably studied by means of "separateness science". That kind of science, however, would - as only part of a more extended science - no longer have the authority to insist that we are here, solely through random causes, in a meaningless universe; more that our consciousness is "merely" the chemical and physical processes of the brain.

"Wholeness science would include and emphasise more participative kinds of methodologies; it would assume that, whereas we learn certain kinds of things by distancing ourselves from the subject studied, we get another kind of knowledge from intuitively "becoming one with" the subject. In the latter case, the experience of observing brings about sensitisation and other changes in the observer. Thus a willingness to be transformed himself or herself is an essential characteristic of the participatory scientist. The anthropologist who would see clearly a culture other than her own must allow that experience to change her so that the new culture is seen through new eyes, not eyes conditioned by her own culture. The psychotherapist who would see clearly his client must have worked through his own neuroses that would otherwise warp perception. The social scientist who would use a participative approach to understanding and guiding organisational arrangements and processes wilt almost certainly he changed through his/her involvement. The scientist who would study meditative processes and those "other states of consciousness" so treasured in the various spiritual traditions has to be wilting to go through the deep changes that will make him or her a competent observer.

Comparison of Two Sciences.

The sort of "wholeness science" being described is summarised in the table below. I believe that the time is ripe to insist on a re-examination of the metaphysical foundations of modern science. Until this is done, research on consciousness-related phenomena will continue to miss the mark because it will continue to be distorted by the misguided attempt to fit it into a basically reductionistic and positivistic framework.

Assumptions, Corollaries and Characteristics of Two Sciences: A Comparison

Separateness Science

1.   Basic ontological assumption:
The universe is made up, ultimately of fundamental particles and quanta which are separate from one another except insofar as there are specifiable connections (such as fields).

2   A scientific explanation of a phenomenon   (understanding of causes in a scientific sense) consists in relating the phenomenon to more general and fundamental relations or "scientific laws." The ultimate scientific explanation would be in terms of the motions and interactions of the fundamental particles and quanta involved. (This desideratum is approached, for example, in thermodynamics or physical optics).

3   All scientific knowledge is ultimately based on data obtained through the physical senses. Such information is, then, ultimately quantifiable.
4. The truest information about the objective reality is obtained through the observer being as detached as possible. There is an ultimate limit to objectivity, in that there is inevitably some "observer effect" in any observation.

5   The universe is scientifically understood   to   be   ultimately deterministic.

6   The material universe evolved to its present state from the "Big Bang" by random physical process and, after the advent of life, mutation and natural selection. Consciousness (whatever it is) is a product of material evolution.

7   There is no evidence for mysterious "drives" or "purposes in evolution.   What appears as a "survival instinct" is merely the result of natural selection; any organisms that did nor have such drive were selected out. There is no scientific evidence for anything in the universe resembling "purpose" or "design". The   biological   sciences   use teleological language for convenience, but what it really' means is that those structures and behaviours that contribute to survival survived.

8   The wide range of more-or-less commonly experienced coincidences" (including the great preponderance of so-called "anomalous" phenomena)- where two or more events appear to be meaningfully connected, but there is no discernible physical connection -must ultimately be shown either to have a physical connection or to be, in fact, merely coincidence.

9   Non-normal states of consciousness, dissociation, etc are phenomena to be studied largely in the context of the pathological, in terms of their effects on behaviourr.

10   The explanations of ontogenesis, morphogenesis, regeneration, and related biological phenomena are to be sought in terms of coded "instructions" in the genes and similar mechanisms.

Wholeness Science

1   Basic ontological assumption:
The universe is basically a single whole within which every part is connected to every other part. The wholeness   includes   every   aspect accessible to human awareness - the physical world as discerned through our physical senses, and all the contents of consciousness.

2   Pragmatically useful scientific explanations enhanc understandings of phenomena by relating them to other phenomena and
relationships. Since things are so interconnected that a change in any
one can affect all, then any accounting for cause is within a specific
context, for a specific purpose. The search for ultimate reductionistic
cause is futile; they are not cause and effect, but rather than the evolution
of a whole system. Order is observed in the physical world, but it is
never free from the possibility of "downwardcausation"   (from
consciousness "down" to the physical).

3   Reality is contacted basically in two ways. One is through physical
sense data. The other is inner, through being ourselves part of the
oneness - through a deep intuitive "inner knowing". Our encountering
of reality is not limited to being aware of, and giving meaning to, the
messages from our physical senses (sometimes referred to as "objective"),
but includes also a subjective aspect in an intuitive, aesthetic spiritual,
noetic and mystical sense).

4   Understanding comes, not from being detached, objective,
analytical, coldly clinical, but rather from identifying with the observed,
becoming one with it. (This is not to deny the usefulness of objective
knowledge, but only the recognition that it leads to a partial
understanding).

5   The concept of a completely deterministic universe (even in a
statistical sense, as in quantum physics) stems from the "separateness"
assumption there is no reason to expect it to be borne out in
experience

6   There is no a priori reason to assume that "scientific laws" are
invariant; rather, it seems more plausible that they, too, are evolving
Hence extrapolation to the "Big Bang" may he suspect. Evidence
seems to point to consciousness either evolving along with, or being
prior to, the material world.

7   Since we humans are part of the whole, and experience "drives" or
"urges" such as survival, belongingness, achievement, and self-
actualisation, there is no a priori justification for assuming these are
not characteristics of the whole. Similarly, since we experience purpose
and "values", there is no valid justification for assuming these are not

also characteristics of the whole. In other words, the universe may be genuinely, not just apparently, telic.

8   "Meaningful coincidences" are not to be explained, but rather apparent separateness.   In other words, the question is not "How can we explain apparent telepathic communication?" but rather, "How can we explain why our minds are not cluttered by all that information in other minds?" Not "How can we explain apparent psychokinetic phenomena?" but rather, "How should we best understand why our minds have such a limited effect in the physical world?"

9   The entire spectrum of states of consciousness are of interest. These include "religious experiences"; experiences of "mystical" states of consciousness, of "other dimensions of reality." These experiences have been at the heart of all cultures, including our own. They have been among the main sources of the deepest value commitments; they may be an important investigative tool, a "window" to other dimensions of reality.

10   The ultimate explanations of ontogenesis, morphogensis, regeneration, and related biological phenomena will probably turn out to have to include something in consciousness analogous to "image" or "idea".

Prof. Willis Harman was President of the Institute of Noetic Sciences and a Vice-President of the Network.

References

Campbell, Donald T. (1974), "'Downward Causation' in Hierarchically Organised Biological Systems," *Studies in the Philosophy of Biology*, eds. F. Ayala & T.
Dobzhansky. Berkeley: University of California Press.

Quine, W.V.O. (1962), *From a Logical Point of View* (2nd ed.). Cambridge, Massachusetts: Harvard University Press.

Sperry, Roger W. (1987), "*Structure & Significance of the Consciousness Revolution, The Journal of Mind & Behaviour*, vol.8 no.1; Winter 1987.

Worldviews in Transition

Mark B. Woodhouse

Deep transformational challenges are currently at work that I believe will result in a fundamental shift in our Western, if not global, worldview(s) in the early decades of the new millennium. By this I do not mean merely that new information is available to fit prevailing theoretical assumptions, or that existing paradigms must be adjusted to accommodate that information. Such changes are a continuing fact of life. I mean, rather, that fundamentally new assumptions, driven by radically different and controversial empirical developments, are emerging. They promise to shift the limits of our thinking and to profoundly alter the way we live on a scale that equals, if not surpasses, the transition from the High Middle Ages to the Enlightenment. This transition will affect everything - from education, health care delivery, and the environment to pure science, religion, and economic/social/political structures. In many instances, it already has.

This transition is occurring for several reasons. To begin, many prevailing assumptions of Western culture have come up against their limits and, in some instances, are creating more problems than they are capable of solving. We have only to look to the deteriorating state of our environment for evidence of this painful drama. Money, technology, and protective legislation — as useful as they are in the short term - cannot substitute for a new vision that connects us to our environment not just in sustainable, but also in sacralized ways. I expect guiding metaphors of materialistic reductionism, fragmentation, fear, hierarchical control (often by the few), and disempowering competition to yield in favor of holism, multi-dimensional realities, mutually empowering cooperation, and the singular importance of compassion and unconditional love - not merely because these are nice ideas, but because the old ways no longer serve us. Along the way, much of human history will be rewritten.

To continue, many transformational challenges in one arena are both conceptually and practically linked to challenges in others. Feminist critiques of patriarchy, for example, have uncovered deep structural similarities in both current health care delivery systems, the rape of the environment, and traditional theistic religion. To effectively change our thinking and our ways in one arena, we shall have to address both conceptual and practical connections to other dimensions of human experience. Moreover, the challenges we face are very deep. For example, fundamental critiques of strict locality, whether in particle physics, distant healing or other transpersonal phenomena, suggest that the perceptual and conceptual boundaries of conventional locality are merely sub-sets of an infinite nonlocal matrix of energy and consciousness in which we live and move and have our being. Finally, ordinary people the world over have had enough and are literally starving, if not for food and shelter, then for love, for awakened political leadership, and a more balanced economic order.

In the limited space available, I shall describe what appear to be some of the most fundamental principles and trends that are both emerging within and guiding this transition of worldviews. The point-counterpoint comparisons that follow are greatly oversimplified, but hopefully will compensate in stimulus value what they lack in elaboration. Each of the "developing" ideas or trends, I believe, is supported by reasonable argument and evidence. But evidence, of course, is not the same as proof, and reasonable persons will disagree. Pure reason, as Kuhn and others have pointed out, does not exclusively motivate either paradigm shifts or the resistance to them.

See *Worldviews in Transition* Table, page 260 -264

The worldview implied by these (re) emerging ideas and trends is still very much a minority position. Each aspect requires extensive elaboration and at least as much critical scrutiny as afforded its "old paradigm" counterpart. In these transitional times, little is guaranteed by way of a finished product. Still, we are better advised to spend less time examining the ships in the harbor, more to looking in which way the winds are blowing. I suspect that by the year 2010 or so - much sooner than many might expect - we shall be participants not just in a new worldview, but in a new world.

Our future is not what it used to be.

Worldviews in Transition

Table

Past/Current	Current/Developing
Matter and energy are coequal realities, each translatable into the other.	Energy or fields of force are fundamental; matter is compressed energy - trapped light
All that we can know exists is confined to three-dimensional sensory awareness.	Reality is multi-dimensional; our physical sensory level is but one of many
Science stresses reductive explanations, which can become a dogma *ofscientism*	Science is expanding outward to systems and complexity theory, upward to the less physical.
Consciousness is a by-product of (or identical with) the neurochemistry of the brain. Consciousness is a passive mirror of external events.	Consciousness is irreducible and extends as a spectrum to other realms. The brain is a filter. Consciousness deeply influences outer worlds
If mind exists, as many believe, it is as a separate(nonphysical) "ghost in the machine."	Energy-consciousness exists throughout the cosmos, including in plants, cells, and animals.
Only sound and the electromagnetic spectrum have "frequencies" that are of much use to us. Standard physics, chemistry, and biology are what we need to control our environments.	Everything has a vibratory signature, from angels and love to disease and the weapons of war. Power accrues to those who understand and access those signatures and their forms.
If God exists, as most believe, "He" is separate from creation and rules through organized religion. Theism prevails	God/Goddess is not separate from creation; accessing inner divinity is a key to spirituality Pan*en*theism is a more inclusive cosmology.

To be "religious" means to have faith in your God, belong to an organization that supports your faith, and to act according to scripture.	Emphasis is on spiritual development over outer forms of religion, including the transformative power of transpersonal experiences.
The paranormal (broadly conceived) violates both science and common sense; it is illusory.	The paranormal is becoming normal. Basic theory is changing to accommodate it.
Being healthy means not having any overt signs of illness or disease. Curing disease is eradicating symptoms and physical pathology.	Health means optimum function of all interrelated physical, emotional, and spiritual systems. Healing is deeper than curing.
Emotions and attitudes have nothing to do with (do not contribute to) physical disease. The physician's job is to fix us, when the machine breaks down, and to make it easier for us to assume less responsibility.	Emotions and attitudes play major roles in health and disease. With professional assistance, we can and should take greater responsibillty for health. Alternative modalities are self-prescribed. Health is a way of life.
Humans evolved from a chemical soup by accident, random mutation, and natural selection. Keep refining Darwin.	Not without periodic "boosts" from sources external to the planet. Inter-species evolution is not biochemically explained.
Human civilisations have existed for no more than seven thousand years — no earlier than 5000 B.C.	Civilisations probably existed tens of thousands of years ago, if not more. The Sphinx dates to at least 10,000 B.C.
Social systems are inherently hierarchical and require "power over" in order to maintain order and advance the common good.	Complexity is hierarchical, but social systems structured on mutual empowerment better support both order and the common good.
Men are inherently superior to women. Western and most other	More than equality, integration of the archetypal feminine nurtures

worldviews are essentially patriarchal, societies sexist.	creative complementarity of male/female energies in each of us.
Disempowering competition is part of the natural order. It's "too bad," but inevitable that many losers must support a few winners. War, poverty, and dropouts are expected.	Creative conflict resolution, win/win mind-sets, and new possibilities for empowerment make war, poverty, crime, and school dropouts not a "natural" occurrence.
Market economies must continue to grow despite the human and environmental costs.	Steady-state economics stresses sustainable resource allocation with minimal destruction.
Charging interest is a perfectly fair and reasonable way for bankers to conduct business the world over. Central banks exist for the common good.	Not when bankers can create nine dollars (with interest!) out of thin air for every dollar placed on deposit, and mortgage pools with small administrative fees would work as well.
Human freedom has expanded dramatically over the past few thousand years. Western cultures are on the whole freer today than in times past. We have more individual rights	Technology and improved living standards have given us more choices. But hidden mechanisms of control, manufactured consent, will be defrocked for true freedom.
Education is left-brained information/skills to help us do something useful and to transmit the values and paradigms of our culture(s). Courses don't fit in a coherent paradigm of human nature and social purpose	Different learning styles, deep critical thinking skills, psychotechnologies, life long learning, and the power of self-image are stressed. Courses do fit a coherent overarching paradigm of human nature and social purpose.
It always costs a greater amount of some form of energy to produce a lesser amount of another form of energy, e.g., the gasoline engine. Energy production is not free. We can increase efficiency, but never over 99%.	Esoteric technologies are emerging to master gravity (thus space travel), produce five times the quality and quantity of food, detoxify the environment, eliminate gas engines, and extract "free" energy from the vacuum field.

The media objectively and truthfully reports most of what we need to know. Investigative journalism tells us the way "things really are."	News that deeply threatens existing power structures is either not reported or unfairly reported. A new world requires full disclosure.
We are on the planet because our parents by design or accident created us. We now have to determine the best way of surviving. Either God put is here to worship Him, or we create our own relative meaning in a chaotic world.	We chose to be here on a soul level to grow in wisdom and alignments with love, to integrate our spirituality with our physicality, and to contribute to the creative evolution of the universe.
When we die, we either rot in the grave or go to (some version of) Heaven or Hell.	Reincarnation promises to become the prevailing "after life" philosophy.
When bad things happen to "bad" people, they deserve it, and when they happen to "good" people, it's rotten luck and/or somebody's else's fault.	We attract, often unconsciously, people or circumstances to mirror what we need to look at in ourselves. Growth requires looking to the pain behind the anger, not moral revenge.
Love is just another emotion that some people are fortunate enough to experience sometimes. Power rests with image, laws, and mechanisms of social control.	Love is at the core of our being, waiting behind the masks of fear to be accessed and unconditionally shared. It is a great source of personal and collective power and healing.
We are fundamentally separate from each other, either as minds in machines or as just the machines (bodies) themselves. We must eternally compete for scare resources and overcome limitation through control.	We are fundamentally connected to one another on other levels as aspects of a whole. Ego is illusory. We can overcome scarcity and limitation by aligning with and drawing from the greater reality of which we are a part.
Science, spirituality, education, politics, etc. are separate agendas whose causes are promoted by	These spheres are integrated into a comprehensive worldview, the parts of which are complementary

specialization, maintaining boundaries, and marginalizing those who question their assumptions too deeply. Science and spirituality either conflict or are irrelevant to each other.	and reinforcing. Those who question fragmentation in the search for wholeness both are, and should be, valued. Science and spirituality are complementary, even synergistic, perspectives.
In theory extraterrestrial races exist somewhere "out there." But they are not here and would have no interest in us, even if they could travel here efficiently. Besides, if they were here, our governments would tell us.	Extraterrestrial races have visited Earth for thousands of years and are currently in, on, or around the planet. If they are not formally recognized as of this writing (1998) they soon will be.
We have precariously abused the environment, but its value is and ought to be subsumed by human interests. It's to our self-interest to manage it more carefully. After all, it is just "biological stuff."	Nature, together with its visible and invisible denizens and realms, feels the effects of human abuse. It commands equal respect and loving resonance more than the belated *quid pro quo* of collective self-interest.
Relationships are often underwritten by the assumption of fundamental separateness, the unarticulated desire to have others compensate for what we lack in ourselves, and associated control and caretaking dramas.	Relationships are underwritten more by an awareness of our underlying unity, the desire to find and integrate within ourselves what we can then use to co-create with partners, and by vulnerability and growth.
Our current worldview(s) have served us well and should be refined, but not abandoned. Judeo- Christian, Cartesian-Newtonian, or Postmodern paradigms will take us into the new millennium. There's no need for alarm or for pie in the sky.	We need a fundamentally new worldview to respond to current transformational challenges. Holism, Systems and Complexity theories, and the Perennial Wisdom underwrite a vision for the next millennium. They are both needed and realistic.

Prof. Mark B. Woodhouse, Ph.D., is Associate Professor of Philosophy at Georgia State University. He is the author of 'Paradigm Wars', which both critically examines and integrally envisions many of the topics of this essay.

264

The Passion of the Western Mind

Richard Tarnas

A fundamental sense of separation is structured into the legitimated interpretive principles of the modern mind. It was no accident that the man who first systematically formulated the separate modern rational self, Descartes, was also the man who first systematically formulated the mechanistic cosmos for the Copernican revolution. The basic a priori categories and premises of modern science, with its assumption of an independent external world that must be investigated by an autonomous human reason, with its insistence on impersonal mechanistic explanation, with its rejection of spiritual qualities in the cosmos, its repudiation of any intrinsic meaning or purpose in nature, its demand for a univocal, literal interpretation of a world of hard facts – all of these ensure the construction of a disenchanted and alienating world view. As Hillman has emphasised: "The evidence we gather in support of a hypothesis and the rhetoric we use to argue it area already part of the archetypal constellation we are in .... The 'objective' idea we find in the pattern of data is also the 'subjective' idea by means of which we see the data."

From this perspective, the Cartesian-Kantian philosophical assumptions that have governed the modern mind, and that have informed and impelled the modern scientific achievement, reflect the dominance of a powerful archetypal gestalt, an experiential template that selectively filters and shapes human awareness in such a manner that reality is perceived to be opaque, literal, objective, and alien. The Cartesian-Kantian paradigm both expresses and ratifies a state of consciousness in which experience of the unitive numinous depths of reality has been systematically extinguished, leaving the world disenchanted and the human ego isolated. Such a word view is, as it were, a kind of metaphysical and epistemological box, a hermetically closed system. It is the elaborate articulation of a specific archetypal domain within which human awareness is encompassed and confined as if it existed inside a solipsistic bubble.

265

The great irony suggested here of course is that it is just when the modern mind believes it has most fully purified itself from any anthropomorphic projections, when it actively construes the world as unconscious, mechanistic, and impersonal, it is just then that the world is most completely a selective construct of the human mind. The human mind has abstracted from the whole all conscious intelligence and purpose and meaning, and claimed these exclusively for itself, and then projected onto the world a machine. As Rupert Sheldrake has pointed out, this is the ultimate anthropomorphic projection: a man-made machine, something not in fact ever found in nature. From this perspective, it is the modern mind's own impersonal soullessness that has been projected from within onto the world – or, to be more precise, that has been projectively elicited from the world.

All of this suggests that another, more sophisticated and comprehensive epistemological perspective is called for. Although the Cartesian-Kantian epistemological position has been the dominant paradigm of the modern mind, it has not been the only one, for at almost precisely the same time that the Enlightenment reached its philosophical climax in Kant, a radically different epistemological perspective began to emerge – first visible in Goethe with its study of natural forms, developed in new directions by Schiller, Schelling, Hegel, Coleridge, and Emerson, and articulated within the past century by Rudolph Steiner. Each of these thinkers gave his own distinct emphasis to the development perspective, but common to all was a fundamental conviction that the relation of the human mind to the world was ultimately not dualistic but participatory.

In essence this alternative conception did not oppose the Kantian epistemology but rather went beyond it, subsuming it in a larger and subtler understanding of human knowledge. The new conception fully acknowledged the validity of Kant's critical insight, that all human knowledge of the world is in some sense determined by subjective principles; but instead of considering these principles as belonging ultimately to the separate human subject, and therefore not grounded in the world independent of human cognition, this participatory conception held that these subjective principles are in fact an expression of the world's own being, and that them human mind is ultimately the organ of the world's own process of self-revelation. In this view, the essential reality of nature is not separate, self-contained, and complete in itself, so that the human mind can examine it "objectively" and register it from without. Rather, nature's unfolding truth emerges only with the active participation of the human mind. Nature's reality is not merely phenomenal, nor is it independent and objective; rather, it is something that comes into being through the very act of human cognition. Nature becomes intelligible to itself through the human mind.

In this perspective, nature pervades everything, and the human mind in all its fullness is itself an expression of nature's essential being. And it is only when the human mind actively rings forth from within itself the full powers of a disciplined imagination and saturates its empirical observation with archetypal insight that the deeper reality of the world emerges. A developed inner life is therefore indispensable for cognition. In its most profound and authentic expression, the intellectual imagination does not merely project its ideas into nature from its isolated brain corner. Rather, from within its own depths the imagination directly contacts the creative process within nature, realises that process within itself, and brings nature's reality to to conscious expression. Hence the imaginal intuition is not a subjective distortion but is the human fulfilment of that reality's essential wholeness, which had been rent asunder by the dualistic perception. The human imagination is itself part of the world's instrinsic truth; without it the world is in some sense incomplete. Both major forms of epistemological dualism – the conventional pre-critical and post-Kantian critical conceptions of human knowledge - are here countered and synthesised. On the one hand, the human mind does not just produce concepts that "correspond" to an external reality. Yet on the other hand, neither does it simply "impose" its own order on the world. Rather, the world's truth realises itself within and through the human mind.

This participatory epistemology, developed in different ways by Goethe, Hegel, Steiner, and others, can be understood not as a regression to naïve *participation mystique*, but as the dialectical synthesis of the long evolution from the primordial undifferentiated consciousness through the dualistic alienation. It incorporates the postmodern understanding of knowledge and yet goes beyond it. The interpretive and constructive character of human cognition is fully acknowledged, but the intimate, interpenetrating and all-permeating relationship of nature to the human being and human mind allows the Kantian consequence of epistemological alienation to be entirely overcome. The human spirit does not merely prescribe nature's phenomenal order; rather, the spirit of nature brings forth its own order through the human mind when that mind is employing its full complement of faculties – intellectual, volitional, emotional, sensory, imaginative, aesthetic, epiphanic. In such knowledge, the human mind "lives into" the creative activity of nature. Then the world speaks its meaning through human consciousness. Then human language itself can be recognised as rooted in a deeper reality, as reflecting the universe's unfolding meaning. Through the human intellect, in all its personal individuality, contingency, and struggle, the world's evolving thought content achieves conscious articulation. Yes, knowledge of the world is structured by the mind's subjective contribution; but that contribution is teleologically called forth by the universe for is own self-revelation. Human thought does not and cannot mirror a ready-made objective truth in the world; rather, the world's truth achieves its existence when it comes to birth in the human mind. As the plant at a certain stage brings forth its blossom, so does the universe bring forth new stages of human knowledge. And, as Hegal emphasised, the evolution of human knowledge is the evolution of the world's self-revelation.

Such a perspective suggests of course that the Cartesian-Kantian paradigm, and thus the epistemologically enforced double bind of modern consciousness, is not absolute. But if we take this participatory epistemology, and if we combine it with Grof's discovery of the perinatal sequence and its underlying archetypal dialectic, then a more surprising conclusion is suggested: namely, that the Cartesian-Kantian paradigm, and indeed the entire trajectory into alienation taken by the modern mind, has not been simply an error, an unfortunate human aberration, a mere manifestation of human blindness, but has rather reflected a much deeper archetypal process impelled by forces beyond the merely human. For in this view, the powerful contraction of vision experienced by the modern mind has itself been an authentic expression of nature's unfolding, a process enacted through the growingly autonomous human intellect, and now reaching a highly critical stage of transfiguration. From this perspective, the dualistic epistemology derived from Kant and the Enlightenment is not simply the opposite of the participatory epistemology derived from Goethe and Romanticism, but is rather an important subset of it, a necessary stage in the evolution of the human mind. And if this is true, several long-standing philosophical paradoxes may now be cleared up.

I shall focus here on one especially significant area. Much of the most exciting work in contemporary epistemology has come from philosophy of science, above all from the work of Popper, Kuhn, and Feyerabend. Yet despite this work, or rather because of this work, which has revealed in so many ways the relative and radically interpretive nature of scientific knowledge, philosophers of science have been left with two notoriously fundamental dilemmas – one left by Popper, the other by Kyhn and Feyerabend.

With Popper the problem of scientific knowledge left by Hume and Kant was brilliantly explicated. For Popper, as for the modern mind, man approaches the world as a stranger – but a stranger who has a thirst for explanation, and an ability to invent myths, stories, theories, and a willingness to test these. Sometimes, by luck and hard work and many mistakes, a myth is found to work. The theory saves the phenomena; it is a lucky guess. And this is the greatness of science, that through an occasionally fortunate combination of rigor and inventiveness, a purely human conception can be found to work in the empirical world, at least temporarily. Yet a gnawing question remains for Popper: How, in the end, are successful conjectures, successful myths, possible? How does the human mind ever acquire genuine knowledge if it's just a matter of projected myths that are tested? Why do these myths ever work? If the human mind has no access to priori certain truth, and if all observations are always already saturated by uncertified assumptions about the world, how could this mind possibly conceive a genuinely successful theory? Popper answered this question by saying that, in the end, it is "luck" – but this answer has never satisfied. For why should the imagination of a *stranger* ever be able to conceive merely from within itself a myth that works so splendidly in the empirical world that whole civilisations can be built on it (as with Newton)? How can something come from nothing?

I believe there is only one plausible answer to this riddle, and it is an answer suggested by the participatory epistemological framework outlined above: namely, that the bold conjectures and myths that the human mind produces in its quest for knowledge ultimately come from something far deeper than a purely human source. They come from the wellspring of nature itself, from the universal unconscious that is bringing forth through the human mind and human imagination its own gradually unfolding reality. In this view, the theory of a Copernucus, a Newton, or an Einstein is not simply due to the luck of a stranger; rather, it reflects the human mind's radical kinship with the cosmos. It reflects the human mind's pivoral role as vehicle of the universe's unfolding meaning. In this view, neither the postmodern skeptic nor the perennialist philosopher is correct in their shared opinion that the modern scientific paradigm is ultimately without any cosmic foundation. For that paradigm is itself part of a larger evolutionary process.

We can now also suggest a resolution to that fundamental problem left by Kuhn – the problem of explaining why in the history of science one paradigm is chosen over another if paradigms are ultimately incommensurable, if they cannot ever be rigorously compared. As Kuhn has pointed out, each paradigm tends to create its own data and its own way of interpreting those data in a manner that is so comprehensive and self-validating that scientists operating within different paradigms seem to exist in altogether different worlds. Although to a given community of scientific interpreters one paradigm seems to be superior to another, there is no way of justifying that superiority if each paradigm governs and saturates its own data base. Nor does any consensus exist among scientists concerning a common measure of value – such a conceptual precision, or coherence, or breadth, or simplicity, or resistance to falsification, or congruence with theories used in other specialities, or fruitfulness in new research findings – that could be used as a universal standard of comparison. Which value is considered most important values from one scientific era to another, from one discipline to another, even between individual research groups.

What, then, can explain the progress of scientific knowledge if, in the end, each paradigm is selectively based on differing modes of interpretation and different sets of data and different scientific values?

Kuhn has always answered this problem by saying that ultimately the decision lies with the ongoing scientific community, which provides the final basis of justification. Yet, as many scientists have complained, this answer seems to undercut the very foundation of the scientific enterprise, leaving it to the mercy of sociological and personal factors that subjectively distort the scientific judgement. And indeed, as Kuhn himself has demonstrated, scientists generally do *not* in practice fundamentally question the governing paradigm or test it against other alternatives, for many reasons – pedagogical, socioeconomic, cultural, psychiological – most of them unconscious. Scientists, like everyone else, are attached to their beliefs. What, then, ultimately explains the progression of science from one paradigm to another? Does the evolution of scientific knowledge have anything to do with "truth", or is it a mere artifact of sociology? And more radically, with Paul Feyerabend's dictum that "anything goes" in the battle of paradigms: if *anything* goes, then whey ultimately does *one* thing go rather than another? Why is any scientific paradigm judged superior? If anything goes, why does anything go at all?

The answer I am suggesting here is that a paradigm emerges in the history of science, it is recognised as superior, as true and valid, precisely when that paradigm resonates with the current archetypal state of the evolving collective psyche. A paradigm appears to account for more data, and for more important data. It seems more relevant, more cogent, more attractive, fundamentally because it has become archetypally appropriate to that culture or individual at that moment in its evolution. And the dynamics of this achetypal development appear to be essentially identical to the dynamics of the perinatal process. Kuhn's description of the ongoing dialectic between normal science and major paradigm revolutions strikingly parallels the perinatal dynamics described by Grof: The pursuit of knowledge always takes place within a given paradigm, within a conceptual matrix – a womb that provides an intellectually nourishing structure, that fosters growth and increasing complexity and sophistication – until gradually that structure is experienced as constricting, a limitation, a prison, producing a tension of irresolvable contradictions, and finally a crisis is reached. Then some inspired Promethean genius comes along and is graced with an inner breakthrough to a new vision that gives the scientific mind a new sense of being cognitively connected – reconnected – to the world: an intellectual revolution occurs, and a new paradigm is born. Here we see why such geniuses regularly experience their intellectual breakthrough as a profound illumination, a revelation of the divine creative principle itself, as with Newton's exclamation to God, "I think Thy thoughts after Thee!" For the human mind is following the numinous archetypal path that is unfolding from within it.

And here we can see why the same paradigm, such as the Aristotelian or the Newtonian, is perceived as a liberation at one time and then a constriction, a prison, at another. For the *birth* of every new paradigm is also a *conception* in a new conceptual matrix, which begins the process of gestation, growth, crisis, and revolution all over again. Each paradigm is a stage in an unfolding evolutionary sequence, and when that paradigm has fulfilled its purpose, when it has been developed and exploited to its fullest extent, then it loses its numinosity, it ceases to be libidinally charged, it becomes felt as oppressive, limiting, opaque, something to be overcome – while the new paradigm that is emerging is felt as a liberating birth into a new, luminously intelligible universe. Thus the ancient symbolically resonant geocentric universe of Aristotle, Prolemy, and Dante gradually loses is numinosity, becomes seen as a problem full of contradictions, and with Copernicus and Kepler that numinosity is fully transferred to the heliocentric cosmos. And because the evolution of paradigm shifts is an *archetypal* process, rather than merely either a rational-empirical or a sociological one, this evolution takes place historically both from within and without, both "subjectively" and "objectively." As the inner gestalt changes in the cultural mind, new empirical evidence just happens to appear, pertinent writings from the past suddenly are unearthed appropriate epistemological justifications are formulated, supportive sociological changes coincidentally take place, new technologies become available, the telescope is invented and just happens to fall in Galileo's hands. As new psychological predispositions and meta physical assumptions emerge from within the collective mind, from within many individual minds simultaneously, they are matched and encouraged by the synchronistic arrival of new data, new social contexts, new methodologies, new tools that fulfil the emerging archetypal gestalt.

And as with the evolution of scientific paradigms, so with all forms of human thought. The emergence of a new philosophical paradigm, whether that of Plato or Aquinas, Kant or Heidegger, is never simply the result of improved logical reasoning from the observed data. Rather, each philosophy, each metaphysical perspective and epistemology, reflects the emergence of a global experiential gestalt that informs that philosopher's vision, that governs his or her reasoning and observations, and that ultimately affects the entire cultural and sociological context within which the philosopher's vision is taking form.

For the very possibility of a new world view's appearance rests on the underlying archetypal dynamic of the larger culture. Thus the Copernican revolution that emerged during the Renaissance and Reformation perfectly reflected the archetypal moment of modern humanity's birth out of the ancient-medieval cosmic-ecclesiastical womb. And at the other end, the twentieth century's massive and radical breakdown of so many structures – cultural, philosophical, scientific, religious, moral, artistic, social, economic, political, atomic, ecological – all this suggests the necessary deconstruction prior to a new birth. And why is there evident now such a widespread and constantly growing collective impetus in the Western mind to articulate a holistic and participatory world view, visible in virtually every field? The collective psyche seems to be in the grip of a powerful archetypal dynamic in which the long-alienated modern mind is breaking through, but of the contractions of its birth process, out of what Blake called its "mind-forg'd manacles," to rediscover its intimate relationship with nature and the larger cosmos.

Prof. Richard Tarnas Ph.D. is professor of philosophy at the California Institute for Integral Studies and author of 'The Passion of the Western Mind', from which this piece is adapted.

An Extract From the Introduction To the Wider Horizons Course, 22nd – 29th August 1986

George Blaker

Perhaps the best way to start is by telling you what we were trying to do when the Scientific and Medical Network began the first of these Wider Horizons Weeks about ten years ago. Of course they are different each year. They grow and change with the people in them. But throughout we wanted to offer a vision of the way the world could work, or does work, from a spiritual viewpoint. We started by asking a number of questions, such as what is our position, as human beings, in relation to the world about us? What <u>are</u> we? I have a body, but I am not my body. I have emotions, but <u>I</u> am not my emotions. You have a body, you have emotions, you have a brain, but you, the vital conscious and unconscious you, are not just these things, you are something more. Those who feel, or know, that they have a soul - well, that is getting a lot nearer to what we are considering, but again, you are something more even than your soul. So what are we? Where do we come from? What are we heading for? What is the purpose of life here on Earth? What personal philosophy shall we adopt to guide us through it all?

We need to know the answers to these questions, at least in their general direction, before we can determine rationally how we want to respond to the things that happen to us and to what purposes we want to address our skills and energies throughout our lives.

Our personal philosophy, or the way we look at the world, needs, I suggest, to be of a kind that our highest, inner, spiritual nature will regard as satisfactory. What we do here and now, and especially **how** we do it, has to be **eternally** acceptable to ourselves, so far as we can make it so, otherwise we shall run into trouble.

May I say a word here about religions and materialism, because the proponents of each of these often feel that it is up to them to give answers to the questions I referred to, and so they try to do that **within**

the set framework of their beliefs. But we have to try to be free and open to any conclusions that the facts, as we understand them, may point to.

The best religions tend to start off with a source of pure spiritual inspiration, expressed in such sayings as "Love thy neighbour as thyself ", things that we can recognise as being profoundly wise, conveying far greater depths of wisdom than just the superficial meaning of the words. That outpouring of the Spirit is not in itself a religion at that stage, but a teaching and a way of life. Just what we are looking for! Then the religion comes in when men, very human and fallible men, build things onto the teaching; a hierarchy of priests gets set up, theologians arise to intellectualize about it, the religion becomes institutionalized, and after a relatively short time begins to go off the rails. It becomes entrenched in a fixed set of ideas, tied to the past and no longer relevant to a human advance on a wide front. The faithful adherents of the religion continue to acclaim it fervently, but the spiritual inspiration quietly moves away and manifests somewhere else within the people's culture.

It was only about 400 years ago that Copernicus and then Galileo, with his telescope and many astronomical discoveries - and despite the fact that the Inquisition forced him to recant - managed to provide a good example of the non-religious force, the scientific force, being brought in to break down forms of thought that had been useful in their time but had hardened into barriers to the further progress of the human mind.

Then what happens? Does science go on leading the way, keeping to the true path of progress? No.' Science, like money, is in itself neutral, and can be good or bad, according to the purpose for which it is used, and it soon began to pursue false goals - excessively materialistic goals. Science was progressively taken over by scientific materialism until, in its turn, it went too far and became, in certain crucial ways, a barrier to the further development of human awareness.

In the last hundred years or so science has made such tremendous strides in widening our understanding of physical matter, and so our power to manipulate it, that many people have been carried away by the sheer brilliance of its results and have concluded that the Universe follows only physical laws, that everything has a physical cause and results, like life itself they say, from the chance interplay of random forces and - putting the doctrine in its extreme form - is meaningless and without purpose except insofar as man, regarded under this hypothesis as the peak achievement of evolution, can bring any meaning into it, starting from scratch with the resources he can control.

That is not science. It is scientific materialism, a deviation from the real thing. By "science" I mean the laws of Nature as progressively uncovered to man's understanding. Scientific materialism is a particular interpretation of what lies behind all creation, invented by those people who have been overwhelmed by the vastness and complexity they discovered in physical laws and physical reactions, and concluded that these were so far reaching that nothing more was needed to explain the Universe. And that view was widely accepted throughout the world.

So there are these two world views, the religious and the materialistic. For most of the 2,000 years now drawing to their close, if we in Europe had held the first of these views, the dogmatic religious one, with an all-powerful God who could do anything he wanted and yet allowed all sorts of horrors to be perpetrated, we should not have been corrected by the official channels of learning. Indeed in one form or another the churches or monasteries or their equivalent would have taught it.

Today, by contrast, we are unlikely to be corrected in our official institutions of learning if we infer that we are meaningless and inconsequent specks of water and a few chemicals in a vast physical universe, created without purpose by the chance interactions of enormous random forces. We are more likely to be encouraged to go on thinking that way, a complete reversal of direction since the Middle Ages, and we are unlikely to get any useful answers from the official teaching we receive, to the fundamental questions that we started with We need to find better answers for ourselves. How do we do that?

One way to explore what the answers might be is to consider a series of propositions, or insights, or ideas, and I would like to put forward about eight of them. I think they will all arise in one form or another in the discussions that you will have this week.

1.   The proposition that we must start with is that man/woman - is primarily a spiritual being, not physically based at all, but only temporarily inhabiting a physical environment. Spirit means different things to different people, but what is meant here is that there is a non-physical living force - we can call it Spirit - that is at the heart of all things, and that it is ultimately a person's spirit, working through the whole of his/her being, not only through the brain or body, that activates the rest, and moreover it is permanent. It does not die. It is our innermost core. It goes on for ever, taking with it all that we have learnt by experience in our soul, mind, emotions and body. In other words the human being is something much bigger and finer and better than the little selves we know now, - something bigger and finer and better **in the process of being created** for some job that lies ahead of us.

2.   The second proposition I'd like to talk about, closely related to the first, is that human life does not begin at birth and end at death-of-the-physical-body, but is a continuous process of development, beginning long before birth and going forward in an unbroken continuity through the incident of death to an unfolding life in other environmente of as real and active a character, probably more real and more active, than we can experience here on Earth.

When Wordsworth wrote:-

"The soul that riseth with us,
Our life's star,
Hath had elsewhere its setting
And cometh from afar,"

he was not the only one to think like that. The same thought is to be found in the poets of many lands and of different times. I think it is important that people in Western countries should receive naturally into their ordinary thinking the fact that life doesn't suddenly stop, but that whatever happens to the physical body, their lives will go on. I don't know whether any of you happen to have come across, as I have, anyone who has nearly died and was then revived and could remember what had happened to him while he was knocked out. I think of a young man I know who was very fond of motorbikes. Incidentally I cannot see a motorbike travelling at speed and taking a curve leaning, as they do, at an incredible angle to the ground, without imagining that it only needs a patch of oil on the road for that bike to be careering out of control straight into the oncoming traffic on the far side of the road. Anyway this particular young man had an accident. He could not remember very much about the accident itself, but he was aware that he had had a head-on crash with an oncoming car. The next thing he knew was that he was up in the air above the road, calmly looking down on the scene of the accident. He saw people getting out of their cars, and he could see his own body lying under the hedge on the far side of the road where it had been thrown by the crash. Soon he saw an ambulance arrive and people picking up his body and putting it into the ambulance which then drove away. Not long after that, as it seemed to him, he woke up in hospital, but the memory of what he had seen from his vantage point floating in the air above the accident remained very vivid.

One of the mistakes we have made is that the subject of life after death, which has many practical implications for life here and now, should have remained for so long something that is a matter of religious belief, or disbelief, rather than of scientific exploration. But that is changing a little now.

We have to envisage that there are other worlds that are at least as real to those who live in them all the time as this heavy Earth is real to you and me now, including that world to which most of us may expect to go when, having finally worn out these physical bodies, which are so useful for living in a physical environment, we shall have died and discarded them. Undoubtedly one of the large blocks of evidence that has to be looked at here is the descriptions and explanations of life in non-physical states of existence that come to us from sensitives of all kinds, trance mediums, telepathic mediums, inspirational writing, sometimes automatic writing, clairvoyants, people who can see auras, and so on. There is a great deal of literature about this, and the underlying consistency and reasonableness common to most of these accounts is well worth paying attention to, despite some differences due to the varying circumstances of the perceivers.

4. Proposition no. 4 is that the human being is not just the person we are aware of through our five ordinary senses and the consciousness of our physical brains, but is a far more **extensive** and **perceptive** being than that, with etheric, emotional, mental and spiritual aspects, and vehicles for these, with relatively vast capacities and potentialities of which, in waking life, we are nearly unconscious. We are linked with them all the time, but they only register through our brain, at present, to a tiny extent. This can be illustrated by a number of different kinds of experience and phenomena. Out-of-the-body experiences, such as the one I have just mentioned, are an instance of these. Thousands of such cases have been recorded, and it may be worth quoting just one more example.

Many of these cases concern people who were forced out of their bodies by nearly drowning, or by some accident in which they were nearly killed, or by illness, becoming unconscious as we call it; which means that the consciousness ceased to operate through the brain, but went on functioning uninterruptedly in the astral or soul body, and the person was able to bring back the memory of that consciousness when s/he re-entered the body. One case, recorded by Dr. Leslie Weatherhead, was of a woman who, when she began to recover from her illness, described how she felt herself pass out of her body through the head and float upwards, though she could see that she was still attached to her body by a kind of silver cord. She looked down from above, with disinterested detachment she said, at her body lying on the bed below. Then she saw her husband come into the room, gently shake her shoulder, pause and then rush for the telephone to call the doctor. She felt herself being drawn back into her body. Then she opened her eyes and, after a little while, mentioned to the doctor and nurse that she had been interested to watch them at work. They smiled at this, and told her that as she was unconscious and had nearly died, she must have been dreaming. But they stopped smiling when she told them in detail all that they had done, where they had stood, and even what her husband had said to the doctor on the telephone.

Now the point is that things like that do happen to people, and they cannot just be dismissed because they don't fit into our ordinary understanding of how life works. Their importance lies in their implications. They are part of the evidence that consciousness exists separately from the body, and can function outside the body.

An indication that, in our total make-up, we are much more perceptive beings, with much more extended powers of awareness than we can appreciate through our physical senses alone, is afforded by those kinds of experience that are related to intuition, and one of those is precognition, or knowing about something before it happens.

I'll give you an example concerning a taxi driver whom I knew, and with whom I discussed what happened. He was worried about his accounts and was working on them at home, with his relief driver in the room with him. His young daughter came home from school and said that she had to write about the siege of Jericho for her homework, and could he tell her where to find the story? He said: "Don't bother me now dear, I'm doing my accounts - page 193 line 25". He didn't think about what he was saying, the answer just came out like that, and he went on with his accounts. A little later, when his daughter casually thanked him for the reference he had given her, which was correct, he was quite badly shaken. He didn't understand what had happened₂ because he had no idea of what the answer should have been. Line 25 on page 193 **was** the beginning of the story of the siege of Jericho, (Book of Joshua, Chap. 6, verse 2), but he said: "I had no idea of this when I said it. My mind was not on her problem at all. I had not previously read the particular Bible she was using (The Revised Standard Versibn), so it could not have had anything to do with memory

On points of detail it may be noticed that it was not the chapter and verse numbers that he gave, which any devout person familiar with the Bible might have known by heart, but the page and line numbers from an edition of the Bible that he did not ¹⁻now, so that he could not have known what pages the story would have come out on in the printing. And his fellow driver was present and able to confirm that he had given the numbers which his daughter had then found to be correct).

It is a common characteristic of intuitive knowing that the information comes through most satisfactorily when the intellect is either switched off or is completely absorbed or distracted by something quite different.

5.   My next suggestion, no. 5, is that life on Earth can usefully be regarded as a kind of University, or school, in which we go through a course, prescribed specially for us, to provide us with just the conditions we know we need in order to learn certain spiritual lessons, or, as I prefer to put it, to acquire certain spiritual qualities and skills and strengths that we know we shall need for use later on. These conditions take account of and are related to, or even caused by, what has been achieved in all our previous existence.

6.   That leads into the idea of Karma. As we sow, spiritually, so shall we reap. It is not something imposed on us from outside. The quality of what we think, say and do here will be drawn to us as part of our character at some later time, somewhere, and so will become an experience to be lived through. If for instance we have not responded to someone's desperate need, we shall experience being neglected until the lack of caring in our character has been corrected by a deepening of understanding due to our knowing, now, more about what it means to be left in a crisis without caring help. As Charles Kingsley might have expressed it, we should "Do as we would be done by because we shall be done by as we did". So we should, but not for that reason alone. Every thought, word and deed of ours has its effects. The physical effects may seem unimportant and be short-lived, but the moral effects are "worked into the character of the self", as Dr. Radhakrishnan put it. We are continually shaping our own selves by our thoughts, words and deeds, which become a self-made limiting factor in our own existence, or a liberating factor permitting greater growth, or, more probably, a bit of both together. These experiences will help us to understand both sides of a situation and to discriminate between right and wrong attitudes in ourselves.

7.   These experiences that we have earned - joyful as well as regretful - may come to us elsewhere or on this Earth again. So we pass on into considering reincarnation, for which the evidence is now

281

quite good. A large proportion of the world's population accepts it as fact, so we would do well to take a close look before we dismiss it as unfounded superstition.

May I make a small digression here to tell you the short story of a little Indian boy, a recent immigrant to Britain? He was asked what animal he would choose to keep as a pet, if he could have one. He chose a cat. So then he was asked, in school, to write an essay about the cat, and I am able to quote to you the whole of what he wrote. It went like this:-

"The cat is a square animal, with four legs, one at each corner. It also has nine lives, but it doesn't use these in Europe because of Christianity".

I think we should study the evidence, and the work of Dr. Guirdham on the Cathars and that of Dr. Kelsey, Dr. Ian Stevenson and others is of value here. (For lack of space and because the best cases are relatively well known, the example given in 1986 is omitted here).

8. Finally the last of the chosen thoughts, that ALL LIFE IS ONE. I put it last of the eight because although this sense of union, of oneness with the living essence that floods through the whole manifested Universe, is something that many have felt at one time or another, and although it is an awareness that is experienced quite commonly in some parts of the world, it is I think the one that is the most difficult for a Westerner to assimilate, or indeed to see any meaning in at all.

Starting at the more physical end of the spectrum of language, and then moving on towards the more poetical, we could first describe things, I suppose, as being dynamic concentrations of energy in one vast system of interacting energy fields. Like that we can begin to conceive that all things <u>are</u> one and that anything done anywhere may have effects throughout the system.

At this point I'd like to give you a quotation from that eminent physicist Albert Einstein, because after all he made a tremendous contribution to science, and anything he had to say on this topic of oneness should give us reason to think. What he said was this:-

> "A human being is part of the Whole called by us the Universe, a part that is limited in time and space. He experiences himself, his thoughts and feelings, as something separated from the rest – a kind of optical illusion of his consciousnesa. This illusion is a kind of prison for us, restricting us to our personal desires and to affection for a few persons nearest to us. Our task must be to free ourselves from the prison by widening our circle of compassion to embrace all living creatures and the whole of Nature in its beauty. Nobody is able to achieve this completely, but the striving for such achievement is in itself a part of the liberation and a foundation for inner security."

I think that is a remarkable perception for a scientist of world stature to have had.

Turning now to the poetical end of the spectrum of language, Rabindranath Tagore put the same thought of one-ness in these words:

> "In the music of the rushing stream sounds the joyful assurance "I shall become the sea.' It is not a vain assumption" he wrote; "It is true humility, for it is the Truth. The river has no other alternative."

In other words our awareness will merge into the Consciousness of God, and the consciousness of God will, ultimately, become open to us. But of course we have an unimaginably huge distance to go yet. And a lack of humility quickly becomes a barrier. We have to remember that it is possible to drift into eddies and go backwards.

One thinks more easily of this idea of the unity of all life as a mystical insight rather than as a scientific concept, yet science itself is playing no small part in awakening us to the recognition of it through its discoveries about the nature of matter and of energy fields and the interactions of things on eachother like the physicists who have shown that solid matter is not solid at all, but is composed of sort of mini-galaxies of whirling energies. There are biologists and meteorologists a conscious being, **regulating** the physical and chemical condition of the planet's atmosphere, so that acidity and temperature and the gas composition of the air, including the oxygen level, are maintained, and have been for thousands of millions of years, in the condition that maximises the probability of growth of the entire biosphere. Other scientists are showing that when some people go into trance or deep states of meditation and claim to enter different states of consciousness, the process of doing so seems to synchronise with changes in their brainwaves that can be measured by instruments. Others are photographing fields of force of some kind, emanating from various living things, from plants to human beings, and this may in time throw scientific light on the nature of the human aura, which sensitives have always told us, is visible to them sometimes, and can give them information about people, including their health and emotional states, and can sometimes be used for diagnosing health hazards long before any physical symptoms have appeared. Others again are exploring telepathy, which undoubtedly is occurring all the time; and psychokinetic force, by which solid objects can be moved without any physical contact with them; the probability of non-physical memory storage is another. There are many more such things. Intuition is one of them.

On intuition I can quote from Professor George King, at that time of the Electronic and Electrical Engineering Dept. of the University of Surrey. He wrote:- "I am familiar with the absolute necessity of intuition for making other than pedestrian advances in science and technology. ... There are some really excellent engineers who are poor at logic, but they know intuitively the right way to get something built to do a given job. There are also logical ones who are nevertheless ineffectual people." King suggests that intuition is what makes the difference between those students who will become good engineers and those who will rank as ordinary, "yet we do not know how to teach it", he points out, or even perhaps how to avoid damaging its usefulness by imparting too rigid logic."

King is supported in this in the medical field by Sir Peter Medawar and others. Echoing the same thought a physician who writes under the pseudonym of Dr. Andrew Yorke has said "Many of the finest academicians are not good healers. Many a country G.P. works wonders."

What is the importance of all this? It does seem likely that the path of evolution for mankind is going to be by way of an extension of consciousness, so that we become directly aware, in our minds, of a much wider range of things going on than we can encompass at present. The study of psychical or paranormal phenomena is of value for two reasons. It gives factual clues as to what to expect of the invisible world around us that is outside the reach of our five senses; and realisation of the significance of this introduces us, as it were, to what is to come, and points to the fact that the prevailing materialstic interpretation of life will cease to be tenable, thus freeing people to choose whatever they want to choose from a far more rewarding system of thought in which they see themselves as spiritual beings first and foremost and realise that life does have the tremendous purpose for them of spiritual and every other kind of expansion of awareness and development generally.

But expansion of awareness will inevitably bring with it when it comes. It is essential that mankind should respond responsibity to the new knowledge. We can safely consider it as our job to use the knowledge we have gained on the way - gained, that is, in the course of life's spiritual journey -to help life on Earth - all life on Earth - to reach a more SPIRITUAL state. And there is no getting away from the fact that an essential way to use the inner knowledge to further this aim is to improve the spiritual quality, the motives and aspirations, the inner quality of thought and consequent action of each individual, which means by ourselves. For this we have to sit quietly in the silence of the inner shrine at the centre of our being and keep bright and steady the flame that burns on the alter there, for we shall inevitably find ourselves radiating out into the world just what we actually are.

May I end with another quotation, expressing my personal wish for you? It comes in a Muslim setting, and one can imagine the background of the desert, complete with its camels, outside Damascus, but it is of universal application. It is taken from James Elroy Flecker's

Song of the South Gate Holder singing "0 spiritual pilgrim rise[1]', and this is the part I quote for you:-

> "God be thy guide from camp to camp;
> God be thy shade from well to well:
> God grant beneath the desert stars
> Thou hear the prophet's camel bell."

The prophet's camel bell being, of course, the still small voice within, the guidance of the Spirit, God, by whatever name you like to call it. Thank you for listening.

George Blaker is President of the Network

Spiritual Vision and Environmental Responsibility

Dr. Peter Leggett

The human body consists of millions upon millions of cells. They are of many different kinds and have many different functions. But all are conscious , that is, they have the capacity to be aware and to respond, though they are not, of course, self-conscious. In some strange way there is within the human body a hierarchy of beings. Few cells function independently, near all function as one of a small (relative to the totality of cells)group, such as the heart. Proceeding in this way we eventually arrive at the human and self-conscious being.. whose consciousness informs the whole body. In this picture there are several points of interest.

Until we arrive at the human and self-conscious being whose consciousness informs the whole body, all lesser beings are part of something greater than themselves. Harmony prevails if every being in the body, whether humble like the cell or exalted like the heart, fulfils its responsibilities and is afforded the conditions under which it can perform its rightful function. Disharmony occurs when some being in the body no longer fulfils its responsibilities, with the result that the body no longer functions as it should. An obvious example is

286

cancer. In colloquial terms the cancer cells kick over the traces and embark on a policy of ruthless self-aggrandisement. In due course this leads to either the destruction of the cells concerned, together probably with a host of "innocent" cells as well, or to a condition in which the body can no longer function and there is death.

It is now suggested that something analogous applies to planet Earth our home. It is pointed out that the human body has a life of its own. In "Gaia; A New Look at Life on Earth" and "The Ages of Gaia" Professor James Lovelock suggests that the Earth too, has a life of its own, a suggestion referred to as the Gaia hypothesis after the Greek goddess of that name. In this analogy a human being would be to the Earth what a cell is to the human body. What we rely on for the body's harmonious functioning has been largely disregarded I relation to the planet. The ruthless self-aggrandisement of cells and the subsequent manifestation of cancer is closely paralleled by much of humanity's attitude to the Earth.

A very significant feature of this allegory is the manner and extent to which the hierarchy of being is interdependent. No being exists for itself and itself alone; each influences directly what is 'below', and limits the manifestation of what is 'above'. Moreover the picture provided by this allegory indicates the existence of many levels of awareness, and so suggests the existence of many levels of consciousness. And one is tempted to wonder whether in this allegory Christ corresponds to the heart, and whether the Lord of this World, the God of this planet, in whom we live and move and have our being corresponds to the individual consciousness which controls and permeates a human body. And what of the sun? Is what we see the cloak of a greater being? Besides acknowledging the sun as that on which all life depends, is there perchance a subtle and deeper reason why in some ancient civilisations the sun was worshipped as a god? In this context the famous Hindu prayer, the Gayatri, merits attention:

> O Thou who givest sustenance to the Universe
> From whom all things proceed
> To whom all thing s return
> Unveil to us the face of the true Spiritual Sun
> Hidden by a disc of golden light.

That we may know the Truth
And do our whole duty
As we journey to Thy Sacred Feet

The heart of this metaphysic is the belief in spiritual development, both of the individual and of humanity, associated with which is the concept of reincarnation, oar serial existence, for which there is increasing evidence. Such a concept provides point and purpose, which today are lacking for many. Furthermore it underlines the importance of responsibility, both individual and collective. By analogy with a school, it is surely very unwise to risk destroying the school in which one is being taught, if for no other reason that that one's education would be brought to an abrupt halt and there may be no other suitable school in which one's education can continue.

Faced with the situation as it is today what can the ordinary individual actually do?

An appropriate starting point is attitude of mind, one's own and other people's. But before considering the mind of others, it is wise to note one's own, and make sure one is free of prejudices, divisive nationalism, religious antipathies, and is reasonably well informed about the problems being discussed. Having faced oneself, it is legitimate to consider the attitude of others and to explain to them the dangers with which we are now threatened. During the last few years there has been an astonishing and most encouraging increase in concern for the environment, but it is doubtful how many how many of those who have become interested are aware of the seriousness of what threatens us. To enlighten them - and this means the people we meet in the normal course of life - is very important. Though fear, fear of what may happen if we fail to do what needs to be done, may not be the ideal motive, it has its place in the scheme of things. Over and beyond this is the vitally important role of faith, a realisation that all life is interconnected - the holistic view - and an appreciation that human life is no mean destiny.

Spiritual evolution is a slow process and to accomplish the change outlined takes time and cannot possibly be achieved in a single life; hence the purpose and place of reincarnation. This metaphysic has three implications which are directly relevant to today's environmental problems.

It puts the human predicament into a far wider perspective than is customary. It suggests that the Earth is far being "the only pebble on the beach", and that we may soon need to consider the role which the Earth and the life it supports is called upon to play within the solar system (albeit within the solar system the only life likely to be visible to physical sight). It then underlines the paramount necessity of respect and care for all life, not just human life. Finally it stresses the overwhelming necessity of tackling energetically, and at once environmental problems.

Dr. Peter Leggett was Vice-Chancellor of Surrey University and a Vice-President of the Network. This piece is extracted from his book 'Facing the Future'.

Postscript
Max Payne

It is clear that the coming 3rd millennium demands a new understanding of the bounds of human knowledge. Current science has been brilliantly successful, but its achievements have been gained by a deliberate process of exclusion and narrowing down to a thin focus on selected aspects of physical experience. A whole wide range of inner conscious experiences including the moral, the intuitive, and the spiritual , have all been intentionally left out. The time has come to recognise this. Reductionist materialism is not an assumption which follows from simple common sense. It is a pragmatic scientific technique. Anyone who elevates it to a fundamental principle of the universe is being as dogmatic as the sort of fanatical religious believer which most reductionist materialists affect to despise.

It is necessary to play the game of paradigm shifts at least two chess moves ahead. Much of science, especially the life sciences, is still locked into a narrow materialism. It ignores the total reality of what it is to be human, and has not even caught up with the full implications of modern quantum physics. Upsetting this narrow dogmatism is the first move. On the other hand although contemporary civilisation is the product of modern science, much of modern culture is anti-rational and anti-scientific. Popular culture is hedonistic, and commercial competition seems to lead the mass media into a continuous downward spiral of vulgarity... The high arts are imbued with the Dada spirit of "find a rule and break it". Art galleries exhibit piles of bricks and dung, and contemporary music tends too often to be a set of discordant sound experiments. Post modern deconstruction of meaning and political correctness stalk the humanities departments of universities. The second move in the game of paradigm shifts will therefore be to reaffirm the basic values of science. Modern scientific knowledge is brilliant, but limited, yet the values of scientific inquiry transcend any particular structure of scientific knowledge. Ptolemaic astronomy, Newtonian physics, Einstein's relativity, quantum physics, and whatever leaves them all behind next, all of them depend upon self-critical openness, fidelity to experience, a relentless search for perfection, and humility before the truth.

Reinterpreting science for the 21st century means reaffirming the values of scientific inquiry in a civilisation which is danger of forgetting them. This is particularly important if the new science is to recognise the reality of mystical experience and the dimension of the paranormal. There is overwhelming evidence for telepathy and psycho-kinesis, but to say so is in danger of opening the flood gates to a tide of credulity and superstition. Spirituality is the name we give to the highest, noblest and most mysterious aspect of human experience, but the spiritual transforms too easily into the religious, and throughout history religion has been a source of intolerance, fanaticism, and obscurantism. The next problem for those at the cutting edge of new thought is how to tread the noble middle path between scepticism and credulity. A congress of physicists meeting to discuss the unification of the four fundamental forces will begin with a hundred plausible theories, but at the end none will be left standing.

Those who are now turning to a new understanding of consciousness and spirituality must aspire to the same ruthless humility in the search for truth. *Max Payne is a former lecturer in philosophy and Chair of the Network Trustees.*

CHAPTER 6:
Implementing a New Vision for the Third Millenium

Edited by Alan Mayne

Introduction

The Network's vision of future human affairs began to be formulated even before the Network was formed. In 1973, the founders of the Network already sought to engage the interest of scientists and medical people at the top of their professions, to include those who felt inspired by the need for a spiritual understanding of life, and to attract the interest of younger people who could contribute positively to the thought of the next generation. In the words of one of the founders, George Blaker (1998), they wanted to convey "the absolute necessity for for a majority of people in general to understand that, without a transition from our evolving but materialistically based culture to a broader spiritually inspired understanding of the world and its inhabitants, the new, just, fair, sustainable and peaceful world order that should succeed us could not become established."

This chapter outlines some specific contributions made by Network members to a broad vision of the future of human affairs, in the context of new thinking by many other people for this purpose. It includes articles by Barbara LeRose and me on education and by James Robertson on human fulfilment and on new economics, within the wider context of my own linking ideas and general exposition of the chapter's themes. These themes reflect and illustrate what I perceive as the Network's emerging and evolving universalist philosophy.

The chapter first covers new thinking in the areas of education, politics and society, economics, business, global ethics, and spiritual values. It then turns to the responsibilities of scientists and medical practitioners. Finally, it discusses some challenges faced by the Network, and indicates what it could achieve within its own future vision.

New Education

Education starts in the family, but should also reach out into the local community, the wider global community, and the universe. Education should be broad-based, to fulfil individual potential, and support cooperative social living, citizenship, and altruistic social purpose.

I first came across Dr Barbara LeRose's ideas on education, when she gave a short presentation at the 1998 Network Annual Gathering about her work for many years on the education of gifted children and other children in schools in the USA. Her contribution to this chapter contains key ideas extracted from her long paper, on which she based her presentation. It begins with the abstract of her full paper, then concentrates on the theoretical approaches, including systems thinking and new paradigms, which have influenced her work.

Her Research findings are summarised in the full paper.

At least two very important messages come across. The educational profession very urgently needs new thinking but most of its members strongly resist new ideas; many of the relevant principles and paradigms are already in being, and others are emerging. Secondly, it is not enough to help gifted children to achieve their full potential; schools and colleges should actively seek out and endeavour to develop the talents and giftedness that are present, in greater or lesser degree, in *all* their students.

The Next Step

Barbara LeRose

The traditional view of education, which began centuries ago and grew with the scientific/industrial revolution, no longer provides us with sufficient reference points to a changing world. The scientific disciplines of the 20th century have revealed to us a world vastly different from the one we previously perceived. The 'new physics' has shifted the 'terra firma' under our feet, changed the configuration of the environment around us, and moved the far shore of our vision. While the various sciences have successfully *applied* these new understandings to our lives, *education* remains frozen in place, essentially unchanged, while learning needs to have out-distanced attainments and the traditional transmission of fragmented knowledge has hidden the wider perspective needed now.

The scientific/industrial world-view, reflected so well in the schools, incorporated efficiency and specialization and high standards for the few (perhaps 15% of the student population). The educational system which resulted is better organized to discourage students - to weed them out - than it is to encourage and support them. The costs of the 'weeding' are extremely high. Few observers believe that our K-12 schools are adequate for today's needs. Textbooks and curriculum focus largely on the mastery of discrete, low-level skills and isolated facts, and deny opportunities for students to master subject matter in depth, learn more complex problem-solving skills, or creatively apply the skills they do learn.

Over the history of Western education, goals such as these have been the most difficult to achieve, and have succeeded only at the margins of the educational establishment. Once confined to our best public and independent schools, they are now not only appropriate, but mandatory, for all children. There was a period when we did not need everybody to be truly educated; now we do. These goals represent standards that are not simply higher than current ones, but qualitatively different.
The challenge to education at the close of the 20th century is insistent, complex, and demands a new world view. Concerns of equity have joined common cause with those of economic reality. Together they compel us to action. We cannot continue as we have in the past.

The time has come to move and, because the time to change is already upon us, it seems that education may have to build a suspension bridge to the future — even while we are crossing it.

'Bridge-building' tools are provided by three seminal concepts:

(1)   Kuhn's **Paradigm Shift**, which gives us a model of change in world view

(2)   The General System Theory of **Self-Organization**, which gives us an expanded definition of 'science' and a paradigm for education; and

(3)   Gowan's **Structured Ensemble**, which gives us a working model of educating for the 21st century.

The Paradigm Shift

The ability of sufficiently flexible/adaptive living systems to perceive a major paradigm shift *before* all of its aspects are fully manifest appears to be a crucial element of survival - whether of a culture, and institution, or an individual. Successful orientation to a profoundly changed world depends on the development of skills, abilities and capacities *before* they are demanded.

The conduct of basic research, aimed at providing more dependable knowledge about the teaching process, must be paradigm-based, and the paradigm must accurately reflect the social, economic, and cultural context of today's world. What is needed to advance educational practice is a serious study of the *process* of applying the new theory into systematic general practice. In other words, *how* to make education *change*. When our instincts, behaviours, strategies and ideologies - despite their record of success - begin working against us, when they are in fact part of the problem, we must ask new questions: How can the *demands* of the present age be effectively integrated into our mentality?

By 1997, Kuhn, the quintessential hard scientist, under attack from his peers, restricted his use of the term 'paradigm' to "the usual English word for the standard examples employed in language teaching — extended to standard scientific problems" (Kuhn 1977, p 231). Used less conservatively, a paradigm can be viewed as a lens which provides a conceptual illumination of an otherwise dimly lit environment. For a particular era, a paradigm could be defined as a central vision of what the world *is* and what it *can be*. In this usage, a paradigm can serve at once as both a master pattern and a guide for exploring the world of experience; it constitutes a kind of theoretical touchstone *by* which everything - for a time - can be measured and *to* which everything can be related.

> "Consensus", Kuhn (1977, p 231) wrote, "is not prerequisite to a sort of progress in the natural sciences, any more than it is to progress in the social sciences or the arts. It is, however, prerequisite to the sort of progress that we now generally refer to when distinguishing the natural sciences."

Whether or not the 'pre-paradigm' state fairly describes the social sciences generally, it clearly describes education. Unlike engineering or agriculture, education has failed to make the steady, normal progress of paradigm-based science. Scientific development depends in part on a process of non-incremental or revolutionary change. In education, change is not revolutionary or even incremental. What we have is the one-step-forward, two-steps-back, of non-science. Periodically, everything old becomes new again - and again - and again.

To receive - and then act upon - new perceptions of responsibility for nurturing the fullest possible development of *all* students, may well be both education's **major reason for being** in the emergent era - and society's best hope for survival. A Paradigm Shift for education implies achieving new levels of organization: to teach more complex cognitive processing, not just assume it; to 'domesticate' increasing creativity, not just hope for it; and to move beyond the boundaries of prevailing thinking patterns, not just be imprisoned by them.

Koplowitz suggested that there are two higher cognitive levels of intelligence beyond the stages of intellectual development spelled out by current psychology: (1) a systems level, in which the individual understands complementarity, homeostasis, and interdependence, and sees that variables cannot be separated; and (2) unitary operational thought in which the individual understands that causality, which had been thought of as linear, is seen in unitary operations, connecting all events with each other.

In a society which is producing more people, more materials, more things, and more information than ever before, **Systems Level Thinking** is indispensable in meeting the challenge of this *complexity*.

Laszlo's Seminal Idea:
A Paradigm for Education

The founders of the general systems movement felt that the compartmentalizing of science was inhibiting the recognition of common patterns and laws in diverse phenomena, and the cross-fertilization of techniques and methodology in diverse disciplines. General systems reflected a theoretical effort to reach out to, or bring in, specialist perspectives to compare notes and mutually recognize isomorphies, to find fruitful analogies or perhaps, at least, a 'damn good metaphor'. General systems thinking can usefully be brought to the critical need for a conceptual educational science - eventually providing a multi-disciplinary model for developing holistic solutions for the holistic problems of education.

Laszlo's synthesis of the fundamentals of systems theory brings together the major threads of the established view of systems. Embodying both the organismic and cybernetic models, it represents systemic invariants which have been identified empirically in a wide range of specialized disciplines. Laszlo's theory of natural-cognitive systems is stated in a set of four variables: ordered wholeness, self-stabilization, self-organization, and hierarchy. *Together they represent the philosophical basis of a set of principles and a new scientific paradigm.*

Within the systems view, the conventional model of emergent evolution is a 'step' pattern, a succession of logistic 'S' curves - a long gradually changing phase followed by a sharply accelerating phase of development, which then levels off at a new plateau which is followed by a steep rise, and so on. In theories which recognize both 'level' and 'complements', these successive phases of 'slow' and 'rapid' change reflect the alternate ascendancy of one polar tendency over the other.

In his classic work *The Survival of the Wisest*, Salk (1975) employed the growth curve in order to show "what the time in which we live now is like".

296

Salk employed the growth curve in his
classic work *The Survival of the Wisest* in
order to show "what the time in which
we live now is like"

Figure 5.1 *Growth Curves*

The extent to which circumstances differ at different points in time
along the curve is graphically suggested by breaking the continuity at
the point of inflection so as to create two curves, A and B, and using
these curves as symbols of the shape of the past and of the future; see
Figure 5.1.

To quote from Heilbroner, in Salk (1975, p 18ff): "We live in a
time very beautifully shown in the *AB* diagram ... a time in which the
prevailing systems of social organization are coming apart at the seams
... Now that is a real dilemma: it asks us on the one hand to prepare
people for the *B* stage ... and, on the other, to prepare them for the *C*
stage, which is still a long way down the road."

There are two different types of change: one that occurs within a given
system which itself remains unchanged; and one whose occurrence
changes the system itself. This will prove to be a key concept in the
application of self-organization theory to education.

Put to use in the service of change, organization and coherence
are powerfully evocative cognitive principles - consider the possibilities
of the growth curve instead of the *normal curve* as a model for educating
children.

To systematically increase society's capacity to predict the future;
to meet changing survival needs; and to plan for change, requires more
people, with more fully developed abilities, to think more creatively.
For students to learn that they are not only affected by the received

environment - but, also, that they are able to *affect* their perceived environment - the educational experience must be qualitatively different. The vital act of the new learner is participation. There must be a profound change in the present organizational patterns, reflecting newly defined organizational goals. New basic skills must supersede those of the old transmissive model. *Reform and revision are necessary, but not sufficient.*

Recurring 'visions' of new models for education, which reflect a shift from the traditional focus on transmitting isolated pieces of culturally consensual information to developing generalizable systems of self-organizing principles, have characterized the work of innovators from Montessori to Bruner, visions which were all momentarily entertained, but eventually rejected, by the main body of education.

The attempt to organize a structural change in education from the traditional pattern of *transmission* of *information* to one of *processing* complex *thought* was, metaphorically speaking, like introducing a foreign entity into the 'body'.

These recurring attempts to reform education were doomed to fail, because neither the context nor the other concepts of education changed — the total system, into which discovery, learning and other innovations were introduced, remained stable.

For example, heavily endowed experimental programmes and textbooks pointed with pride to their 'discovery' experiences and they were beautifully presented - but they are beautiful examples of programming, deliberately leading the pupil to prescribed conclusions. 'Discovery' learning must be A PART OF A WHOLE SYSTEM LEVEL CHANGE.

Branch Curves

In the 'lag time' between dissolution of an old paradigm and the full recognition of a new one, 'innovations' are said to identify those events and things which cannot be made to fit into the fading system. They are what Kuhn termed 'anomalies'. Persistent 'intuitions', recurring over time, these innovations may be viewed as the forerunners of systems-level change. The existing system will resist them - with good reason - for they serve clear notice of its impending demise.

Since we are 'absolutely conditioned' in the old paradigm, change requires tremendous energy, because it is not just learning new stuff but doing it in the face of massive resistance in the service of regulating the status quo.

The solution to the problem of changing education will not be found at the level of improving the efficiency of current practices. It must be sought at the next level of organization: rethinking the way we teach children in an era in which the greatest natural resource may well be creative human thought.

Chaos: Peaks and Valleys

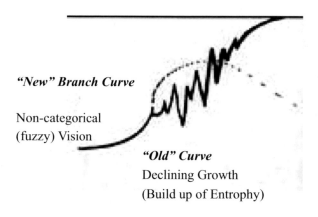

"New" Branch Curve

Non-categorical
(fuzzy) Vision

"Old" Curve
Declining Growth
(Build up of Entropy)

Figure 5.2 shows what happens during the transition from an old paradigm to a new paradigm. Although the transition may look like 'chaos', when it is viewed as Self-Organization, we see an essential tension between the old pattern, struggling to survive, and a new pattern, struggling to emerge. The term 'transcendence' may prove to be a literal description of a phase relationship between two brain processes: the analytical and the holistic. A 'vision' emerges and is then actualized, piece by piece, as parts of a new system.

An Example of an Anomaly:
Gifted Education

Gifted education is an anomaly for traditional education. In all of its variations, it is a concept which does not fit the traditional pattern. While anomalies channel the 'vision' of a new paradigm, they are not that vision, but parts of a whole which will be greater than the sum of its parts.

It may well be that, at the time of a major paradigm shift in education, a much larger pool of creative people than children identified as 'gifted' will be needed to accomplish the step from before to after the transition; genius may in act need to be multiplied.

The 'gifted' may be only, as Gowan (1977) noted, the forerunners of a time when the methods, which we engaged to address the needs of 15% of children, will become a primary model for realising the creative potential of all children.

According to Gowan (1977, p 18), the gifted comprise the "most easily identifiable pool" with the potential to be creative, but, if we are going to survive as a culture, we are going to *need* a lot more people to be a lot more creative. In the successful development of the individual towards actualizing his/her full human potentialities, creativity is "the unfailing earnest".

Through a real understanding and the use of process tools, students could be enabled to create - not just find - new patterns of (self)organization in their world. This model suggests a radical departure from the traditional transmissive paradigm.

The Transforming Experiment
Still Lies Ahead

If the cultural imperative makes creativity our educational objective, then the answer is *not* to take away the potentiality-enhancing effort directed toward individuals showing *greater* potential, in a misguided attempt to be 'fair', but to increase the *pool* by directing the effort to *all* children and establishing creativity schools!

A view of potential human development as 'self-organization' offers education an opportunity to:

(1)   assume a place as 'real' science, so that sustained progress in *educational theory and practice* can rest firmly on a *shared paradigm*;

(2)   bring education into harmony with natural process and actively, as Jonas Salk (1975) put it, "become involved in our own evolution";

(3)   reverse the waste of human potential of students who continue to be programmed for obsolescence in a 'world' which no longer exists;

(4)   foster higher-level processing, thereby increasing the potential for the maintenance, nurturing, and development of a much greater pool of creative productivity;

(5)   assume an informed stance to the role of technology and the implications of the information explosion — achieving an interface between technology and *learning* before it is engulfed in 'data-pieces';

(6)   develop a general perspective for relating events and things in an interdependent world an an instructional model for studying inter-disciplinary problems - replacing a system which is rigidly disciplinary;

(7)   recognize landmarks in the levels of individual development, to guide the shifts from egocentrism to interdependence of members of a world community.

We must take the next step to successfully implement, and also sustain, the necessary changes in schools.

The *application* of the basic principles of Self-Organization Theory to developing an educational systems model leads to the specific programme objectives of providing a programme structure which

(1)   nurtures potential development growth through the systematic achievement of increasingly higher levels of awareness of the whole

general system and its inter-related subsystems, with intense work in specialized disciplines as preparation for systems thinking;

(2)   is designed to maximize the opportunity for creative production in individual areas of high potential through a generalizable ability to think at higher levels; and

(3)   fosters the excitement, energy and joy of learning through instruction which is sufficiently complex to provide challenge and motivation.

Gowan's Seminal Idea: A 'Structured Ensemble'

John Gowan (1977) made a remarkable forecast: "If we may be permitted a peep at the future, we see an integrated science of human development and talent. ... All of psychology will be welded together in a 'structured ensemble' greater than interest in the gifted, greater than interest in creativity, greater in fact than anything except the potential of human kind itself."

After a paradigm shifts, when it comes back together, every piece needs to be looked at differently, the good 'old stuff' doesn't die, but it must be reconceived and it will fit in differently.

Gowan repeatedly pointed out that, by the middle of the 21st century, it will seem incomprehensible that creativity - as a science - was not taught in our schools. If we accept the proposition that students are living systems who self-organize in an interactive, interconnected relationship with the people, events and things in their environment, then it follows that their educational experience must be profoundly different and grounded in a conceptual whole - a 'structured ensemble'. In the light of new goals, all institutional functions and components must be systematically and differently interrelated. These include how the system works (its entities, attributes and relationships and how they interact and develop over time) and the design of the 'systems space' (the programme in its environment). The first major change calls for a new pattern of key *relationships*, made explicitly to create the context for implicit understanding of the *self-organization* process.

302

Dr. Barbara LeRose is Research Associate, Racine Unified Schools, USA

Education and Its Future Development

My own ideas about education and its future development were formulated most fully in the ninth issue of **New Paradigms Newsletter** (Mayne 1990), which began with a feature on "The Nature of Education", considering both traditional and existing approaches and new developments and paradigms. Its short articles covered: the aims and scope of education, approaches to education, approaches to schooling, educational initiatives, the content of eduction, educational methods and technology, and the future of education.

Some of these ideas were included, together with summaries of the ideas on education of Parker Rossman (1992), Robert Muller (1992) and others in Section 3, "A World Brain as an Education System", of my Critical Introduction to the new edition (Wells 1995) of H. G. Wells's book *World Brain,* which considered how far Wells's pioneering ideas on information, World Brain/World Mind, education, and politics, could be applied and extended to address today's human situation. The themes of this section were: a World Brain as a learning system, a World Brain as a teaching system, the purposes and functions of education, towards a unified global curriculum, and the emerging global education network.

The following brief formulation of my ideas on the future of the UK National Curriculum was written in May 1997, but has not previously been published. It should be considered in relation to Robert Muller's (1992) ideas for a holistic world core curriculum, emphasising the great importance of both family and individual, and appears below.

My Ideas About a National Curriculum for the 21st Century

Alan J. Mayne

Ideally, education should be concerned with the development of the individual and social potential of all people. A UK National Curriculum for the future should develop enough knowledge and skills to equip a young adult for life in the 21st century. Each of its elements should start when the child is ready to begin learning it. The curriculum should be adaptable to individual needs and the advancement of individual abilities.

The first objective of education is to find and then enlarge the talents of each individual. Here, it is necessary to develop each individual's character, capacity for independent thinking, ability to find a purpose in life, individual initiative, self-actualisation and, especially, 'learning how to learn'.

The first dimension of the curriculum should aim to impart to each individual basic information, knowledge and understanding about the following subjects: (1) ability to speak, read, write and communicate in English; (2) mathematics; (3) information studies, including computing, information technology and use of libraries and the Internet; (4) technology and design; (5) at least one or two modern languages; (6) geography and environmental studies; (7) history, current affairs and futures studies; (8) the arts, including literature, drama, dance, visual arts and music; (9) health and physical education; and (10) 'unified practical philosophy', to give a holistic overview of individuals in society, world, and universe.

The second dimension, thinking and being, should teach each individual the essentials of general types of individual and social know-how and skills in preparation for everyday life: (1) rational, intuitive and creative thinking; (2) ethical and moral education for harmonious living with other people; (3) education for citizenship, showing each person how to live as a responsible member of a family, local community, nation, humanity, and planet; (4) education for everyday life, including common sense, practical living skills and know-how; and (5) education for work, gradually developing preliminary work experience in various useful tasks.

The third dimension, teaching and learning, should include: (1) learning basic skills by observation, imitation, practice and discipline; (2) finding and developing individual talents through observation, discovery, and enjoyable creative expression; and (3) learning effective team activity through mutual learning and intercommunication, at first in small groups but later also in larger groups; leading to (4) learning to learn and a desire for lifelong learning.

New Politics and New Society

An in-depth study of today's global political scene and of many current and emergent paradigms shows that there *are* positive ways of addressing the present human situation. My forthcoming book *From Politics Past to Politics Future* (Mayne 1999) offers an integrated analysis that could help to lay the foundations for a positive new approach to politics and government in the early 21st century In it, I aim to provide: (1) a broad and fairly comprehensive introduction to contemporary and future politics and government; (2) a holistic, multidisciplinary synthesis; and (3) a starting point for exploring human problems and constructive solutions and responses.

I emphasise that global problems and their resolution must be addressed as a unified whole, allowing adequately for their complex interactions. I outline a possible holistic politics, incorporating the positive aspects of many paradigms, and I present some guidelines for achieving a good human future. I include a large annotated bibliography and other extensive reference material, and refer to a very wide range of political movements, ideas, and paradigms, involving many different individuals.

I challenge any attempt by any existing ideology or paradigm to dominate current political thinking. In particular, I question the current hegemony of global capitalist thinking over a wide range of political movements, together with the prevalent assumption that 'socialism' has no ideas worth considering further. A much broader range of possible viewpoints needs to appear in the current arena of political discussion, and this is one area where Network members could usefully contribute; only thus can the necessary strands of eventual solutions be identified and brought together.

The book's chapters about new paradigms will be of special interest to such members, as they outline and discuss ideas by many new thinkers that have already been formulated or are still emerging. Chapter 10 "Paradigms and Politics" includes a summary of the 'living systems paradigm' that I have outlined as a possible new paradigm for politics, which views humankind as a living system and could provide new insights into the current human and global situation. Within such a framework, politics and governance should play the essential part of endeavouring to ensure that necessary products and services are provided to humanity as a whole and to its individual cells (people) and groups of people in the best possible ways. The chapter also includes subsections on new economics and new business.

Chapter 11 "Spiritual Politics" presents a view of politics that is motivated by an altruistic approach to living in general and politics in particular. It first considers ethical approaches, including global ethics, which are addressed later in the present chapter. It then discusses instances of spiritual politics within a religious context. It finally presents examples of spiritual politics that appear in New Age philosophies of life, which tend to be 'holistic', by comprising all aspects of life, and 'universalist', by emphasising the common ground between different religions and spiritual traditions. It includes an outline and review of the book *Spiritual Politics* (McLaughlin & Davidson 1994), which is especially notable.

Chapter 12 "Towards a New Political Paradigm" provides a preliminary formulation of a possible way to develop and evolve a form of holistic politics that could adequately address the present very critical human and global situation. It outlines and attempts to explain some essential concepts and components of such a politics. They include: a strong methodological foundation, the statement of suitable human and global goals that are likely to be widely agreed, the identification and clarification of problems and issues, the enhancement and extension of existing policy-making processes, the development of cooperative politics and adaptive political systems, the concept of unity in diversity, and the combination of all these essential elements into a political synthesis. Such a synthesis should be based on a more participatory form of democracy, in its true sense of "government of the people, by the people, for the people", originally defined by Abraham Lincoln.

The evolution of such a holistic, spiritual political system and process, based on a constructive analogy with a healthy living organism, would at the same time lead to the development of a global civil society that is at the same time a multi-level community and network. The society's constituent communities would range from the family and neighbourhood to the global community of humanity and our whole planet, all linked together by a web of networks spreading worldwide. Such a society could meet both individual and collective needs in the best possible, most creative and constructive way, combining individual initiative with mutual support wherever it is needed. Network members have important ideas to contribute here; for example, Yvonne St. Hill's (1998) paper, presented at the 1998 Network Annual Gathering, outlined new holistic practical approaches to development which will be especially useful in the developing countries.

James Robertson is one of the best-known members of the Network. He has a vision of future human society where people would be more self-reliant, while belonging to a wider community, and would be able to fulfil their potential more than ever before. The first of his two articles appears below, and is based on extracts from Chapter 16 and the Epilogue of his book *Beyond the Dependency Culture* (Robertson 1998a). We are grateful to the publisher, Adamantine Press, for its permission to reproduce them.

Towards Self-Reliance and Human Fulfilment

James Robertson

The vision of a future that fosters self-reliance and enables people to develop themselves has been voiced by increasing numbers of like-minded men and women over the past twenty years. It now influences mainstream thinking and mainstream agendas to some extent.

There has been a decline in confidence in conventional approaches to the worldwide problems of poverty, unemployment, social breakdown and ecological destruction. Public opinion is becoming increasingly sceptical about the capacity of governments and other established institutions to deal with these problems. Non-governmental organisations (NGOs) and people's movements around the world are campaigning with increasing vigour for alternatives. For example, **The Politics of the Real World** (Jacobs, 1996) is a statement of concern by over thirty of the UK's leading voluntary and campaigning organisations. Political rhetoric, on the Left now as well as on the Right, favours policies that will foster self-reliance, not reinforce dependency.

But there is still no general understanding that the basic questions are: What kind of society, and what kind of world, do we want? Do we want a society that fosters self-reliance and equality, or one that reinforces dependency? In deciding what to do or whether a particular initiative is a good one, it still is not generally accepted that the touchstone is: How can the people involved in this problem acquire the capacity to deal with it for themselves? Will this initiative empower all the people affected by it to become more self-reliant?

Nor is it yet widely understood that a principal cause of dependency - and of the poverty, unemployment, social exclusion and environmental damage that it causes - has been the 'enclosure' by rich and powerful people and organisations of more than their fair share of common resources and values, and the exclusion of the majority of people from them. The enclosure of land and the consequent conversion of peasants into paid labourers was a key feature of the early stage of modern economic development, and the same process still continues in 'developing' countries today. Reversing the effects of enclosure will be a key feature of post-modern liberation from dependency. No longer will arguments of logic or justice be found - only selfish arguments will remain - for allowing some people to continue enjoying much more than their fair share of the commons without paying for it. The demands of economic efficiency, social cohesion, environmental sustainability and quality of life, as well as fairness and justice, will all be seen to require an end to the private enclosure of common resources.

Some relevant measures towards such an end - the replacement of taxes on employment by environmental taxes, the reduction of taxes on income, and the need to rationalise social benefits - are already on the agenda at the European level and in European nations. But they still have to be understood as potential steps towards recognising the following rights for all citizens:

> (1)　　(in the form of a Citizen's Income), the right to an equal share in the commons created by nature or society at large;
> (2)　　(by ceasing to tax employment, incomes and value added), the right to enjoy to the full the values people themselves create by their own work and skill and enterprise.

This combination of common and individual rights is one point on which my thinking has developed over this twenty-year span, as I have sought to work through various implications of a systemic, worldwide shift from dependency to self-reliance.

The state would pay a Citizen's Income (CI) as a tax-free income to every man, woman and child as a right of citizenship. Because CI could not be funded only out of income tax, it is necessary to consider proposals for CI along with proposals for tax reform. Taxes that could be used to finance CI include land taxes and 'ecotaxes'.

Such a comprehensive reform package could be phased in over a period of ten to twenty years, to include:

> (1)　　phasing out incomes and profits taxes and value added tax;
> (2)　　replacing them with taxes and charges on the use of natural and social sources of wealth (land tax and 'ecotaxes');
> (3)　　phasing in a Citizen's Income, paid to all citizens as a right, which would replace existing tax allowances and many existing social benefits.

This package reflects the vision of a *new social compact*, in a *people-centred society*. It would reward people, not tax them, for their useful work, for the value that they add, and for their contributions to the common good. The amounts that people and organisations are required to pay to the public revenue would reflect the value that they subtract by using 'common' resources. All citizens would be equally entitled to share in the annual revenue so raised, partly from services provided at public expense and partly from a Citizen's Income.

Institutional Change

As an energetic institutional reformer in the 1960s and early 1970s, I had come to see that, without more citizen involvement, reform was always likely to be too little and too late, and often misconceived; see Robertson (1971). Existing leaders whose powers and influence, skills and and self-esteem, are linked to today's ways of life and thought and organisation, are strongly motivated to ignore and conceal the need for radical change and to discourage serious practical study and discussion about the form it should take. Even when the need for some change is accepted, reform remains largely an insiders' game, in which the minority section of the population that operates within the superstructure - politicians, top industrialists and financiers, government officials and other professionals and careerists - continue the ongoing competition amongst themselves for promotion and influence and power over the rest of society. So reform tends to happen only when it is long overdue, and then in a hurry, in an atmosphere of intrigue, and without full public understanding of what is involved.

So I was ready to see that, instead of shuffling institutional functions around, a more important and more fundamental question was: How, as citizens, can we liberate ourselves from our present degree of dependency on the institutional superstructure as a whole? The enthusiasm with which I embraced this new insight gave some readers and listeners the impression, in the later 1970s and early 1980s, that I thought the post-industrial revolution would come about by people doing their own thing, without regard to the need for action to bring about changes in society's institutions. This impression needs to be corrected.

The post-industrial, post-modern revolution will involve change across the whole spectrum of economic, social and political life. People's lifestyles and work; technologies; the built environment and transport; education; the institutional structures of business and government; money and finance, including taxes and benefits; ideas and theories about economics and politics and society; ethical and spiritual values - all of these are bound up with one another. The scope for change in any is limited by absence of change in others. For example, the scope for people to change to more self-reliant forms of work is limited so long as the social welfare system refuses benefits to unemployed people unless they seek an employer to give them a job. The scope for people to reduce their dependence on cars is limited, so long as the pattern of the built environment (e.g. the location of shops), the absence of good public transport, and the comparatively low price of petrol and diesel, make it cheaper and more convenient for most people to own and use cars if they can.

So the important question is not whether change is needed in the established institutional framework of society. The answer to that question is obvious. Our institutions are crying out for change. A society's institutions, such as its system of taxes and benefits, encourage certain kinds of behaviours and activities and discourage others. One feature of a good society is that its institutions are designed to make the better choice the easier choice for its citizens. In other words, the institutions of a good society in the post-modern age will encourage activities and behaviours, attitudes and dispositions, that contribute to equitable, sustainable, self-reliant development, and discourage those which do not.

The important question is how these institutional changes are to be brought about. And here there is a serious problem. On the one hand, most of the practising expert insiders - in the taxes and benefits system or any other particular institution or complex of institutions and policies - will tend to resist change and mystify the whole topic. On the other hand, non-expert outsiders, even if they know that existing institutional structures and policies have perverse effects, will often lack the time and energy, and the commitment and confidence, to campaign effectively for change. The readiness of many Church people to accept the economic values of business and finance, even when these are obviously contrary to ethical and spiritual values, is a case in point.

And most people who want to resist particular instances of social or environmental damage or to change particular aspects of the world for the better, find it easier to focus on specific issues - resisting a motorway, supporting organic food and farming, or joining a local LETS, for example - than on campaigning for systemic changes in the institutional circuitry of society to make it more favourable to those concerns.

Accepting both those sides of the picture, the evidence still points to the conclusion that - difficulties though there may be - the initiative for institutional and policy change, and much of the groundwork and energy needed to get radical new proposals on to mainstream agendas, must come primarily from independent citizens outside the system. There is an important role for exceptional people inside the political parties, government, business, finance and the whole range of professional and academic walks of life, who see that change is necessary and begin to prepare themselves and their institutions to respond to pressures for it. But the actual pressures must come from active, committed citizens outside. It is they who have to provide the motor force for the changes that will liberate people from crippling dependence on institutions.

The Pace of Change

I may sometimes have been over-optimistic about the pace of change. It is probably inevitable that change normally comes more slowly than expected by those who want it and see why it must come. In 1960, I travelled with the Prime Minister, Harold Macmillan, on his 'Wind of Change' tour of Africa. As Macmillan spoke to the South African Parliament in Cape Town about the wind of change that was blowing through Africa, I would not have believed it would be thirty years before liberation from apartheid began to lead South Africa along its new path of democratic, multi-racial development. And, in the past twenty years, I admit I have hoped for faster progress than has actually been achieved in the worldwide process of post-industrial, post-modern liberation and decolonisation discussed in the various chapters of this book.

But two points are pertinent. First, putting out these ideas and proposals for replacing dependency with self-reliance is not about predicting when they may come to fruition, but about communicating the need and the possibility to act on them. A more academic approach might have predicted they would take a long time to build up momentum. But the current human predicament demands that pessimism of the intellect be overridden by optimism of the will. Second, although change may come more slowly than its supporters hope, it often comes more quickly than conventional wisdom and mainstream opinion foresee. The collapse of communism in 1989 is one case in point. Another is a more personal memory of my own. In 1956, I suggested that we should start looking forward to Kenya's eventual independence, and begin to train African Kenyans for judicial and administrative posts. My Colonial Office superiors patted me on the head - "this is just the kind of forward thinking we want from you young chaps" - but assured me that, in fact, it would be at least another twenty years before the question would arise. Less than five years later the new Colonial Secretary, Iain Macleod, announced the forthcoming independence of Kenya. The post-industrial, post-modern breakthrough may prove not to be so far off as it sometimes seems.

In Conclusion

My hope is that, during the few years on either side of the Year 2000, the need to change to a new direction of progress - enabling for people and conserving for the Earth - will become much more widely accepted. The issues discussed in the lectures and papers reprinted here will attract increasing attention and understanding. Recognition will spread that a historical transition of the first magnitude is upon us, and that its impact will be comparable in scope with the change from the European Middle Ages to the modern era some five hundred years ago. But this time there will be two important differences. The impact will be worldwide from the start, and one of the possible outcomes could be catastrophe for the human species as a whole.

As this awareness grows, more and more attention will be given to the practicalities of change. Particular attention will focus on the obstacles to it, and how they can be removed or by-passed. But that is a topic for another time.

James Robertson's most recent book is 'Beyond the Dependency Culture'. He is a Trustee of the New Economics Foundation and co-editor of 'Turning Point 2000.

New Economics

For over 25 years, both capitalism and collectivism have been challenged increasingly by various forms of 'new economics' and 'green' economics, which are based on ethical and environmental principles and go beyond them. In his book *Small Is Beautiful*, E. F. Schumacher (1974) criticised capitalism's current pursuit of profit, argued for a more humane economic system and patterns of work, and proposed a system of 'intermediate technology'. From the 1980s on, a series of *The Other Economic Summit (TOES)* conferences has been held, and the New Economics Foundation has encouraged new economic thinking. In 1985, ideas were shared between conventional and alternative economic viewpoints at a conference at Findhorn, Scotland, on *The New Economic Agenda*. Influenced by this conference, I outlined some ideas for a humane 'world cooperative economy' (Mayne 1986) aiming to combine the best features of free enterprise, market economics, and a judicious element of planning. Such an approach would provided full scope for constructive business initiatives, develop a balanced mixed economy, and ensure that the market remains a good servant and does not become a master or a panacea.

The most notable originators of 'new economic thought' include James Robertson, Herman Daly, Hazel Henderson, Paul Ekins, and Manfred Max-Neef. The books by Robertson (1990, 1998b) advocate a new, worldwide economic order for the twenty-first century, adapted and applied to real human and planetary needs with emphasis on enabling people and conserving the Earth.

Green economics has been discussed by E. F. Schumacher (1973) and many later writers, and now covers a range of new approaches. David Pearce and his colleagues have developed an approach to environmental economics as an extension of orthodox economics. Arthur Dahl (1996) explains why present economic and political systems are not working and integrates economic, ecological, and spiritual aims into a new paradigm for understanding and changing them.

In his classic book *Progress and Poverty*, the American economist Henry George (1879) pioneered an important strand of economic thought, which most mainstream economists ignored or underestimated, but which has attracted attention from a wide range of people for over 100 years. This economic paradigm proposes economic justice as a natural law, based on the values of health, fraternity, and cooperation. It advocates making land public property, and basing taxation largely on the amounts of land that people hold and use. There now seems to be a significant revival of interest in these ideas.

David Korten (1996) presents a strong critique of global capitalism and many of its multinational corporations and financial institutions, but shows how millions of people worldwide have already begun to reclaim their power, rebuild their communities, and heal the Earth. He outlines a citizens' agenda to increase their efforts and empower their local communities through global cooperation. The resulting 'community enterprise economy' would combine the money economy's market forces with the social economy's community forces.

In Mayne (1993), I developed a preliminary version of a 'resources paradigm for economics', and outlined its applications to future patterns of work and constructive activities. I introduced a broad classification of different kinds of economic resources, and discussed how best to use them to meet the whole range of human, environmental, and planetary needs.

In 1997, James Robertson was asked by the European Commission to report on the emergence of an alternative economic approach to sustainable development in Europe, on the basis of recent initiatives, studies and publications. Here he outlines one aspect on which he recommended follow-up. He thinks that some members of the Network might be interested, and he would welcome comments and suggestions about taking it forward.

New Models in Science and Economics: The Scope for Mutual Learning

James Robertson

Since the middle 1980s, a worldwide movement for a new economics has come into existence which aims to transform today's conventional pattern of economic activity and thought into a new economics of person, society and planet. How will the conceptual underpinning of the new economics (and politics) influence and be influenced by post-modern developments in science and philosophy?

Newtonian physics no longer provides the dominant model for science. Systems theory, the study of interactive processes, the morphogenetic and developmental theories of the biological sciences, and mathematical theories about chaos and turbulence, are more typical of today's scientific frontiers. It is beginning to be accepted that scientist are not and never could be value-free observers, and that they cannot be altogether detached from the world which they observe. Scientists belong to the particular society in which they happen to live, and the questions they ask are greatly influenced by social, economic and cultural factors. More attention is now being given to experiential types of knowledge and understanding, acquired not by external observation but by direct participation in the processes about which knowledge and understanding are sought. In the economic and social spheres, this takes the form of participatory study and research. This cannot be divorced from ethical and political issues. The new knowledge it brings cannot be dissociated from action, nor its epistemology from its ethics.

Crucial aspects of contemporary science, including medicine, are about:

   –   the role of information and codes and decision rules in systems of every kind
   –   patterns of energy flow and energy use
   –   processes of structural change
   –   interactive relations between systems and subsystems

    –   factors determining whether a system is efficient, well-functioning, or inefficient, malfunctioning and unhealthy
    –   relations between the measurable and the unmeasurable, quantity and quality, matter and mind; and
    –   the role of ethics in science.

All these have their analogues in economic processes. Economic life is increasingly concerned with information, as well as with material commodities and products. The advent of electronic money reminds us that money is basically a scoring system. It provides information about people's entitlements and obligations. Money is an information system for regulating economic activities, transactions and relationships. Looked at another way, flows and stocks of money reflect and determine flows and stocks of economic energy. Laws, regulations, management procedures and corporate cultures embody decision rules which help to shape economic behaviour. Altering them in the hope of reshaping economic behaviour has been compared with the alteration of genetic codes in biotechnology.

In economics, increasing attention is now being given to relations between - on the one hand - the unquantified, informal, non-monetized sphere of economic activity in which goods and services are directly used by the producer and the producer's family and friends, and - on the other hand - the quantified, formal, monetized sphere in which goods and services are produced for exchange. This parallels the growing attention being given to relations between complementary and allopathic medicine. 'Barefoot' economists, who participate in the economic activity they are studying, may be compared with physicists whose observations affect the behaviour of the particles they are observing. The dual mechanism of cancer growth in biological system - the formation of cancer cells accompanied by the weakening of the immune system - has analogues, such as the spread of crime, in the economic and social sphere. An approach to agriculture which emphasizes pesticides, and to health which emphasizes allopathic medicine, is analogous to an approach to crime which emphasizes police and courts and prisons.

Can analogies such as these be explored scientifically in depth, or are they just metaphorical parallels? Is it possible to establish whether the same or similar structural and (where appropriate) topological and mathematical patterns are found, on the one hand in particular physical and biological functions and malfunctions, and on the other in particular social functions and malfunctions? Do the links between information and energy provide a basis for modelling comparable behaviour in biological and economic systems?

Might it be possible to show, for example, similar patterns in the development of some cancers as in certain unhealthy developments in the economic sphere - such as overdevelopment of Third World cities or of financial flows and financial institutions on the global and national economy? Might this provide insights of practical value in both the economic and the medical sphere?

This is a potentially important topic. Might some members of the Network be interested in taking it up?

New Business

During recent decades, new paradigms have been emerging for more humane, democratic, and socially accountable forms of business. Good principles for the conduct of business include: good business ethics, right human relationships in business, and business responsibilities for the community. The concept of 'social business', pioneered by John Williamson, is that business should be conducted with social benefits in mind, including the application of business profits for socially beneficial purposes.

As early as 1896, the German company Zeiss began to give its workers a stake in its performance; at various times during the 20th century, several other companies began to share profits with their workers and consult them more. From the 1940s on, George Goyder developed his vision of the unity of the business, industrial, and social purposes of a company. He formulated proposals for an extension of company law, which would enable a fair balance to be achieved between the interests of all of a company's stakeholders: shareholders, employees, customers, and society in general. The latest version of his ideas is presented in *The Just Enterprise* (Goyder 1993). A few years ago, the Caux Round Table formulated its "Principles for Business", based on general principles of business responsibility and stakeholding. During recent years, the ideas of stakeholding in companies developed into ideas of stakeholder partnership, which were then extended from business into politics, at least in the UK.

Similar ideas, combined with the idea that 'people matter most', were used by several groups of business people. The most notable of these groups was the Business Network, which was founded by Network members Francis Kinsman and Edward Posey, and in which several other Network members were active. Sadly, the Business Network closed down a few years ago, but its contributions to promoting a more cooperative, supportive, and humane climate in business were considerable. It had networking links with several other countries, especially the USA.

More recently, the Royal Society of Arts in the UK initiated its important Tomorrow's Company initiative, Redefining Work Project, and Living Systems Group. It was at a meeting of the latter group that I first presented my ideas for a Living Systems Paradigm, outlined earlier in this chapter; before and since then, the group has stimulated many other interesting new ideas. Some of its members used to be active in the Business Network.

Again in the UK, Business in the Community has been active for quite a long time, with the aims of integrating the social and economic regeneration of communities with business involvement and successful business practice. In this and other ways, the British business sector is continuing to contribute to local community and social activities; more recently, it has begun to work with the social and economic regeneration policies of the new British Government.
In his book *The Hungry Spirit*, Charles Handy (1997) advocates a responsible individualism, which he calls 'proper selfishness', and applies it to develop the concepts of a more humane 'reinvented capitalism' and 'citizen companies', which use different business methods to work more closely with the community.

In addition, there have been considerable movements for green and sustainable business in many parts of the world. During the late

1980s, the green consumer movement and other green movements began to influencing several large companies to adopt more sustainable business methods. A variety of 'green' entrepreneurs began to emerge. Several important books about green approaches to business were written.

It is very sad that, despite all these encouraging developments, a very large proportion of multinationals and other big business sectors and companies still adopt outdated, often wasteful, business methods, which all too often bring extensive environmental damage and degradation, and increase poverty and the gap between rich and poor in many if not most parts of the world. By thoughtlessly adhering to the old economic and business paradigms, they continue to threaten the prospects for humanity. Korten (1996) has given many examples of the destructive behaviour and harmful influence of many of the world's big companies. All this throws doubt on how far most organisations in business and industry intend to adopt policies that are longer-term and more sustainable, even when they have explicitly expressed willingness to do this in principle.

This means that people of goodwill should redouble their efforts to promote more constructive and cooperative approaches there, through positive use of their power as consumers and as citizens.

Global Ethics and Spiritual Values

Although the specific ethical codes of different cultures and religious groups diverge considerably and occasionally far, the great religions in their original forms have essentially the same basic moral principles. This basic similarity gives some basis for hoping for the emergence of a *global ethic*, which can bring together personal, social, national, and international goals.

Ervin Laszlo's (1977) book *The Goals of Mankind* presents the results of an international survey of national and international goals, which was conducted for the Club of Rome. It surveys current goals and aspirations worldwide, considers what long-term international policies could make the world safer and more humane, and examines how to work together towards these policies. It suggests how to change from goals that are self-centred and short-term goals to those that are humanity-centred, long-term, and in the interest of *all* people.

In 1987, the American journalist and author Rushworth Kidder interviewed 22 leading global citizens and asked each of them a fundamental question about the issues facing humanity in the 21st century. He was unprepared for their deep about a global breakdown in ethics and morality; they seemed to say that a collapse of ethics would doom us just as surely as a nuclear, demographic, or environmental catastrophe. He then conducted a series of interviews with 24 people from 16 countries, seeking their views on a possible global code of ethics for the 21st century. He found that the values that emerged were very much the same, and that many, if not most, people share the same core values, such as honesty, respect for people, responsibility, fairness, compassion, and respect for life.

In 1990, Kidder founded the Institute for Global Ethics as an independent, nonprofit organisation for promoting the discussion of ethics in a global context. It began its work in the USA. Today, it responds to the increasing need to identify and describe ethical standards worldwide. It helps people to find what these values actually are, and to discuss them in inclusive, non-threatening ways that contribute to conflict resolution. It now has about 2000 members worldwide.

Hans Küng's (1992) book *Global Responsibility* argued powerfully for a consensus on basic ethical values among people of all religions and none. Its wide influence led to a Declaration Toward a Global Ethic, which was agreed by the 1993 Parliament of the World's Religions in Chicago. Representatives of the world's great and small religions and of those with no religion signed this statement of a minimal ethic on which all of them could agree. Küng and Kuschel's (1993) book *A Global Ethic* presents the text of this declaration, which was drafted after thorough and extensive consultation between representatives of different religions, spiritual viewpoints, and nations.

The first principle of the declaration is that there should be no new global order without a new global ethic. It insists on the humane treatment of every human being. It has four irrevocable directives, which commit it to cultures of (1) nonviolence and respect for life; (2) solidarity and a just economic order; (3) tolerance and a life of truthfulness; and (4) equal rights and partnership between men and women.

Its principles are based on a realisation that Earth cannot be changed for the better without transforming the consciousness of individuals and those in public life. Already, fundamental changes of awareness have occurred in the areas of war and peace, economics, and ecology, and they also need to be achieved in the area of ethics and values. Even though it will be difficult to obtain a universal consensus on many disputed ethical questions, suitable solutions should be attainable in the spirit of the fundamental principles already developed and agreed. It would be good if as many professions as possible could develop up-to-date codes of ethics. Above all, the supporters of the declaration urged the various communities of faith to formulate their very specific statements about the meaning of life and death, the enduring of suffering, the forgiving of guilt, selfless sacrifice and the necessity of renunciation, compassion, and joy. These statements would deepen and clarify the already discernible global ethic.

Those who formulated and agreed the declaration realised that it was only a beginning, and that much work would need to be done to elaborate its principles and extend its scope. The book *Yes to a Global Ethic* (Küng 1996) took the process is taken one stage further by publishing the contributions of a remarkable group of international figures towards the vision of a global ethic; these people included heads of states and world organisations, religious leaders, scholars, and writers. Contributions came from the worlds of politics and culture, Judaism, Christianity, Islam, and the Eastern religions.

The book also announced the creation of the Global Ethic Foundation, in Tübingen, Germany, which aims to: (1) carry out and encourage intercultural and inter-religious research; (2) stimulate and implement intercultural and inter-religious education; and (3) enable and support intercultural and inter-religious encounter.

Professor Ervin Laszlo is a well-known member of the Network, who is noted for his work on new paradigms, system theory, unified science, and unified philosophy. He is Chairman of the European Academy of Advanced Evolutionary Studies and President of The Club of Budapest. His contri-

bution, given below, was originally published in **Network**, *No. 65 (December 1997) pp 8-9. In it, he discusses consciousness, creativity, and responsibility as three aspects of the problematique of sustained well-being and positive evolution into the Third Millennium. He ends by quoting significant passages, about several of our individual responsibilities, from the* **Manifesto on the Spirit of Planetary Consciousness**, *adopted by the Club of Budapest.*

Consciousness - Creativity - Responsibility

Ervin Laszlo

A new and more evolved consciousness has become necessary in today's world. The rate of change has accelerated to the point where traditional approaches, 'tried and tested' methods no longer produce acceptable results. A new mentality is needed; a new way of envisioning ourselves and the world around us. This calls for a new consciousness, and evolving such a consciousness calls in turn for a significant leap in cultural creativity. With that leap we can not only see the world, and ourselves in it, in a new and more adequate light; we can also take more responsibility for our actions. Consciousness, creativity, and responsibility are three facets of one and the same - the '*problematique*' of sustained well-being and positive human and social evolution at the dawn of the next millennium.

Consciousness

Consciousness research is the new frontier in science. Its promise is not only to give us a better theoretical understanding of the nature and functioning of our mind, but of our-selves, and of our relations to each other and the world around us. The advances are not discipline-specific: they embrace work in quantum physics, biology, as well as psychology and neurophysiology.

Current research is intensely relevant to the problematique of survival and evolution, for it questions the classical empiricist assumption according to which humans would be categorically discrete individuals, enclosed by their skin. Increasing evidence is surfacing concerning subtle yet effective interconnections between human individuals, and between humans and the world at large. This is of the utmost importance in regard to our future. We need to recognize the presence of subtle yet effective connections between human individuals, and between humans and the natural world which is our life-sustaining environment.

In the past few years hundreds of controlled experiments have been carried out on what came to be known as 'transpersonal' connections. There is now evidence of such connections of a kind that is acceptable to the rigorous criteria of the natural sciences. It appears that 'senders' and 'receivers' can interact in ways that exceed the scope of sensory contact and the known means of information transmission. Among other things, identifiable and consistent electrical signals are found to occur with statistically significant frequency in the brain of one subject when a second subject, especially if he or she is closely related or emotionally linked to the first, is either meditating, or provided with sensory stimulation, or attempts to communicate intentionally.

Transpersonal connections also occur outside the laboratory; they are particularly frequent among identical twins. Besides 'twin pain', countless episodes are known of mothers knowing when their sons or daughters are in grave danger, and of wives knowing when their husbands are wounded or killed in an accident or on the battlefield. Communication in the transpersonal mode is also noted in the practice of psychiatrists and psychotherapists. A number of practitioners have noted that, during a session, they experience memories, feelings, attitudes and associations that are outside the normal scope of their experience and personality. At the time these strange items are experienced they are indistinguishable from the memories, feelings and related sentiments of the therapists themselves; it is only later, on reflection that they come to realize that the anomalous items stem not from their own life and experience, but from their 'patients'. Moreover, when entering an altered state of consciousness the patients themselves experience events and recall 'memories' that extend beyond the scope of ordinary sensory experience (Laszlo 1996).

Reviewing findings gathered in the course of over three decades of experience with patients in altered states, Stanislav Grof noted that the standard cartography of the mind needs to be completed. To the 'bio graphic-recollective' domain of the psyche we need to add a 'perinatal' and a 'transpersonal' domain. The transpersonal domain, he claims can mediate connection between our mind and practically any part or aspect of the phenomenal world (Grof 1988, p xvi).

The current findings of consciousness research, above and beyond their theoretical interest, have deep practice significance: people need a kind of consciousness that includes awareness of their linkages to each other and to nature. People and societies cannot indefinitely exploit and degrade nature: they must recognize that they are part of the environment in which they live. Seeing oneself as separate from the world in which one lives only creates a short-sighted struggle that produces ever worse conditions, for it takes place among more and more unequal partners. To live with each other and not against each other; to live in a way that does not rob others of the chance to live as well; to care what is happening to the poor and the powerless as well as to nature; these call for a consciousness not only of our interdependence with others and nature, but of our deep linkages with the human and the natural world (Laszlo 1997).

Creativity and Responsibility

Evolving the required consciousness presupposes intense exercise of the creative potentials inherent human individuals and cultures. Cultivating genuine creativity is a precondition of finding our way toward globally interacting society in which individuals, enterprises, states, and the whole family of peoples, and nations can live together peacefully, co-operatively, and with mutual respect and benefit.

The creative evolution of a new consciousness could instil the required degree of responsibility into human affairs. A person aware that he or she is part of the great web that links people to each other and to the biosphere does not act the same way as one who believes that he or she is categorically distinct and separate from others and the wider environment. With a fuller recognition of our deep linkages, people are likely to take more responsibility for the effect their actions and behaviours produce on others, as well as on nature.

A more responsible attitude is sorely needed. The *Manifesto on the Spirit of Planetary Consciousness,* adopted by The Club of Budapest (1996) and signed by the Dalai Lama and two dozen other spiritual and cultural leaders, noted that in the course of the 20th century people in many parts of the world have become conscious of their rights and of the many persistent violations of them. While this development is important, in itself it is not enough: we must also become conscious of the factor without which neither rights nor other values can be effectively safe-guarded: our individual and collective responsibilities. Let me quote here the Manifesto's relevant passages:

> In today's world all of us, no matter where we live and what we do, became responsible for our actions as private persons, as citizens of a country as collaborators in business and the economy as members of the human community and as individuals endowed with an unique mind and consciousness.

> — **As private persons,** we are responsible for seeking our interests in harmony with, and not at the expense of, the interests and well-being of others; responsible for condemning and averting any form of killing and brutality, responsible for not bringing more children into the world than we truly need and can support, and responsible for respecting the right to life, development, and equal status and dignity of all the girls, boys, women, and men who inhabit this Earth.

> — **As citizens of our country,** we are responsible for demanding that our leaders beat swords into ploughshares and relate to other nations peacefully and in a spirit of co-operation; that they recognize the legitimate aspirations of all communities in the human family; and that they do not abuse sovereign powers to manipulate people and the environment for narrow, short-term, and selfish ends.

> — **As collaborators in business and actors in the economy,** we are responsible for ensuring that corporate objectives do not centre

uniquely on profit and growth, but include a concern that products and services respond to human needs and demands without harming people and impairing nature; that they accord real value to nurturing and life-sustaining activities; that they do not serve destructive ends and unscrupulous designs; and that they respect the rights of all workers, entrepreneurs, and enterprises who compete fairly in local and global marketplaces.

–   **As members of the human community**, it is our responsibility to adopt a culture of non-violence, solidarity, and economic, political and social equality both in our own families and in the family of nations, promoting mutual understanding, empathy, and respect among people whether they are like us or different, and demanding that all people be empowered to respond to the challenges that face them with the material as well as the intellectual and spiritual resources required for this often unprecedented task.

–   **As individuals endowed with a unique mind and consciousness**, our responsibility is to encourage comprehension, empathy, and appreciation for the excellence of the human spirit in all its manifestations, and for inspiring awe and wonder for a cosmos that brought forth human consciousness - and holds out the possibility of its continued evolution toward a planetary dimension, marked by growing insight, understanding, love, and compassion.

With greater recognition of our manifold responsibilities, brought about by a creative evolution of our consciousness, there is fresh hope and a more reasonable expectation that our generation, and that of our children, will come up with the capabilities for meeting the epochal challenges that await all of us at the dawn of the next millennium.

Ervin Laszlo is President of the Club of Budapest and author/editor of over sixty books.

The Responsibilities of Scientists

For many years, scientific and technological advances have been capable of bad as well as good applications, and the effects of these applications have tended to be more powerful the more recently they have occurred. This means that, with the passage of time, the responsibility of every scientist, every engineer, every technologist has been increasing. Each of them needs to be conscious of the potential, as well as actual, effects and ethical implications of the work that they are doing. Special caution needs to be applied by those working on defence and other military projects and by those working in fields with unusual potentiality for unleashing new dangers. Care should also be taken by those working for businesses whose primary objectives are likely to be the maximisation of private profit, rather than pursuing the maximum public benefit. Above all, some effort is needed to think through the longer-term impacts, which can be far from easy to predict.

Scientists, engineers, and technologists, together with some politicians and some intelligent citizens without a technical background, have been aware of these issues for decades. However, the extent to which these responsibilities have been taken seriously seems to have fluctuated. It was strong around the time of World War Two, also fairly strong a few decades ago, and it is becoming strong again today, now that more and more people are becoming aware of ecological and other crises that could arise from the misapplication of scientific knowledge.

Many people now realise that uncontrolled, inappropriate, and irresponsible uses of science and technology have brought about the major threats facing humanity. These dangers include: environmental catastrophe, nuclear disaster, and devastation by chemical and biological weapons or by inappropriate genetic engineering and biotechnology. In the UK about a decade ago, these concerns had already led to the formation of Electronics for Peace (ECP), Psychologists for Peace (PfP), and Scientists Against Nuclear Arms (SANA). In June 1992, they merged and Scientists for Global Responsibility (SGR) was officially launched. It has international links with similar bodies in various parts of the world, including the Union of Concerned Scientists in the USA and the new International Network of Engineers and Scientists for Global Responsibility (INES).

SGR aims to promote and coordinate research, education, and related activities of scientists, and to: (1) ensure the responsible use of science and technology; (2) build international peace, security, and justice; (3) accelerate disarmament; (4) work for global survival; and (5) bring about a transfer of resources from military spending to peaceful and sustainable development. It has a broad range of activities, many of which promote widespread debates and increase public awareness of new scientific work. Areas of special concern to its members at present include: (1) ethics and science, including support for scientists and engineers seeking more socially and environmentally responsible employment; (2) the need for open science; (3) climate change and the technologies that give rise to it; (4) the effects of low level radiation from radioactive discharges; (5) genetic engineering and biotechnology, the main theme of its November 1998 conference; and (6) "Science Matters" briefing papers for secondary school students.

SGR already cooperates with several other organisations in allied fields, and there could be a useful cooperation between SGR and scientific members of the Network. Although the Network Guidelines provide a very valuable starting point, they make little explicit reference to the responsibilities of scientists. That is, they do not make any detailed statement about them, although they are *implicit* in the 'Care of Others' Guideline: "Have respect and empathy for others and be aware of their needs."

The book *Science for the Earth* (Wakeford & Walters 1995) discusses many ways in which science can be 'for the Earth'. It is an outstanding collection of critical reflections on science by 18 contributors, including scientists of various disciplines, environmentalists, and human rights campaigners. Its authors all believe that science can and must radically reform itself, if it is to work really effectively to resist the often harmful effects of the dominant cultural ethos that promotes belief in science's exclusivity, remoteness, superiority, and elitism. This ethos undermines humanity's ability to address many of its most vital and urgent problems, and actually reduces the effectiveness of the contributions that science can make to their identification, investigation, and solution. By beginning a dialogue that must continue if science is to maximise its potential for good, this book is so important that it should be read by as many Network members, scientists, educators, politicians, civil servants, business executives, and other professionals as possible. Several leading members of SGR helped to bring this important project to fruition.

Some of the many valuable insights that its contributors provide are of special relevance and interest to Network members. Science is one of several useful ways of knowing, but it is not the best for every possible situation. It can be applied very effectively and accurately to certain specific areas, but it is much harder to apply to highly complex human and global problems. There is no guarantee that scientists can provide better answers to such problems than people in other walks of life. Scientists and people with Western culture are *not* the only people who can use empirical scientific method well. Many people without formal scientific training have developed important technical as well as social inventions and innovations. Many indigenous peoples have their own effective technologies, which are appropriate and sustainable in their own environments. In contrast, modern science and technology are too often misapplied by vested political, financial, and business interests, with damaging or even disastrous consequences. to the especial detriment of the Third World and its original ways of life. Therefore, all scientists should consider carefully the possible social and human implications of what they do in their work; indeed, they should take global responsibility for it.

In my view, science policy will need to be transformed, so that adequate support is provided for those programmes of research and development that really are beneficial, and much more care is taken to prevent harmful applications and effects. This could be done by having less 'big science' and more 'little science', less pursuit of 'fashionable' orthodox research areas, less reliance on peer review for creative and multi-disciplinary projects, more encouragement of individual scientists' originality and versatility, and exploration of unorthodox ideas and fields. New career structures are needed, to free scientists to use their social responsibility and creativity without threat to their livelihoods.

The Responsibilities of
Medical Practitioners

Most medical practitioners, orthodox and complementary, together with their professional organisations, already have their own codes of practice which state many of their responsibilities. In addition, there are mutual responsibilities for practitioners of each form of therapy to recognise the positive roles of other therapies. All therapies should be viewed as complementary in this sense.

In addition, practitioners of different therapies have a mutual responsibility, *together*, to provide a holistic framework for restoring patients to good health as whole human beings as far as possible and endeavouring to maintain them in good health for as long as possible. Here, practitioners should contribute according the their own knowledge and skills, and according to the strengths of their specific therapies.

HRH the Prince of Wales (1998) has presented very well much of what can be done in these directions and the way in which medical organisations have already begun to address these responsibilities. He refers to a report on integrated health care that was published in 1997, which made 28 specific proposals for further consideration and development. These proposals were based on the findings of work groups on four priority areas: (1) scientific research into the safety and effectiveness of complementary medical therapies; (2) the development of formal standards and systems of professional regulation; (3) improved education and communication; and (4) effective ways of delivering integrated health care to the public. The proposals aimed to stimulate a wider public and professional debate about the possible role of complementary medicine within health care in the UK, and how to achieve the various initiatives that the report suggested.

Ways in which medical and other members of the Network can help include: (1) participation in this debate; (2) providing a forum for the open exchange of views about how to bring together and mutually complement different forms of therapies and approaches to healing; (3) promoting holistic approaches to medicine and mutual cooperation between different practitioners and therapists through their personal example; and (4) exploring emerging new approaches to medicine and healing.

Under the third heading, I would like to mention the outstanding work of Professor Richard Petty, who is promoting a programme and model of integrated medicine at the University of Pennsylvania Medical School, one of the leading medical schools in the USA. His presentation at the 1998 Network Annual Gathering was received enthusiastically.

Under the fourth heading, the emergence of the Network's Energy Medicine Group is of very special interest. It has already brought together a remarkable cross section of Network members covering a wide range of scientific, medical, and philosophical abilities, and provided a very stimulating collection of new ideas at its many events.

It should not be forgotten that the public has legitimate concerns about the malpractice of medicine. Members of the Network have a responsibility to become aware of these concerns and try to address them. Several cases of inadequate orthodox medical treatment, some leading to deaths, have recently been publicised, and I know of at least one other possible case which needs further public investigation. At the same time, some alternative medical therapies should be used with due care, as they *do* have aspects which can be dangerous if not properly considered.

These public concerns may now be greatest in the area of genetic engineering, where they seem to have grown rapidly during recent months. They are well expressed in Mae-Wan Ho's (1998) book *Genetic Engineering* and in the two reviews of that book in *Network* (Bremner 1998 & Taylor 1998). For example, inappropriate use of genetic engineering could aggravate the already serious problem of resistance to antibiotics and lead to the emergence of new pathogens. The book *Genetic Engineering* by Russo & Cove (1998) discusses the potential benefits and pitfalls of genetic engineeering, and aims to stimulate a well-informed public debate about them.

Some Challenges Facing the Network

At the end of his recent review of the Network's first 25 years, George Blaker (1998) quoted several statements by members about the future challenges facing the network. Here are three of them.

> "The Network has an important part to play in the next millennium as science gains an understanding of the true spiritual nature of mankind and becomes more integrated with many of the systems of ancient wisdom."

> "The Network is still undergoing a period of organic growth and must remain flexible in its outlook."

> "We have an ambitious vision. ... We believe that this vision can transcend currently acceptable forms of scientific enquiry and lead to a fuller flowering of the human spirit."

Other challenges facing the Network include: (1) handling the financial and administrative problems arising from its rapid growth to over 2000 members worldwide; (2) addressing the scientific and medical responsibilities reviewed earlier in this chapter; (3) continuing to set up groups and project teams having excellent discussions and doing constructive work including, sometimes, high quality scientific research; (4) becoming an effective Network, which provides the greatest scope for the creative talents of its members and develops new syntheses of knowledge and practical projects from the wide range of ideas and skills that it contains.

What the Network Could Achieve in the Third Millennium

The Network is already likely to achieve much through a continuation and gradual expansion of its present work. It already has an excellent journal, *Network,* a fairly frequently updated Directory that is an in-valuable tool for mutual networking of its members, and a full programme of meeting and associated events. To some members, the highlight of the Network Year is the Annual Gathering, and other Annual events include the May Dialogue and the Christmas Party. In addition, there are meetings several times a year held by each of its groups, including the Consciousness Group, The Science and Spirituality Group, the Science and Esoteric Knowledge Group, the Energy Medicine Group, national groups in several countries outside the UK, and local groups in various parts of the UK itself. Network book prizes are awarded once a year to those members considered to have written the best books.

The Silver Jubilee of the Network, together with the rapidly approaching transition into the 21st century and the Third Millennium, could be a signal for the Network to enhance the extent and range of its activities, and develop an even more significant phase of its work. The potential for its further development could be very great indeed. The Network could help to develop a new universalist philosophy and unified practical philosophy, which would apply global ethics, combined with extensions of the scientific method, to the healing of humanity and our planet. What will actually happen will depend on the imagination, creativity, constructive work, and commitment of its members.

In my forthcoming book *From Politics Past to Politics Future* (Mayne 1999), I discuss three possible scenarios for the future of humanity, and I make it very clear to the reader that the achievement of the Optimistic Scenario will be very difficult, and will require tremendous effort and much mutual cooperation between many people of goodwill. Helping to achieve such a scenario is perhaps the Network's greatest challenge for the years leading into the Third Millennium, but it is also one that it **could** achieve, given sufficient will and commitment among enough of its members.

In the Epilogue to my book, I outline some of the many creative and constructive things that various people, including **us**, could **do**, to help bring about a really positive future for humanity and Planet Earth. We should and **can** (1) become aware of the total human and global situation; (2) adopt a positive attitude to life and living, well grounded in altruism and spirituality; (3) form effective networks to discuss with each other what to do for the best; (4) identify what to do, both individually and collectively; (5) form effective groups and teams to do what we need to do; and (6) have the right ideals, ideas, awareness, will, and commitment.

Some excellent guidance in these directions has been given by Robert Muller, an Honorary Member of the Network, Chancellor of the University for Peace, and former Assistant Secretary General of the United Nations. His contribution follows; it consists of Extracts from a speech delivered at the Conference "Seeking the True Meaning of Peace" in Costa Rica, 26 June 1989.

A Cosmological Vision of the Future

Dr. Robert Muller

As we proceed towards the year 2000, I propose that we should pack this last decade with vision and actions aimed at preparing the next millennium as the cosmic, spiritual millennium of this planet, in order to respond properly to the expectations of God or the cosmos. In order to do this I will propose that a number of major conferences or efforts be undertaken which are not considered in the United Nations. Peace, disarmament, population, the environment, economic development etc., are all subjects being dealt with in the United Nations. But there is a list of others which should be taken up in order to prepare adequately for the next millennium.

First, a major conference should be convened on a *new cosmology*. One would listen to the physicists, to the biologists, to other scientists and to people who have come out with new cosmologies. From their views one would extract a common denominator. They all have very important perceptions. But these perceptions vary with the point of view of their professions: physical, biological, spiritual, social, political, etc. At the end of such a conference we would have a better understanding of what the cosmos is expecting from us in our next phase of evolution.

Second, I would recommend a major conference on a *new philosophy*, a global philosophy. Philosophy is the way of life. What should be the way of life on this planet in global terms, in the light of our fantastic knowledge? Where are the great sages of our time? Where are the positive philosophies that are giving us an explanation and meaning of life and hope for the future?

Third, a *new sociology* is needed which would help us to understand the meaning and role of all the inumerable groups, entities, professions and institutions we have on this planet.

Fourth, we need a *new anthropology* as Margaret Mead proposed. We need world celebrations as we have them in the family, in religions, in nations. Humans and the world have to develop common paradigms, common ideals and benchmarks for the future. The science of the total human race leaves much to be desired. We know more about tribal systems than about the human system.

Fifth, we need an *overall human biology*, a science of human life on this planet. We study more animals and microbes than we study the functioning of the human species. To the biologists this is political. It should not be so. The biologists should tell **us** very frankly and honestly how the human species functions from their point of view as experts in life.

Sixth. we need a *world or cosmic spirituality*. We have here this morning religious leaders of various faiths. It was illuminating. I hope that religious leaders will get together and define before the end of this century the cosmic laws which are common to all their faiths. They have been cosmic experts and interpreters of the heavens for a long time. They should tell the politicians what the cosmic laws are, what God, or the gods, or the cosmos are expecting from humans.

Seventh, we need a *new world policy and political system*. This planet is mismanaged to an incredible degree. If the United States were managed like the world is managed it would be a disaster. Nobody would understand how fifty states - and the world has 160! - each having a president, a flag, an army, an absolute sovereignty could ever work together. Imagine the US government in Washington being only a kind of United Nations without any authority. It would be a disaster.

Well we have this disaster for the world and it is about time we recognised it

Eighth, we need a *proper planetary management.* Private firms and the multinationals must be placed before their responsibilities for the management of the planet. They consider themselves responsible only towards profits and stockholders. Well it is becoming increasingly manifest that this planet was not created for the purpose of making profits.

Ninth, we need a *new world philanthropy.* People are giving their wealth and monies to a hospital, to a local university, to a national foundation or purpose. And the world gets nothing. The University for Peace here in disarmed Costa Rica is one of the most beautiful and useful projects on earth. But where are the philanthropists who are taking an interest in it, with the exception of one or two? And yet it is here in this University where a new Science of Peace must be developed for this planet and thousands of peacemakers educated for a whole series of professions. The people have to take the financing of the world's care in their own hands. We do not even have an intergovernmental world budget. Well, if governments do not want to have a world budget let the philanthropists and the people do it in their own way. A new world democracy will thus be born.

Tenth, we need a *new world education.* Global education, namely the education of the children into our global home and into the human family is making good progress. But we have to go beyond. We need the cosmic education foreseen by the religions and by people like Maria Montessori. We need a holistic education, teaching the holism of the universe and of the planet.

Eleventh, we need a *new world information.* Outer-space inspectors would be shocked by the wrong information that is being spread around this world. We need honest, objective information to guide our way and behaviour and not manipulated information for all kinds of purposes. Proper world information and communications are another subject of paramount importance. The UN and its 32 specialised agencies and world programmes come closest to what such an information system should be.

Twelve, we need a *new world ethics*. What is good for the United States or the Soviet Union - like having atomic arms - can be awfully bad for our planet. I'm sure that God or the cosmos has not created this planet to have all these nuclear detonators in its flesh, in its waters, in its air, and tomorrow in the stars. Our political leaders must be given to understand that they have not only a responsibility towards their people and towards humanity but towards the success of the cosmos process unfolding on this planet. They might finish it or they might help it.

Thirteenth, we need a *new world science and technology*. The scientists and the technologists must assume a cosmic responsibility. What they are doing might be right or wrong for humanity and for our further cosmic evolution. They have to think of the seventh generation.

Fourteenth, we need a *new world economy*. Oikos, economy, means the management of the household. Our household is now the planet. We need a world economy in which all people have decent cosmic lives and perform the functions for which they have been born. It goes far beyond the new international economic order. It is a restructuring of the economy of our planet. We have to put our house, which is the planet, in good order.

Fifteenth, we need a *new world art*. We need a renaissance of art similar to the Italian Renaissance which put things into harmony again. Modem art was the expression of our analytical period. We dissected everything. We have now to put everything into harmony again. We need a holistic, universal cosmic art expressing our faith, sense of beauty and planetary, humanistic and cosmic consciousness as all great poets, writers, painters, musicians and sculptors have done in the past.

Sixteenth, we need a *new world psychology*. We must learn to love the planet and humanity above anything else. Now we are taught to love a nation or a group or a religion and we are ready to kill other human beings, other cosmic units for them. This is contrary to nature and to cosmic, divine laws. We have to love humanity, we have to love the planet, we have to love the universe and to be their instruments during our short years on this planet. A completely new world psychology must lay down our right sentimental priorities.

338

Seventeenth but not least, we must teach the children of this planet a *new art of living*, show them how great life is, how thankful they should be to live today at this time of magnificent consciousness of the universe and incredible knowledge, that it will be their role to be the right managers of the planet, that each of them is a cosmic unit, or as Pablo Casals said, "a true miracle, a potential Leonardo or Beethoven therefore you cannot hurt, you cannot kill another miracle".

In the next century every human being should know that he or she is an Instrument of God, be it as a mother who gives life to a new cosmic unit, or a father who in the family is raising new cosmic units, or an educator who is educating new cosmic units, or doctors, or public servants, or artists, etc. etc. Then we will validate life fully and make children and people proud to be alive. Then humans will respect their cosmic unit as Buckminster Fuller said when he was offered cigarettes, "I will never do anything that might impair the functioning of the perfect cosmic unit I have been given by the universe". This is the language which we should have with children. This would be the real fight against drugs. You do not destroy your cosmic unit by introducing poisonous materials into its functioning. We can validate life to an unprecedented degree and extend it to the largest and smallest limits to the universe. This can be the philosophy of the next century. I would like to conclude by saying that perhaps we should replace the popular recent saying, "think globally, act locally" by "think cosmically, act globally and act locally".

Dr. Robert Muller is a former Under-Secretary General of the United Nations and Chancellor of the University for Peace.

REFERENCES

Blaker, George (August 1998) "Glancing Back and Forth", Network, No. 67, pp 2-4.

Club of Budapest, The (October 1996) *Manifesto on the Spirit of Planetary Consciousness.* The Club of Budapest.

Dahl, Arthur Lyon (1996) *The Eco Principle: Ecology and Economics in Symbiosis.* St Martin's Press, New York, & Zed Books, London.

George, Henry (1879) *Progress and Poverty.* 3rd. ed. 1996, Robert Schalkenbach Foundation, New York, and Shepheard-Walwyn, London.

Gowan, John C. (1977) *"Background and History of the Gifted Child Movement"* in Stanley, Julian et al. (eds.) (1977) *The Gifted and the Creative: A Fifty-Year Perspective.* Johns Hopkins University Press, Baltimore.

Goyder, George (2nd. ed. 1993) *The Just Enterprise.* Adamantine Press, London.

Grof, Stanislav (1988) T*he Adventure of Self-Discovery.* State University of New York Press, Albany, NY, USA.

Ho, Mae-Wan (1998) *Genetic Engineering: Dream or Nightmare?* Gateway Books, Bath, & Access Publishers Network Grawn, MI, USA.

HRH The Prince of Wales (April 1998) "Integrated Health Care: A Way Forward", *Network*, No. 66, pp 14-15, reprinted from the *Daily Telegraph.*

Jacobs, Michael (1996) *The Politics of the Real World.* Earthscan, London.

Korten, David C. (2nd. ed. 1996) *When Corporations Rule the World.* CoPublications & Kumarian Press, West Hartford, CT, USA, & Kumarian Press & Earthscan, London.

Kuhn, Thomas (1977*) The Essential Tension: Selected Studies in Scientific Tradition and Change.* University of Chicago Press, Chicago & London.

Küng, Hans (1992) *Global Responsibility: In Search of a New World Ethic.* SCM Press, London, & Continuum, New York.

Küng, Hans (ed.) (1996) *Yes to a Global Ethic.* SCM Press, London.

340

Küng, Hans & Kuschel, Karl-Josef (1993) *A Global Ethic: The Declaration of the Parliament of the World's Religions.* SCM Press, London.

Laszlo, Ervin (1977) *The Goals of Mankind: A Report to the Club of Rome.* Hutchinson, London.

Laszlo, Ervin (1979) quoted in Stamps, Jeffrey (1979*) Holonomy: A Humanistic Systems Theory.* Dissertation. The Humanistic Psychology Institute, 1979.

Laszlo, Ervin (1996) *The Whispering Pond.* Element Books, Shaftesbury, Dorset, & Rockport, USA.

Laszlo, Ervin (1997) *Third Millennium: The Challenge and the Vision: The Club of Budapest Report on Creative Paths of Human Evolution.* Gaia Books, Stroud, Gloucestershire.

Mayne, Alan J. (November 1986) *The Vision of a World Cooperative Economy,* New Paradigms Newsletter, No. 1, p 6.

Mayne, Alan J. (January 1990) *The Nature of Education,* New Paradigms Newsletter, No. 9, pp 2-8.

Mayne, Alan J. (June 1993) *Ending the Recession,* New Paradigms Newsletter, No. 15, pp 3-8.

Mayne, Alan J. (1999) *From Politics Past to Politics Future: An Integrated Analysis of Current and Emergent Paradigms.* Praeger, Westport, CT, USA, & London.

McLaughlin, Corinne & Davidson, Gordon (1994) *Spiritual Politics: Changing the World from the Inside Out.* Findhorn Press, Forres, Scotland.

Muller, Robert (1992) *A World Core Curriculum,* International Journal of Community Education, Vol. 1, No. 1, pp 2-4.

Robertson, James (1971) *Reform of the British Government.* Chatto & Windus and Charles Knight, London.

Robertson, James (1990) *Future Wealth: A New Economics for the 21st Century.* Cassell, London, & Bootstrap Press, New York.

Robertson, James (1998a) *Beyond the Dependency Culture: People, Power and Responsibility.* Adamantine Press, London.

Robertson, James (1998b) *Transforming Economic Life: A Millennial Challenge.* Green Books, Totnes, Devon.

Rossman, Parker (1992) *The Emerging Worldwide Electronic University: Information Age Global Higher Education.* Greenwood Press, Westport, CT, USA, & London.

Russo, Enzo & Cove, David (1998) *Genetic Engineering: Dreams and Nightmares.* Oxford University Press, Oxford & New York.

St. Hill, Yvonne (1998*) Holistic Lifeways for Holistic Development: Philosophy and Practical Approaches.* Draft Paper presented at the 1998 Network Annual Gathering.

Salk, Jonas (1975) *Educators: Trustees of Evolution?* in Leeper, Robert (ed.) (1975) *Emerging Dimensions in Society: Implications for Schooling.* A.S.C.D., Washington, DC, USA.

Schumacher, E. F. (1973) *Small Is Beautiful: A Study of Economics as If People Mattered.* New ed. 1993, Vintage, London.

Taylor, Roger (August 1998) *Genetic Engineering: A Call to Action,* Network, No. 67, pp 44-45.

Wakeford, Tom & Walters, Martin (1995) *Science for the Earth: Can Science Make the World a Better Place?* Wiley, Chichester & New York.

Wells, H. G. (Mayne, Alan J. ed.) (1995) *World Brain.* New ed. Adamantine Press, London.

A bibliography of significant books on topics of interest to Network members published during the first 25 years of its life

This bibliography has been compiled by Dr Julian Candy with extensive help from friends within the Network, particularly the Editors and Section Editors of this book. Inevitably both the volumes chosen and their annotations reflect some personal bias, and for that reason alone readers and authors should not put undue weight on what is included in or excluded from this list. It is intended to be of interest and use, and in no way aspires to interim or final judgement.

Phrases in the annotations within quotation marks are taken from the text of the book, from associated publicity material or from reviews. Names of Network members past and present are highlighted in **Bold**.

1973   **Schumacher, E F** *Small is Beautiful* Blonde and Briggs
Subtitled 'Economics as if People Mattered', this book had a seminal influence on the development of the 'new economics' .with ideas of sustainability and the promotion of intermediate technology and local economies.

1976   **Capra, Fritjof** *The Tao of Physics*
Fontana A seminal introduction to the links between Eastern mysticism and modern physics. See also 1982, 1996.
Jaynes, Julian *The Origin of Consciousness in the Breakdown of the BicameralMind* AlanLane.
A striking thesis, often cited but seldom rigorously examined, that human consciousness began in Greek times, and that hallucinations in contemporary people represent remaining traces of the preconscious era, as one half brain spoke to the other in the guise of 'voices of the Gods'.

Smith, Huston   *Forgotten Truth*
Harper
Argues that our misreading of science has blinded us to a spiritual truth
encapsulated in the phrase 'Man mirrors cosmos'. Discusses levels of
reality and selfhood and places science within a wider cosmic context
of the primordial tradition.

1977   Popper, Sir Karl & **Eccles, Sir John**   *The Self and its Brain*
Hutchinson.
A rigorous defence of dualist interactionism from a leading philosopher
and neuroscientist. Contains a fascinating appendix of critical dialogues
between the authors.

Wilber, Ken   *The Spectrum of Consciousness* Quest Book.
An exciting and scholarly synthesis of religion, philosophy, physics and
psychology and their relationship to different 'wavelengths' of
consciousness, written by a 23 year old. His many later books (see
among others   1995, 1996) develop and modify the ideas presented
in this first book.

1978   **Koestler, Arthur**   *Janus: A summing up*
Hutchinson
Draws together his thinking about the holarchy and the predicament
of modern man.

1979   Hardy, Sir Alister   *The Spiritual Nature of Man*
OUP
The culminating book of the author's work on spiritual and religious
experience drawn from the database of his research centre in Oxford.

1980   **Bohm, David**   *Wholeness and the Implicate Order*
Routledge.
A quantum physicist links science and philosophy in his vision of the
universe as an implicate order within which all is enfolded and which
manifests explicitly as matter and consciousness.

Merchant, Carolyn   *The Death of Nature*
Harper & RowA history of science illustrating the role of patriarchal
conceptions of nature.

1982   **Capra, Fritjof**   *The Turning Point*
Wildwood House.
Modern physics has moved beyond Newton and Descartes, and is
leading our culture towards a holistic systems-based world view. See
also 1976, 1996.

1983   Fox, Matthew   *Original Blessing*
Bear & Co.
A passionate presentation of 26 polemical theses on what is wrong with
most modern Christian thinking and what is right within the larger
Judeo-Christian tradition, giving an integrated view of justice and the
environment.

Trevelyan, Sir George   *Magic Casements*
Gateway
An inspiring anthology of poems subtitled 'The use of poetry in the
expansion of consciousness'. Contains many of the poems he used to
recite at conferences.

1984   **Prigogine, Ilya** & Stengers, Isabelle   *Order out of Chaos*
Heinemann
The authors link their studies of the thermodynamics of non-
equilibrium states to the themes of order and chaos, claiming that the
new order which represents creativity and growth arises 'from the edge
of chaos'.   They relate this in turn to aspects of the history and
philosophy of science.

1985   Eliade, Mircea   *A History of Religious Ideas*
Collins
A three volume magnum opus based on the premise that the sacred is
an integral element in the structure of consciousness rather than simply
a stage in its history. Vol. 1: From the Stone Age to the Eleusinian
Mysteries; Vol. 2: From Gautama Buddha to the Triumph of
Christianity; Vol. 3: From Muhammad to the Age of Reforms.

Grof, Stanislav   *Beyond the Brain*
SUNY Press
A psychiatrist's account of a therapeutic regression procedure which
provides a more far-reaching account of the unconscious than Freud

and which suggests we are each on a spiritual journey which began before we were born into our present life. See also 1998.

Needleman, Jacob   *The Way of the Physician*
Arkana
Written for practitioners and patients, the author advances the thesis that physicians are now 'the dispirited pawns of the medical arms race', and need to become 'wise healers working on the heart rather than mechanics who fix bodies'.

1987   Jahn, Robert & Dunne, Brenda   *Margins of Reality*
Harcourt Brace Jovanovich
An engineer and a psychologist from Princeton University report experiments that show the influence of mental intention on the output of a random number generator. This work has since been replicated and extended by them and others.

LeShan, Lawrence   *The Science of the Paranormal*
Aquarian. Subtitled 'Telepathy, clairvoyance, precognition and psychic healing in the light of modern science'.
Presents the case for a multi-tracked universe where what is impossible and 'paranormal' on one track is perfectly possible and normal on another.

Stevenson, Ian   *Children who Remember Previous Lives*
University of Virginia
A lucid and compelling presentation of 25 years of research on children with memories of previous lives. Presents typical cases along with an exhaustive analysis of possible theoretical explanations. His two-volume monograph *Reincarnation and Biology* and his summary book *Where Reincarnation and Biology Intersect* (both 1997) take the research further by correlating theses memories with birthmarks and even birth defects.

1988   Gleick, James   *Chaos: making a new science*
Penguin
A readable and comprehensive account of the mathematical discoveries and shifts in patterns of thinking that have produced chaos theory.

Sheldrake, Rupert   *The Presence of the Past*
Collins

A biologist develops the concepts of *formative causation* and *morphic fields*, which ensure the influence of like upon like through space and time, and which explain the mystery of biological form. See also 1994.

1989   **Griffiths, Bede**   *A New Vision of Reality*
Fount
An exposition by a spiritual master of the inadequacy of a purely materialistic world view, and of the   coherence between the world's spiritual traditions.

Chopra, Deepak   *Quantum Healing*
Bantam
Brings together research in Western medicine, neuroscience, physics and Ayurveda to show that the human body is controled by a network of intelligence grounded in what the author calls quantum reality. Argues that this intelligence has the potential to change basic physiological patterns and initiate healing.

Mahrer, Alvin   *Experiencing*
University of Ottawa Press
Presents a humanistic view of psychodynamics, early development, the social environment and the philosophy of sciencce.

Penrose, Sir Roger   *The Emperor's New Mind*
OUP
An eminent physicist claims that it is in principle impossible to build a machine that is conscious, and in substantiating this illuminates links between physics, mathematics and philosophy. The debate is carried forward in his *Shadows of the Mind* OUP 1994.

1990   Eisler, Riane   *The Chalice and the Blade*
Mandala
Surveys 30,000 years of history to show that dominator cultures, though common, are not universal, and proposes ways of moving towards a partnership culture in which the different .characteristics of women and men can truly complement each other.

Feuerstein, Georg   *Yoga: the Technology of Ecstasy*   Crucible
A scholarly and wide-ranging exposition of the historical and cultural context of the many practices which make up the tradition of Yoga.

Lorimer, David   *Whole in One*   Arkana
The Director of the Network uses a comprehensive survey of modern
and ancient thought to set the Perennial Wisdom in a present-day
context, and couples this with an examination of the near-death and
related experiences to draw out significant implications for global and
personal ethics.

Ravindra, Ravi   *The Yoga of the Christ*   Element
A verse by verse exegesis of the Gospel of St John from an Indian
perspective, which illustrates its coherence with other traditions and
especially with the *Bhagavad Gita*. See also his *The Yoga of the teaching
of Krishna*.

Zohar, Danah   *The Quantum Self*   Bloomsbury
The author develops a new model for consciousness based on findings
in subatomic physics, and examines the implications of this view for
our relationships with each other and our wider society. See also her
The Quantum Society Bloomsbury 1993.

1991   **Baring, Anne** & **Cashford, Jules**   *The Myth of the Goddess*
Viking Arkana
A beautifully illustrated and scholarly exposition of the place of the
oddess in the history of Western culture: first central, then eclipsed,
now re-emerging.

Broughton, Richard   *Parapsychology: the controversal science*
Rider
A comprehensive overview of parapsychology demonstrating that
parapsychologists frequently apply more rigorous criteria to their
findings than colleagues in much 'conventional' scientific research.

Burrows, Brian, **Mayne, Alan**, Newbury, Paul   *Into the 21st Century*
AdamantineProvides a starting point for exploring the complex web of
human and global problems in more depth.

Lovelock, James   *Gaia, the practical science of planetary medicine*
Gaia Books. The book that put the concept of the earth as a living
organism on the map.

Perry, Whitall   *A Treasury of Traditional Wisdom*
QuintaEssentia
An astonishing 'well chosen, organised, cross-referenced, indexed, and bibliographed' compendium of extracts which affirm and explore one man's vision of the perennial wisdom.

Schuon, Frithjof, ed **S H Nasr**   *Essential Writings*   Element
A theologian 'depicts... the traditional doctrine of the nature of the One...' and develops many related themes, drawing out not only the 'remakable harmony which exists in various traditions' but also the significance and value of orthodoxy. The introduction by Nasr is itself illuminating and inspiring.

Tarnas, Richard   *The Passion of the Western Mind*
Ballantine
A lucid and exciting overview of 3000 years of Western civilisation, which sets the transformative crisis of the modern era within a larger perspective: one in which the the masculine aspect of consciousness strives to reunite with the feminine and thus with the ground of its being.

Varela, F J, Thompson, E, & Rosch, E   *The Embodied Mind*
MITPress
Making common ground between cognitive science and Buddhist meditative psychology, relating phenomenology and evolutionary theory to the problem presented to conventional science by subjectivity.

1992   Davies, Paul   *The Mind of God*   Simon& Schuster
A cosmologist speculates about where his studies are leading us.
Sogyal Rinpoche

The Tibetan Book of Living and Dying   Rider
A Tibetan master lays out in accessible yet profound fashion the majestic vision of life and death that underlies his tradition.
Sogyal Rinpoche

Goldsmith, Edward   *The Way: an ecological world-view*
Themis
A radical critique of the modernist world-view that presents the underlying principles of an ecological world-view reflecting the original earth-oriented religion of traditional societies.

1993   **Dossey, Larry**   *Healing Words*
HarperCollins
A description by a cardiac physician of the power of prayer for healing, and an exposition of the concept of three 'eras' in medicine: mechanical / doing, meaning / mind, and nonlocal / being. His later books expand   these themes.

Gore, Al   *Earth in the Balance*   Penguin
A powerful, well researched, realistic and highly influential analysis of the environmental situation and our political response.

Zajonc, Arthur   *Catching the Light*   B a n t a m
Though a comprehensive study of light and vision, a physicist 'blends science with literature, religion, philosophy and morality'.

1994   **Harman, Willis** with **Clark, Jane**
New Metaphysical Foundations of ModernScience
Institute of Noetic Sciences. The authors edit and introduce fourteen essays which challenge the ontological and epistemological assumptions that underlie our current science, and in their final chapter describe the characteristics of a 'science of wholeness'.

Goodwin, Brian   *How the Leopard Changed its Spots*
Weidenfeld & Nicolson
A new view of biology which challenges the Darwinian claim that natural selection and adaptation can explain the structural differences between species, and postulates rather that every organism is a dymanic self-organising process. The author shows how this view can be expanded into a post-modern science of qualities.

Irwin, H J   *An Introduction to Parapsychology*   McFarland
A textbook introduction to the field based on the author's undergraduate course.

Sheldrake, Rupert   *Seven Experiments that Could Change the World*
FourthEstate
A 'do-it-yourself guide to revolutionary science', which describes experiments which are inexpensive and simple to do but which call in question aspects of traditional science. See also 1988.

Skolimowski, Henry   *The Participatory Mind*   Arkana
Sets out a 'new order of reality, a new concept of mind', in which Western consciousness returns to and reintegrates the spiritual.

Tart, Charles   *Living the Mindful Life*   Shambhala
A workbook for 'waking up', based on an integration of science and ancient wisdom and related to the author's experience in transpersonal psychology, about which he has written extensively.

1995   **Fenwick, Peter & Elizabeth** *The Truth in the Light*
Headline
An exploration of over 300 near-death experiences, with thoughtful commentary and intriguing speculations   concerning their origin and significance.

Wilber, Ken   *Sex, Ecology, Spirituality*   Shambhala
A monumental volume of 800+ pages, extensively referenced and annotated, in which the author lays out in detail his vision of the 'spirit of evolution'. It is based on profound scholarship, and describes the progressive actualisation of the cosmos through the hierarchical transformation of matter and consciousness towards the non-dual. It is both easy to read and inspirational in the deepest sense. See also 1977, 1996.

1996   **Anderson, William**   *The Face of Glory*   Bloomsbury
A discursive account, personal yet universal, of the sources of divine creative energy in the Great Memory, and of its outpouring into so many fields of human endeavour.

Bortoft, Henri   *The Wholeness of Nature*   FlorisBooks
Three essays which describe and put in a contemporary context the scientific methodology adopted by the German poet and scientist Goethe. They draw out its relevance to current endeavours to escape from the constraints of current materialistic 'observer' science and thus

to develop a truly participatory science which values and validates the subjective.

Capra, Fritjof   *The Web of Life*   HarperCollins
An attempt to create a 'holistic theory of living systems' using a new scientific language in which the interrelationships between psychological, biological, physical, social and cultural phenomena can be described and communicated. See also 1976, 1982.

Clarke, Chris *Reality through the Looking-Glass* FlorisBooks
Quantum theory provides us with an alternative to the picture of the world provided by traditional science and its conventional view of spacetime. An exploration of such alternative realities leads into mystical experience, and thus into 'reality-in-relation', from which a new world view and a more comprehensive science can emerge.

Laszlo, Ervin   *The Whispering Pond*   Element
A vision of the cosmos as interconnected and all-embracing. The author describes the emergence of a new and more complete science which will encompass the paradoxes and anomalies within traditional science, and which will recognise the quantum vacuum as a unifying source of energy and information. Speculative, realistic and inspiring.

Holdgate, Sir Martin   *From Care to Action: making a sustainable world* Earthscan
Sets out the political and societal implications of the principle of sustainability, emphasising the positive and attractive consequences of this alternative to unbridled individualism and consumerism. It is extensively referenced.

Wilber, Ken   *A Brief History of Everything*   Gill & Macmillan
An excellent introduction to his views in easy to assimilate question and answer format. Without index, notes or references, it almost fulfils the promise of its title! See also 1977, 1995.

Woodhouse, Mark   *Paradigm Wars*   Frog
A wide-ranging and perceptive exploration of worldviews in science, medicine, healing, and education, emphasising ways in which they might be integrated. Energy monism is described in detail, together with its links with the New Physics and mystical experience. Reincarnation,

abortion and extra-terrestrial visitation are other aspects of human experience which are embraced within this vision.

1997   Pert, Candace   *Molecules of Emotion*   Simon & Schuster
A scientist's lively account of how her research led from the discovery of many of the neuropeptides which mediate the connection between mind and body to an understanding of the central role of the emotions in the   unity that is the 'bodymind'.

Radin, Dean   *The Conscious Universe*   HarperEdge
A meticulous and comprehensive overview of research into parapsychology, with detailed analysis both of the experiments and of the statistical methods used to evaluate them. The author concludes (many consider correctly) that the evidence for the reality of *psi* is overwhelming. The reasons for dogmatic scepticism are discussed, as are some of the implications for science and our view of the world.

1998   **Austin, James**   *Zen and the Brain*   MIT Press
A remarkable and wide-ranging exposition of the links between Buddhism and neuroscience, in which a   neurologist 'interweaves the most recent brain research with the personal narrative of his Zen experiences'.

Grof, Stanislav   *The Cosmic Game*   Newleaf
Summarises the findings and conclusions of his extensive work in transpersonal psychology, and draws out their relevance for a new view of human nature and our place within the cosmos. See also 1985.

Robertson, James *Beyond the Dependency Culture* Adamantine Press
Advocates a new world-wide economic order for the 21st century, adapted and applied to real human and planetary needs, with emphasis on enabling people and conserving the earth.

Chronology of Meetings
1973-1998

September 1973 – inaugural meeting

January 1974 – Seminar at the University of Surrey on *The Significance of the Paranormal*

September 1974 – First Wider Horizons seminar for students.

November 1974 – Healing Seminar, Hawkwood College

April 1975 – Weekend Conference, Surrey University, *Ideas on the extension of individual awareness beyond the two ends of earthly life*, with Sir George Trevelyan, Paul Beard, Charles Davy and Dr. Peter Leggett.

April 1976 – *Towards Wider Horizons of Healing*, University of Reading

May 1977 – Network May Lectures, *Science, Mind and the Spirit of Man.* Speakers: Dr.. E.F. Schumacher, James Robertson, Prof. Derek Bryce-Smith and Dr. Peter Leggett.

October 1977 – Series of regional conferences – *Education – to What End?*

February 1979 – Weekend on *A Holistic Approach to Cancer*

April 1978 – May Lectures, *Mystics and Scientists*, jointly with Wrekin Trust, Winchester. Speakers: Dr. Fritjof Capra, Prof. Arthur Ellison, Dr. Brian Inglis, John Davy, Prof. Derek Bryce-Smith.

May 1979 – May Lectures, *Spiritual Impulses Leading to Change*, London. Speakers: Ronald Higgins. Prof. Christopher Magarey, Canon Peter Spink.

May 1980 – May Lectures – *Bridges Across the Abyss – Visions in Science and Medicine.*

March 1981- *Towards a Healing of Science*, Emerson College.

April 1982 – *Science, Technology and Consciousness Change*, with Richard Michell, Sidney Sussex College, Cambridge.

May 1982 – *Wholeness and Healing*, Iona

July 1982 – *Past Lives and Present Problems*, with Dr. Denys Kelsey, Oxfordshire.

March 1983 – *Through the Gateway*, with Sogyal Rinpoche, London.

September 1983 – *Expanding Awareness: Creating Our Collective Future*, Speakers: Peter Russell, Alistair Shearer, Michael Shallis.

September 1983 – *A New Science of Life*, by Dr. Rupert Sheldrake, joint meeting with the Business Network, London.

May 1984 – Iona Gathering (reported by Dr. Sylvia Darke in No. 27)

May 1986 – May Lectures – *Intuition and the Energy of Money*. Speakers: Lionel Fifield and David Lorimer

November 1986 – *Sound and Healing* seminar, Sussex. Speakers: Prof. Joscelyn Godwin, Catherine Thom.

May 1987 – May Lectures – *Emerging Models and Values in Western Science*. Speakers: Prof. Arthur Ellison, Dr. Christopher Thomson

July 1987 – *Healing and the Clairvoyant Reality*, by Dr. Lawrence LeShan

November 1987 – *Do We Need Enemies and Scapegoats?* Speakers: Dr. James Thompson, Dr. Nicholas Goodrick-Clarke, Prof. Adam Curle, Brigadier Michael Harbottle,

Autumn Lectures, 1987 – *Creativity and the Renewal of Civilisation*, by William Anderson, *Beyond Reductionism in Evolution*, by Prof. Brian Goodwin, *Psychoneuroimmunology*, by Dr. Dudley Tee.

April 1988 – *The Presence of the Past*, by Dr. Rupert Sheldrake

May 1988 – May Lectures – *From Mechanism to Organis: Reanimating the World.* Speakers: Dr. Mae-Wan Ho, Dr. Patrick Pietroni, Dr. Rupert Sheldrake.

July 1988 – *The Theory and Practice of Psychic Healing,* by Dr. Lawrence LeShan.

December 1988 – *The Search for Understanding in Science and Religion* – Rev. Dr. John Polkinghorne, FRS

January 1989 – *A Modern Survey of Apparitions and Death-Bed Visions,* by Prof. Erlendur Haraldsson

March 1989 – *A World Free of Nuclear Weapons – Is it Desirable? Is it Possible?* by Prof. Joseph Rotblat, FRS

May 1989, May Lectures – *The Ecological Crisis as an Evolutionary and Spiritual Challenge.* Speakers: Prof. Henryk Skolimowski, Monica Bryant, Peter Russell.

July 1989 – *Music, Cosmology and Number,* by Professor Joscelyn Godwin.

July 1989 – First Annual Meeting at Dartington.

September 1989 – *Healing and Parapsychology in the Soviet Union Today,* by Barbara Ivanova

October 1989 – *Chaos: The New Mathematics of Unpredictability,* by Dr. Ian Stewart.

Spring 1990 – *Gaia Lecture Series: Gaia, Tropical Forests and World Climate,* by Peter Bunyard. *Gaia and Evolution,* by Prof. Brian Goodwin and Dr. Mae-Wan Ho. *Gaia and the Rebirth of Nature,* by Dr. Rupert Sheldrake. *Gaia and the Oceans,* by Dr. Michael Whitfield. *Gaia, Human Values and Sustainable Development,* by James Robertson.

May 1990 – May Dialogue - *Evolutionary Crossroads.* Speakers: Dr. Richard Dawkins, Prof. Brian Goodwin, Prof. Tim Ingold, Dr. Robert Foley.

July 1990 – Annual Gathering at Winchester, Hants. Theme: *Presuppositions and Values in Modern Science.*

October 1990 – *The Near-Death Experience and the Ethic of Interconnectedness,* by David Lorimer.

January 1991 – *The Green Man,* by William Anderson and Clive Hicks.

May 1991 – May Dialogue – *Science, Consciousness and the Human Spirit.* Speakers: Prof. Chris Clarke, Dr. Richard Dixey.

July 1991 – Annual Gathering, Gaunts House, Dorset.

August 1991 – *The Challenge of the Ideological Vacuum,* a colloquium at Westminster College, Oxford.

April 1992 – Mystics and Scientists Conference – *The Nature of Light,* Winchester. Speakers: Dom Bede Griffiths, Prof. John Barrow, Dr. Jacob Liberman, Nicholas Hagger, BK Jayanti, William Anderson, Clive Hicks, Thetis Blacker, Sir George Trevelyan

May 1992 – May Dialogue – *Science, Religion and the Ecological World-View.* Speakers: Dr. Rupert Sheldrake, Edward Goldsmith.

May 1992 – *Medicine and the Feminine Principle.* Speakers: Dorothy George, Stephen Wright, Liz Hopper, Dr. Graham Curtis-Jenkins, Dr. Su Pembrey, Dr. Sheila Cartwright.

July 1992 – Annual Gathering at Hawkwood College, Stroud. Theme: *Upheaval in Social and Spiritual Structures.*

October 1992 – *Science and the Paranormal* – Lord Ress-Mogg.

March 1993 – Continental Meeting at Obernai, France. Theme: *Integrating Science and Medicine with Spirituality.*

April 1993 – Mystics and Scientists Conference – *The Life of the Heart,* Winchester. Speakers: Dr. Larry Dossey, Fr. Matthew Fox, Satish Kumar, Anne Baring, Dr. Philip Kilner, Catherine Thom, Dr. Helen Ford.

April 1993 – *New Science, Education and the Experience of Living Nature.* With Dr. Rupert Sheldrake, Kevin McCarthy, David Lorimer

April 1993 – *Illness, Health and Healing* – Daskalos (Dr. Stylianos Atteshlis)

April 1993 – *Catching the Light – An Entwined History of Light and Mind* – Prof. Arthur Zajonc.

May 1993 – May Dialogue – *Mind, Behaviour and the Law.* Speakers: Prof. Alexander McCall Smith, Dr. Peter Fenwick, Prof. Bill Fulford.

May 1993 – *Healing with Love.* Workshop with Dr. Leonard Laskow.

July 1993 – Annual Gathering, La Bussière Abbey, France. Theme: *Science and the Perennial Wisdom.*

October 1993 – *Sustainable Human Development – The Long and the Short of It* – Dr. Alexander King.

October 1993 – Continental Meeting at Hilversum, Holland. Theme: *Self-Regulating Processes in Nature; from Cell to Man.*

April 1994 - Mystics and Scientists Conference – *Birth and Rebirth,* Winchester. Speakers: Dr. Michel Odent, Dr. Roger Woolger, Pearl Goodwin, Prof. Ravi Ravindra, Bronwen Astor, Peter and Bojanka Ganev.

March 1994 – *Bede Griffiths' Vision of Reality* – Dr. Rupert Sheldrake

April 1994 – Continental Meeting, Oberhofen, Switzerland. Theme: *The Explorable Reality.*

April 1994 – *Knowledge and Perception in Yoga and Physics* – Prof. Ravi Ravindra.

May 1994 – May Dialogue – *Rediscovering the Soul.* Speakers: Prof. Keith Ward., Dr. Mary Midgley.

July 1994 – Annual Gathering at Stowe Theme: *Models of the Human Being.*

October 1994 – Continental Meeting, Rila, Bulgaria. Theme: *The Human Being, a Multidimensional Reality: From Earth to Cosmos and from Body to Spirit.*

October 1994 – *Universalism and the New Metaphysics.* Speakers: Nicholas Hagger, Geoffrey Read, Dr. Alison Watson, Dr. Christopher Macann,

April 1995 - Mystics and Scientists Conference – *The Water of Life,* Winchester. Speakers: Dr. Michel Odent, Dr. Jacques Benveniste, Dr. Rowena Pattee Kryder, Alan Hall, Beata Bishop, David Lorimer, Christopher Seebach.

May 1995 – May Dialogue – *Time, Chaos and Creativity.* Speakers: Prof. Ilya Prigogine, Prof. Brian Goodwin, Rev. Prof. John Polkinghorne FRS.

June 1995 – Meeting in St. Petersburg. Theme: *Parapsychology, Evolution and Consciousness*

July 1995 – Annual Gathering at Gaunts House, Dorset. Theme: *The Role of Fields in Science and Medicine.*

August 1995 – *Beyond the Brain: New Avenues in Consciousness Research.* St. John's College, Cambridge. Speakers: Dr. Stanislav Grof. Prof. Charles Tart, Dr. Peter Fenwick, Prof. Stuart Hameroff, Prof. Willis Harman, Dr. Ervin Laszlo, Anne Baring, Prof. Chris Clarke, Dr. John Beloff, Prof. Guy Claxton, Prof. David Fontana, Prof. Brian Josephson, David Lorimer, Dr. Edgar Mitchell, Dr. Marilyn Schlitz, Dr. Max Velmans.

October 1995 – Continental Meeting, Hydra, Greece. Theme: *The Winds of Change: Science, Medicine, Humanity.*
October 1995 – *The Memory of Water* – Dr. Michel Schiff.

November 1995 – *Humanity and the Sacred* – Prof. Brian Goodwin, Dr. Rupert Sheldrake, Edward Goldsmith

December 1995 – *Consciousness, Spirit and Death* – Dr. Peter Fenwick, Rev. Prof. Paul Badham, David Lorimer.

January 1996 – *Science and Spiritual Values* – Prof. Tim Ingold, Dr. Mary Midgley, Max Payne.

February 1996 – *Towards a Unified Theory of Science and Religion* – Rev. Prof. John Polkinghorne FRS, Prof. Chris Clarke, Lord Ress-Mogg

February 1996 – *Full Catastrophe Living* – Prof. Jon Kabat-Zinn.

March 1996 – Continental Meeting, Schloss Weissenstein, Germany. Theme: *Metaphors in Science, Medicine, Psychology and Spirituality.*

April 1996 – *Matter, Life and Soul* – Prof. Russell Stannard, Dr. Ervin Laszlo, Prof. Chris Isham.

April 1996 – *Planetary Consciousness and World Problems* – Dr. Ervin Laszlo.

April 1996 - Mystics and Scientists Conference – *The Nature of Energy: Science and the Subtle,* Winchester. Speakers: Fr. William Johnston, Dr. Joan Borysenko, Dr. Hermann Scheer, Mary Ison, Peter Harper, Paul Devereux, Prof. Chris Clarke, Dr. Ervin Laszlo, Gillian Wright.

April 1996 – *Exploring the Heart of Healing* – Dr. Joan Borysenko.

May 1996 – May Dialogue – *The Participatory Mind.* Speakers: Prof. Henryk Skolimowski, Dr. David Peat, Dr. Jean Hardy, Jules Cashford.

June 1996 – *The Coming Transformation of Work* – James Robertson.

July 1996 – Annual Gathering at De Voorde, Holland. Theme; Building Bridges between Orthodox & Alternative Views

October 1996 – Continental Meeting, Prague. Theme: *Reconciliation: Inner/Outer, Private/Public, East/West.*

October 1996 – *God, Chance and Necessity* – Prof. Keith Ward.

October 1996 – *Emotional Intelligence and Lifelong Learning.* Speakers: Mike Eales, Dr. Peter Fenwick, Prof. Paul Robertson, Prof. Guy Claxton, Anne Baring.

November 1996 – *The Placebo Response: Biology and Belief.* Speakers: Prof. Herbert Benson, Dr. David Reilly, Prof. Patrick Wall, Dr. James Hawkins, Dr. David Peters, Prof. Edzard Ernst, Andrew Vickers, Dr. Elizabeth Stroebel, Tuvi Orbach, Prof. Linford Rees, Prof. Cecil Helman, Dr. Peter Fenwick, Dr. Jos Kleijnen, Dr. Michel Odent.

December 1996 – *Psi-Explorer* – Dr. Mario Varvoglis

April 1997 - Mystics and Scientists Conference – *The Spirit of Science and the Science of the Spirit.* Speakers: Dr. Rupert Sheldrake, David Lorimer, Danah Zohar, Warren Kenton, Prof. Arthur Ellison, Prof. Derek Bryce-Smith, Dr. John Crook, Prof. Ursula King, Prof. Kurt Dressler.

May 1997 – May Dialogue – *Science, Heresy and the Challenge of Revolutionary Ideas.* Speakers: Prof. Chris Clarke, Prof. Brian Goodwin, Prof. Arthur Ellison, Dr. Peter Mansfield.

May 1997 – Continental Members' Meeting, Denmark. Theme: *The Significance of Polarities and Paradox.*

July 1997 – Annual Gathering at St. Aidan's College, Durham. Theme: *Putting the Heart into Science and Medicine.*

August 1997 – *Beyond the Brain – Frontiers in Consciousness and Healing.* St. John's College, Cambridge. Speakers: Anne Baring, Barbara Brennan, Dr. Peter Fenwick, Prof. David Fontana, Tom Hurley, Dr. Kim Jobst, Dr. Ervin Laszlo, Dr. Jean-Marc Mantel, Dr. Andrew Powell, Prof. Kenneth Ring, Dr. Anthony Stevens, Dr. Roger Woolger, Gillian Wright.

October 1997 – Continental Meeting, Budapest. Theme: *Consciousness, Creativity and Responsibility.*

April 1998 – Mystics and Scientists Conference, *The Breath of Life,* Warwick. Speakers: Dr. Neil Douglas Klotz, Dr. Philip Kilner, Jill Purce, Dr. Joy Manné, David Lorimer, Peter Glover, James Gregory.

May 1998 – May Dialogue – *Healing or Curing? Is there a clash of world-views underlying alternative and bio-molecular medicine?* Speakers: Dr. Stephen Fulder, Dr. Kim Jobst, Dr. Susanna Graham-Jones.

May 1998 – Continental Meeting in Kiev, Ukraine. Theme: *The Integration of Orthodox and Complementary Medicine.*

June 1998 – *Science and Esoteric Traditions* – Geoffrey Farthing, Hertha Larive, Prof. Peter Stewart, David Lorimer

July 1998 – *Head, Heart and Healing* – Prof. Mark Woodhouse.

July 1998 - *The New Scientific Paradigm, Opening our Minds and Hearts* Dr. Brian O'Leary.

July 1998 – Annual Gathering at Warwick University. Theme: *Empowering Transformation in Science, Medicine and Education.*

October 1998 - Continental Meeting in Cortona, Italy. Theme: *Prospects for a New Reniassance.*

INDEX